HIMMLER'S DOUBLE

HIMMLER'S DOUBLE

David Isherwood

The Book Guild Ltd
Sussex, England

First published in Great Britain in 2004 by
The Book Guild Ltd
25 High Street
Lewes, Sussex
BN7 2LU

Typesetting in Baskerville by
Keyboard Services, Luton, Bedfordshire

Printed in Great Britain by
CPI Bath

A catalogue record for this book is available from
The British Library

ISBN 1 85776 870 1

For the support of my wife Anne and our family in this project and to the memory of my elder brother John Isherwood who was an inspiration to me.

Heinrich Himmler,
Norfolk, England, 1948

The speculative drawing of 'Himmler in 1948' by kind permission of
Melissa Dring, the acclaimed English Portrait Painter and Forensic Artist.

Preface

On May 8th 1945, hostilities in Europe came to an end and the war with Nazi Germany was finally over.

On May 22nd 1945, British soldiers arrested three Germans at a checkpoint in Bremervörde, south of Hamburg. At a prison camp next day, one of those prisoners admitted to the British officer in charge, that he was Heinrich Himmler. Himmler had been in total charge of Hitler's SS, which included the Gestapo, the concentration camps and extermination camps.

The former Reichsführer of the SS, was the only top Nazi who was not already dead or captured and thus his value as a prisoner of the Allies was immense. He was taken to a safe house in Lüneburg used for questioning important prisoners.

There during a body search by a British doctor, Himmler bit on a phial of poison which he had secreted in his mouth. Despite strenuous efforts to resuscitate him, Himmler was pronounced dead.

American and Russian officers were called to view the body and photographs were taken. Everyone was satisfied that Heinrich Himmler died on May 23rd 1945. His death was officially announced on BBC radio.

On May 25th, an autopsy was carried out on the body and it was decided to bury it in secret. Only a few British soldiers ever knew of the location of the grave.

The other two prisoners that had been arrested were found to be Himmler's SS Aides. They confirmed that their third colleague was Himmler.

That is the accepted version of history...

Almost at the end of December 1945 and known only to two other persons, the real Heinrich Himmler landed clandestinely on the East Coast of England to start a new life under a false identity. It was certainly not a re-incarnation.

Himmler's clairvoyant had told him back in 1943, 'People may still search for someone believed to be dead, but no one looks for someone who is known to be dead.'

The events leading to this story have remained dormant for over fifty years. Only now can one of the war's strangest secrets be finally told.

Chapter 1

My brother's phone message had been short and to the point; he informed me that Uncle Bernard was dying. He had only a few months to live and he wanted to see me.

I think I had only ever seen Uncle Bernard about six times in my life, at weddings and funerals. Although he had married my mother's sister, some unspoken family attitude had always made me feel that he was the 'black sheep' of the family and no one had ever explained why.

Now here I was in 1998, driving across the flat windswept fens of Cambridgeshire in the direction of Wisbech to see him at his house near Cromer on the English East Norfolk Coast. My wife was working that weekend and so I was alone in my car. I have always found long journeys alone ideal for reviewing one's thoughts. Apart from the semi-hypnotic movement of the windscreen wipers, which fought against the sweeping rain to clear the screen, I began wondering why I had set out at all. Although my aunt had died in 1990 and I knew that Bernard had other relatives on his side of the family, perhaps I secretly thought he intended to leave me something and I suppose I was as greedy in that respect as the next man.

As the miles to Cromer reduced in number, I remembered day trips in my youth to that area with its beaches and pier. I had always found the sea fascinating.

I pulled into the small village of Eastrepp near Cromer at about 2 p.m. The rain had abated, but a strong wind off the sea a few miles away swept the clouds across the sky. Uncle Bernard had a detached house on the village outskirts and I recognized his car on the drive.

I rang the bell and after a few seconds I could see a shape through the frosted glass slowly approach from inside the house.

'Ah! You have come, lad!' was my uncle's greeting. It was nice of him to call me lad, I must have been pushing fifty at that time. I have never been very good with illness myself. I can recognize someone is ill in hospital, but illness otherwise means to me that perhaps an arm or leg was in plaster. Possibly for the first time, even I could see the man who stood in front of me was very ill. He had a grey pallor to his face and there was a slight sheen of sweat about him, although it was none too warm.

He invited me into the living room and sank with deep racking coughs into a worn armchair. I chose a hard seat and sat down nearby. Various medicines and bottles of tablets littered the table and bore witness to uncle's condition.

I asked if I could make him a drink, but he declined. As his breathing grew easier, he looked at me quizzically and a faint smile came to his lips.

'They tell me you are a bit of a historian, lad; interested in the Second World War and all that?'

'Certainly!' I replied. 'I've always been interested in that part of history.'

He didn't answer for a moment, as if considering his options. At length he replied, 'Well I have something for you, something both of interest and of potential value. I reckon you are the only one in my family who can do something with it.'

I was intrigued. Uncle asked me to pull a chest out from under a table at the side of the room. It was metal, with a rounded top and a hasp lock. As it was fairly heavy, I pulled it over to within easy reach of his chair. He leaned forward to open the chest, then, as if the effort was too much, sank back in the chair with another bout of coughing. 'My lungs are…' he searched for a word … 'kaput!' An interesting word to choose – German, I thought.

He asked me to open the chest and to look for a brown paper parcel, which I soon uncovered. In delving into the contents of the chest, I also unearthed a small photograph of a young man in military uniform. I had seen lots of similar wartime photos, but this young man looked somewhat familiar. The photo also showed the German Eagle surmounting a swastika on the hat. 'Who is this?' I began to enquire, as I looked up and focused on his face, before the answer became

2

obvious. It was my uncle! My uncle Bernard, who seemed about as English as was possible, even with a Norfolk accent, was formerly an officer in Hitler's army.

He grinned at me and explained, 'I was born Bernt von Eichwald on an estate near Stettin. During 1944 I was taken prisoner at Caen in France and brought to England. I stayed here after the war's end and eventually married your mother's sister. My name was Bernard Oakwood by then, I merely anglicized my name.' He chuckled. 'It wasn't the done thing for an English girl to marry a German so soon after the war's end, but we both loved each other and she stood by me.'

'What about the estate in Stettin?' I queried.

'Oh! That went long ago. Stettin is now part of Poland. You don't think after forty years they will ever give lands back to their rightful owners, do you? Anyway, enough of that, this parcel is for you. It contains a story that was written down by a friend of mine, Erich Koch. He was also a German officer during the War and a childhood friend of mine from Stettin. Unlike me, he wasn't in the Wehrmacht – the army – he was an SS officer.'

My eyes widened. Uncle Bernard continued, 'Oh! I know what you must be thinking, most British people associate Hitler's SS with the concentration camps, or the Gestapo, and that of course was true, but there were hundreds of thousands of SS soldiers involved in the fighting as well. You read the story and see if you can turn it into a book. Erich died last year in a car accident. It was his wish for the story to become known, but not during his own lifetime. Now he is dead and I soon will be, I pass his story to you to try and keep my word to him. Don't read it here. Take it away with you and read it in peace. It will be one more thing off my mind. I know I haven't got long to live, but the good Lord has given me long enough to settle my affairs, before I am moved to a hospice.'

I offered uncle my thanks, made my farewells, and wished him well. He had daily nursing care in the mornings and evenings and someone brought him a hot meal daily. There was not a great deal more that I could do for him, or that he would let anyone do.

Driving back from the East Coast to the Midlands, I placed the parcel on the empty passenger seat. Although I should not

3

have done it whilst driving, I tugged at the string on the parcel as I drove along on the quieter stretches of road. One final tug allowed about ten numbered children's exercise books to tumble on to the seat. I fished about for one from the middle of the pile and opened it on the steering wheel of the car as I drove along.

I didn't intend to read the contents, just glance at it. When I judged it safe to do so, I darted a glance down to the neat handwriting of the exercise book and read about ten words before lifting my eyes to the road once more. After repeating that process three times, the meaning of the words I had read permeated my tired brain. The words indicated that one of the top Nazis of Adolf Hitler's Third Reich, was still alive years after the end of the Second World War. According to the history of that period, it was well documented that Himmler had committed suicide in May 1945. I closed the book and carefully put it back down on the passenger seat with the others. 'Bloody hell!' I exclaimed. If the story was true, it could be a real 'diamond' of a tale. I increased the pressure on the car's accelerator, to get home a little quicker.

This is Erich Koch's story. It is his own account, chronologically arranged, with descriptions of other events taken from conversations, which either he or the author had at a later date.

The author wishes to declare that in trying to write what Himmler may have said, the views and opinions expressed are not the same as the author's.

War always brings changes.

I volunteered to serve my country at the age of seventeen in 1940 with thousands of fellow young Germans. The SS seemed to have the Elite divisions and that attracted me. I did well during training as an infantry-man, but I was kept behind to help train others, instead of being posted to a division. Apart from a brief period in Belgium, I had never left Germany and certainly not seen any front-line fighting. The losses of SS officers eventually created another chance for me when I was selected as an SS officer cadet.

4

Despite the strenuous training as an SS officer cadet, fate had posted me to SS headquarters rather than to a Waffen (armed) SS division fighting alongside the German Wehrmacht (army). I worked at the Prinz Albrecht SS headquarters in Berlin in 1943, alongside several other young SS officers, on the various minor tasks passed down by more senior officers.

I was a young SS untersturmführer (second lieutenant) and I had been ordered to investigate clairvoyants, in order to see if anyone did possess the ability to foresee the future. There were even rumours that Hitler himself consulted astrologers. I had spent weeks investigating lots of people. They were mainly frauds, tricksters and quacks and I was growing more and more anxious. The SS did not tolerate failure too readily, and I was really pleased when my researches brought me to meet a man named Kaminski from Krakow in Poland. Kaminski, it seemed, did have some sort of unexplainable powers and a high degree of accuracy.

I had never even seen Heinrich Himmler who was Reichsführer of the SS, other than at a distance at parades, or on newsreels. Although I worked at a very junior level in the headquarters of the SS organisation, my position was at present too lowly to meet, or even be spoken to by, the Reichsführer.

After passing my reports about Kaminski upwards, other more senior SS personnel brought them to the attention of Himmler himself. He became interested and gave instructions for Kaminski to be detained by the Gestapo and taken by train to Paderborn in Germany. From there he was taken to a small village nearby.

In recent times, Himmler had the local villagers moved elsewhere and used the local castle as his own temporary headquarters, or private retreat. The place was called Wewelsburg, and the castle had three turrets, in a triangular disposition. It had a moat around one side, now dry, and the castle itself was situated on a cliff which dropped down to a river. The castle was guarded by a small SS garrison, which was increased when Himmler himself was in residence. A small concentration camp was situated nearby. The prisoner workforce did any maintenance work to the castle and its surroundings that might be needed, but not, of course, when Himmler himself was staying there.

Kaminski was made comfortable in a room and could exercise

at will with an escort, although only within the castle and its grounds, initially. It was made clear to him that he was in protective custody and his future depended on his performance. Himmler formulated some questions and had them passed down for investigation by the officer who had discovered Kaminski, which was myself.

I travelled to Wewelsburg castle and held a meeting with Kaminski alone, some hours after his arrival. Entering his guarded room, we regarded each other. I was twenty years old, upright, with short blond hair and he was about fifty-five years old with a slight stoop and dark hair which was much longer than was usual in Germany.

'I hear that you have a great talent, Herr Kaminski,' I stated warmly.

'Your Excellency, any reports that you might have heard may be wildly exaggerated!'

'We shall see,' I said curtly. 'Reichsführer Himmler has given orders for me to ask you to make certain predictions about the future in writing. Some of these requests mean nothing to me personally, you must understand. The first request is: what will be the future for Rudolf Hess, who was Hitler's deputy, until he flew to England on a peace mission and remained there as a prisoner? The second is: what will the major changes in the war be? The third is more speculative. If it ever came about that the Allies should win this war – how could Reichsführer Himmler ensure that he survived to carry on the fight elsewhere? This would mean, of course, that enemy forces occupy the Reich.'

For some minutes both of us sat in silence, facing each other, at a table in Kaminski's room. It was as if he was trying to read my thoughts.

At length, he remarked, 'The Reichsführer asks a great deal of me. How do I know that the predictions I make will be believed?'

'It seems that Reichsführer Himmler himself hopes something from your answers will indicate, if your prediction is accurate or not. He told me to warn you about what you reveal, but that no harm will befall you for predicting the truth.' I replied.

Kaminski raised his eyebrows and held both hands together on the table with fingers touching, as if in prayer. 'I must have your assurance that the conditions necessary for my work will be met, or I will be unable to make any predictions. I need no disturbance or noise from the guards. I need to work in my room for hours at a time and concentrate. If the guards wish to check me, a hole can be drilled in the door. I will need to work with my door shut. Your guards must wear slippers or just socks on their feet. It is imperative that my concentration is not distracted by noise. I will come out of my room for food when I need it and I will sleep whenever I wish, for as long as I wish, to refresh myself. I cannot say how long it will take – only that it may take several days. You, or others, are not to ask about progress, and in return I will report when I am ready, either to you, if you are here, or to the officer of the guard.'

'These conditions are acceptable,' I told him. In fact I would have agreed to almost anything to get a result that would satisfy Himmler. 'I will be returning to Berlin for a few days and so I will brief the guards. Their commander outranks me, but I have the Reichsführer's carte blanche in this matter.'

'So let it be written, so let it be done!' Kaminski replied, with a faraway look in his eyes.

I left for Berlin the next day to return to my office duties and send my report 'upstairs'. Announcing my arrival back to Himmler's main aide, I was told that the Reichsführer would see me personally at 18.30 hours that evening in his office. It would be the first time that we would actually meet. For me it was a great honour, but I was also frightened. 'Reichsheini' (our nickname for the boss) had tremendous power; in fact in direct terms he probably had more power than Hitler himself did. He was a man who had not risen to this position by chance, nor did his underlings remain at Berlin HQ if they made many mistakes.

At 18.20 hours, I went up in the lift to the floor where Reichsführer Himmler had his office suite. I announced my appointment to a female secretary, who checked in her book. She then pressed a button on her desk and an orderly appeared. I was taken down a corridor and the orderly caused me to pause at one point. An X-ray machine concealed against a thin partition of the wall revealed to a hidden watcher that no weapon was concealed on me, and we proceeded. At an office door the orderly knocked, and at the sound of a voice, opened the door to allow me inside.

Rudolf Brandt, the Reichsführer's main aide, greeted me in the office. 'Everything satisfactory, Koch? Go in when I tell you. Be brief, because he has to go to the Chancellery very shortly.'

I merely nodded my understanding. It was a bit like waiting to see the headmaster at school.

After a few minutes, I was admitted to the inner sanctum. Heinrich Himmler, Reichsführer of the SS, sat behind his desk writing. I took a deep breath, approached the desk, snapped to attention, threw out my right hand in salute with a crisp '*Heil Hitler*' and clicked my heels.

'Reichsführer! Untersturmführer Koch begs to report that the clairvoyant Kaminski is installed at Wewelsburg castle to work on the predictions as ordered,' I stated.

Himmler made no immediate reply, apart from a wave of his arm to acknowledge the salute. He regarded me from behind his pince-nez for some moments.

'Good!' he said at last, speaking rather quietly. 'When can we expect some results?'

'Kaminski asks for several days, Reichsführer. About Wednesday next week, I should think,' I replied.

'Try and be more precise in future, Koch. Very well, report back with news, when you have it.' Himmler resumed writing and the interview was at an end. I soundlessly released my pent up breath. So far, so good.

I busied myself with other duties, until a phone call from the guard commander at Wewelsburg, informed me that Kaminski was ready to talk.

Brandt was told and made arrangements for the necessary travel orders for me to return. Himmler had stipulated to Brandt that the predictions were to be collected personally and not committed to the post. Brandt chose me for the task because I had already met Kaminski. In retrospect, I imagine it was that chance decision that changed my future life for some years.

I travelled to Paderborn by train and, from the station, was driven by kubelwagen car to the castle. The guard commander greeted me and conveyed me to Kaminski, then left us alone.

Kaminski was quick to pass me a large envelope.

'My predictions are written out in here,' he announced. 'Do you wish to read them, or shall I seal the envelope?'

'Please seal it, Herr Kaminski. It will be for the Reichsführer's eyes only,' I answered quite truthfully. Whatever Kaminski had predicted, I did not wish to know unless Himmler decided to tell me, and I thought that was unlikely.

'So be it then,' said Kaminski and licked the envelope seal and closed it. 'One further request, Excellency,' he continued. 'These words of mine must be seen, word for word, as I have written them. They must not be typed or grammatically improved in any way for the Reichsführer. The essence of my predictions are in the word,' he added cryptically.

I gave Kaminski that assurance and bade him farewell. As I walked out of the room, he called after me, 'I hope to see you again soon.'

I remember half turning and then I hurried outside to the waiting kubelwagen.

I need not have hurried after all, because when I arrived back in Berlin, Himmler was away visiting the Führer Adolf Hitler, at the 'Wolf's Lair' in Rastenburg, East Prussia. In fact, it was some days before Himmler returned to Berlin by plane.

At 18.30 hours on the evening of his return, I was allowed into Himmler's office.

'Well, Koch, what has this fellow got to say for himself?' Himmler snapped.

'Reichsführer! Herr Kaminski requested that you read his words unaltered and neither typed nor grammatically improved. I have not seen what he has written and he sealed this envelope himself, in my presence,' I blurted out rapidly, proffering the envelope politely to Himmler.

To my surprise, Himmler declined to take the envelope, leaving his hands on the desk.

He smiled and asked, 'Will you please open the envelope for me, Koch?' He was ever wary of poison, in any shape or form, and envelopes could have sharp edges.

I opened the envelope and removed the several folded sheets, which I offered to Himmler. He took the pages carefully and lightly and placed them on his desk in front of him.

'Take a seat, Koch,' he remarked in a more benevolent tone, without looking up. He switched on his desk lamp and started to read. Kaminski had altered the order of his replies from that of the original questions, but the content was clear enough:

9

'Despite great efforts, the forces of the Reich will eventually be defeated, when the enemy advances from both East and West. Your southern Ally (Italy) will collapse and your partners in the East will turn against Germany, as the Red tide advances.

'The greatest general of all time (a reference to Hitler) will survive attempts on his life, but will ultimately make the final sacrifice. Leaders in other countries will precede him, but their passing will make no difference. Germany will lose territory, will be divided and occupied by its enemies for many years. Yet, as before, it will rise more strongly than ever.

'When Germany ends this war, the victors will accuse their enemies of great crimes. The leaders who survive and are found will be tried for these crimes in courts. Some will lose their lives. Others will be imprisoned and largely forgotten.

'Your own future is largely in your own hands. Men may still search for a man that they believe might be dead, but no one will look for a man that they know to be dead.'

Himmler reached for a cup of coffee and took a sip from the cup, as he continued to read.

'The prisoner you refer to as Rudolf Hess, in England...' Himmler spluttered.

'Are you all right, Reichsführer?' I enquired.

'Yes! It is nothing!' replied Himmler without looking up, reading the words again.

'The prisoner you refer to as Rudolf Hess, in England, will survive the war. He will live a long life, before death claims him.'

Himmler looked up at me and I paled under his gaze. He pushed back his chair and stood up and started pacing the room, seemingly deep in thought. At length, he addressed me without looking at me.

'Did Kaminski say anything else to you at Wewelsburg?' he enquired.

I swallowed hard and wondered if Himmler was clairvoyant also, before continuing, 'As I left the castle, Reichsführer, Kaminski said the essence of his predictions were in the word.'

'Well then, Koch,' Himmler answered eventually, clapping his hands together in enthusiasm, 'you might have just found me a real clairvoyant.' He turned and beamed a smile at me, which was in itself not an everyday sight. I let my pent up breath slowly deflate and breathed more easily. I found a meeting with Himmler made me very tense until I got more used to it. Himmler seemed to examine me through his glasses. I started to feel uncomfortable again.

'Koch, can I trust you?'

'Of course, Reichsführer!' I exclaimed, as I sprang to my feet and stood to attention, clicking my heels together loudly.

'I rather thought I could,' continued Himmler, 'but I mean real trust, Koch.' He paused for a few moments, as if to measure his words. 'Have you ever heard of *Sippenhaft?*'

'I cannot say that I have, sir,' I asserted.

Himmler explained that it was a status where failure or treachery could not only have an effect on the individual, but also on his or her family. Thus for example, someone's failure could cost their own head and that of their relatives also. I gulped involuntarily.

'Are you prepared to be bound by such a commitment to loyalty?' Himmler asked.

'Certainly sir!' I found myself exclaiming. How could I say otherwise?

Himmler regarded me for some seconds in silence. I felt a bead of perspiration fall down my back.

'Good! Good!' he said. 'I note your willingness. Please go to the desk and sit and read what Kaminski has written.'

I did as I was ordered. Himmler waited patiently, until at last I looked up. 'Well, what do you make of it?' he demanded.

I rose to my feet once again, 'Reichsführer, I cannot believe that our forces will be defeated and this could come about. London lies in ruins under our bombs and the U-boats are sinking many ships in the Atlantic.'

'Perhaps so,' said Himmler. 'However, the scenario described could happen! What do you think of the next section?'

'Reichsführer, I can read what it says, but I cannot understand what it states, about no one looking for someone known to be dead,' I replied.

'What about the last section?' Himmler continued to probe.

'I regret sir, that I can see nothing remarkable in what it says,' I told him.

'Nor should you find it remarkable,' Himmler said quietly. 'However, as Kaminski told you, the essence of the prediction was in the word. *The prisoner you refer to as Rudolf Hess in England*. That is it in a nutshell! Your Kaminski has indicated that he has seen something known by only about twelve other people in this country.'

I must have still looked puzzled and Himmler looked at me for a few more seconds thoughtfully. 'Koch, you are about to hear a State secret, so remember to be discreet in what you may say.' Himmler moved closer to me and almost whispered in my ear. 'The prisoner I refer to as Rudolf Hess in England ... is not Rudolf Hess, but since Hess has disappeared and a Hess has turned up in England, why should anyone doubt that it is the real Hess?'

The expression on my face must have been a picture of bewilderment, so much so that Himmler started to chuckle. He slapped me on the back and said very quietly, 'We sent a double!'

I digested the information in silence. Himmler awaited the obvious question. I bit my tongue and kept quiet.

'Good!' Himmler observed. 'I think that you have just experienced the first unspoken lesson. You and I may sometimes be working a little more closely together in future. You are not permitted to discuss this matter with anyone. I need someone that I can trust implicitly and you will have more tasks given to you to work on. You may go now. I will pass on orders for you in a day or so.'

Over the next few days, then weeks and months, I was ordered to prepare all sorts of reports and outline plans. One or two were to surface later in the war and affect Himmler and myself personally. These were the plan to have small units of resistance nests codename '*Werwolf*', situated in Germany and elsewhere, to strike back at any enemy that temporarily occupied German soil, and a report on the future development of small U-boats (midget submarines).

One of the seemingly strangest tasks that Himmler passed down to me, was to examine British prisoner of war camps, within Germany and elsewhere, to find out the names of any disaffected prisoners who might be sympathetic to Germany.

I had been taught English at school and had taken holidays in England before the war. The bustle of London, contrasting with the sleepy Oxford and Cambridge of pre-war days, seemed another world away at that time.

This all took time, but I did not have to visit every camp personally. Some camps were visited and others replied to the questionnaire that I sent to the camps' administration.

At length, I submitted a written report to Himmler that I had identified sixty such people amongst the British prisoners of war and their Commonwealth allies. Without seeing me personally, Himmler sent me a written order to have these men removed from their camps and sent to a barracks at an SS garrison near Heidelberg. He also sent me instructions as to what he wished me to tell these men, once they were assembled.

After a week or so, I heard that every one of the prisoners listed had arrived and settled down in the barracks. I departed for Heidelberg the next day by train and arrived late in the evening.

Heidelberg seemed to be unaffected by the war. Naturally there were uniformed members of all the forces in evidence, but the city had missed Allied bombing so far. It was an environment where I hoped I could relax a little without constant air raid warnings, spending hours in air raid shelters and other privations of Berlin life.

I was shown into the presence of the SS standartenführer who commanded the garrison. He wanted to know why he was being expected to look after British prisoners of war? It was the 'why' question that I would experience in most areas that I visited, and I had a brief effective reply.

'It is a secret matter of State, Standartenführer! I am acting on the Reichsführer's personal instructions. Would you be so good as to allow your staff to allocate me quarters for the night and to advise the British prisoners that there will be a briefing for all of them to attend at 09.00 hours tomorrow. Someone must make sure they will be there.'

'Of course! Of course! We are always ready to assist the Reichsführer,' replied the standartenführer, in a much more friendly tone. 'Would you care for a schnapps in the officers' mess before a meal?'

'Thank you, but I must decline, as I have to read the Reichsführer's instructions for tomorrow again,' I said. 'If you will excuse me, I will retire to my quarters for the night.'

'As you wish, Untersturmführer. By the way, this letter arrived for you,' stated the officer, and he handed it to me.

The standartenführer led the way out of his office and brushing his own aide aside, conducted me to a bedroom in the officers' quarters. Like a hotel manager, he told me that an orderly would awaken me at 06.00 hours with coffee, if that might be convenient. I confirmed that it was acceptable. I rather enjoyed this 'acting upon the instructions of the Reichsführer' because it meant getting my own way.

In the bedroom, having shut the door, I threw my case, greatcoat and hat on to the bed and looked out of the window. Some distance away stood another similar walled barrack with windows on several levels. I was tired, but I sat at the table and re-read Himmler's instructions for the morning a couple of times. I then opened the letter I had been given and found instructions from SS HQ in Berlin, describing what to do about any prisoners who declined the Reichsführer's offer.

Later, as I lay in bed in the darkness, I reflected on the recent turn of events. I was a trained soldier, but was attached to Himmler's headquarters, far from any fighting on the ground. I thought about my parents and sister, at their home near Stettin in northern Germany. They were at present on the von Eichwald estate, and hopefully safe from the bombing; although, as a port, Stettin would become a target for the Allies sooner or later. I also thought of Kaminski, presumably safe, but a prisoner in Wewelsburg castle. The matter that returned to my thoughts again and again, was the 'forbidden' question. If a double had been sent to England, where was the real Rudolf Hess?

At length, I fell asleep, until I was awoken next morning by an orderly bringing coffee. I rose, washed, shaved and dressed and walked down to the mess for some rolls with slices of sausage and jam. I sat by myself, and other officers entering the mess shunned my company. It seemed that no one wished to brush shoulders with a personal envoy from Himmler.

Having satisfied my hunger, I was directed by an orderly to the barracks where the British prisoners had been housed. Guards stood at various points around the perimeter of the barracks, both to guard the prisoners within and to keep other SS soldiers away. A rottenführer (corporal) was in charge of the guard. The orderly introduced me and then departed.

'Tell me Rottenführer, do you speak or understand any English?' I enquired.

'None at all, sir!' replied the guard, as he stood at attention.

I gave the guard my orders, 'Accompany me into the barracks mess hall, round up the prisoners, bring them into the hall and stand by the door to await any further instructions.'

'At your orders, sir!' bellowed the guard, and he doubled away into the barracks.

I followed at a more leisurely pace and made my way into the mess hall area, where already some of the prisoners were assembling. I waited at the far end from the door. As the movement and shuffling of feet subsided, I could see that the guard had also come into the room and was standing by the door, as instructed.

I addressed the waiting prisoners in my rusty English. 'Please sit down, gentlemen,' I began pleasantly.

The prisoners did as they were told and apart from the noise of moving benches on the wooden floor, nothing else was said. When silence had again prevailed, I began to speak to them.

'Most of you here today regard yourselves as Anglo-Saxons, although some of you are from British Commonwealth countries. Saxony is a part of Germany. Most of our ancestors came from there. We Germans and British are brothers of the blood, separated by many generations. We ought not to be fighting each other. Some of you know that when you were living in England, you had the same enemy as we had here in Germany. The Communists are our common enemy. That is whom we should both be fighting. Russia must be laughing at us, to see our great nations trying to destroy one another, so that they can follow with their Communist ideas, into nations already weakened by war.'

A muttering amongst the prisoners revealed that my rusty English was being understood and the point that I was making was 'getting home' to the men.

I continued a little more confidently, 'We have brought you here because we believe that you are intelligent men, whether you are officers, NCOs, or privates. Some of you may have a German parent, or knowledge of the German language. Please put up your hands.' About one dozen hands rose in the room.

'Gentlemen, I am commanded by SS Reichsführer Heinrich Himmler himself. He wishes to inform you that if you will work with us, instead of against us, we will enroll you in a separate unit of British troops to be called the Britisches Frei Korps. You would have a uniform, pay and good conditions as our own soldiers. You would not be sent to the front-line and your task would be to recruit others to the Korps from amongst those prisoners of war where you were yourselves a short time ago.

It will be an SS Korps. You should understand that we have soldiers in our SS from many nations. Some make up complete divisions: French, Belgians, Dutch, Danes, Norwegians, Finns, Italians, Slovenes, Croats, Serbs, Albanians, Hungarians. We have a Russian Army under General Vlassov fighting with us, besides SS soldiers from parts of Russia you have probably never heard of. We even have Indians in the SS, besides people from neutral countries such as Sweden and Switzerland. They all recognize the common enemy as Communism, which is often aided by the activities of Jewish businesses in our countries.'

I paused and continued in a softer voice, 'No one will be forced to join us. If you decide that this is not for you, please raise your hands and arrangements will be made for you to go back to your camps.'

The moment of truth had arrived. I waited patiently. Around the room, men talked in small groups for several minutes.

Finally, I brought discussion to an end. 'Well, gentlemen! Time for talk is over. Would anyone who does not wish to proceed with us please raise your hand.' Around the room a total of four hands were raised.

After a few seconds searching the remaining faces, I addressed the guard in German, 'Take the four prisoners who raised their hand to the guardroom to await collection.'

The guard saluted and gathered up the four men and led them away. After they had departed I ordered the remaining men to stand up.

'Attention!' I drew out the word as I had heard it in London some years ago. Fifty-six men stood at attention facing me. 'You will be informed of what is going to happen, after the next few days. During that time, you will be given some practice in German military terms and commands. The German speakers can help the others. You will also be given some drill, to prevent you from getting too rusty and finally, as we realize

16

that former prisoners will not be on peak fitness, we will toughen you up on elements of the assault course for training SS soldiers.

If you do not look forward to that, may I point out that as prisoners you have been without women for a long time. There is a brothel here and, as soldiers, you may go there in the future. Some of you may not like that idea, but as we say here in Germany – I do not know if it translates well – all cats are grey at night!'

The assembly digested the last piece of information and a few grinned. 'Gentlemen! Welcome to the SS Britisches Frei Korps! *Heil Hitler*!' I announced.

Around the hall the assembled men threw up their right arms and echoed the salutation '*Heil Hitler*'. The SS Britisches Frei Korps had arrived in being.

I then left the men to their own devices. The guards would remain for a few days, until the former prisoners' security arrangements had been made. I walked from the barrack, around the edge of the square where new German SS recruits were being drilled by NCOs and arrived at the guardroom.

The four POWs sat contentedly enough on a bench seat against the wall, under the gaze of a guard with a rifle. The guard snapped to attention and I saluted. Addressing the prisoners, I enquired what their names were and searched for them on my list. Having found the names, I extracted their file details from my briefcase and clipped them together. I then crossed off the four names from the list.

'Well then!' I said pleasantly. 'You men will remain here in the guardroom until an escort arrives to take you back to your camps.'

Turning to the guard, I addressed him in German and ordered him to lock the prisoners in the cells until their escort arrived to take them away. After this had been done, I requested that I might use the telephone.

I consulted the instructions in the letter, telephoned the number given and reported to the other end that I was acting on Reichsführer Himmler's orders and that four British prisoners of war were to be picked up from the Reinhard SS barracks, to be escorted back to their camps. The man on the other end acknowledged the call and the conversation ended.

Following my written instructions I got out a blue pencil and marked each file with two large letter Ns, then signed each file with my full name and rank. After asking that my thanks be conveyed to the standartenführer, I left the four marked files with the guards, for the escort to collect. I then departed by kubelwagen for the railway station to return to Berlin.

Hours later, as the rails drummed their rhythm, I again thought about 'NN', and wondered what it meant. It would be a long time before I did realize what it signified.

About one and a half hours after Koch had left the Reinhard barracks a small lorry arrived at the entrance. The driver showed the guard an order and the lorry was allowed in through the barrier and parked in front of the guardroom. Two men in civilian working clothes got out of the cab and identified themselves to the guard commander as SD men (Sichertheitsdienst – which was the part of the SS that dealt with security matters).

One of them showed the guard their order to collect the British prisoners. Whilst one guard went to unlock their cell doors, another guard passed the four files marked 'NN' to the SD men. As the prisoners assembled, one of the SD men signed a form, as a receipt for the prisoners passing to their custody.

With a minimum of fuss, they gestured for the prisoners to climb up into the rear of the covered lorry outside. Inside the lorry, sat three further SD men, two of whom held machine pistols cradled in their laps. The tarpaulin cover was dropped over the rear, the lorry drove out of Heidelberg and east on a road which ran along the river Neckar. The scenery was pretty, but unfortunately the prisoners could not see it. As the lorry got to the small village of Zwingenberg, the lorry turned north on a small winding track for a kilometre or so and stopped.

There was no one about, nor any dwelling in sight. One man got out of the cab and walked to the rear of the lorry and flipped up the tarpaulin.

'Come', he called to the prisoners in basic English. 'Toilet halt! Long time to camps!'

The prisoners climbed down from the lorry and their guards climbed down after them. The two with machine pistols took up positions at either side and took out cigarettes to smoke. The third guard remained behind the prisoners, with his colleagues from the cab. The Germans began to chat in a friendly way and the prisoners turned away and undid their trouser flies. After a few seconds two guards to the rear of the prisoners, pulled pistols with silencers from their clothing and each shot two prisoners, so quickly that none of them realized what had happened.

As the bodies dropped to the grass at the side of the track, the guards watched them for signs of life. There were none. One guard stepped forward to check for pulses, as another colleague climbed back into the lorry and threw out a bundle of canvas to the ground outside. As the guards with machine pistols kept watch, the other SD men wrapped the bodies in canvas and bound the bundles, then placed them back in the lorry.

The lorry was driven a little farther to a turning point and turned around to rejoin the main road again. The SD men drove eastwards once more, until they arrived at a town that had a crematorium, and the bodies were discreetly delivered. Under an arrangement between the local SD and the crematorium, within a few hours the bodies would have disappeared for ever.

It was not uncommon for such things to happen in secret in Hitler's Germany. People could suddenly disappear as if they had never existed. They might disappear at night or in daytime, according to circumstance, as if into a fog that made them invisible. They were people whose files were marked NN for *Nacht und Nebel* (night and fog) by the Nazi machine. Those initials meant death, or disappearance into a concentration camp. In most cases their relatives and friends would never hear from them again.

The Britisches Frei Korps members in the Reinhard barracks had no reason to doubt that the four men had been taken back to their old camps. The bulk of prisoners who had remained in their prisoner of war camps for British and Commonwealth soldiers believed that some of their number had been taken away to another camp, because they had not returned. After a while they forgot about them.

19

I was completely unaware at that time of what had happened to those four prisoners. For the SS hierarchy in Berlin, it meant no loose ends.

Chapter 2

Himmler contemplated the idea of finding a double for himself. He already had a great interest in twins and far away in occupied Poland that interest had led to research on twins both living and dead.

The railway engine snorted clouds of smoke and steam as it pulled a string of cattle trucks up the slight gradient in southern Poland. The engine driver leaned out of the side to look along the track. Some landmarks distinguished themselves in the vast panorama of ploughed fields, grassland, hills and woods sprinkled with towns and villages, which had lined each side of the track in the last two days.

The driver turned to the fireman, who was bending to thrust another shovelful of coal into the roaring firebox.

'Not long now, Hans! Only another few kilometres,' he remarked.

Hans looked up and saw the shape of a wooden guard tower slide past the engine. (The outer perimeter ring of guard towers was situated some kilometres from the three main camps at Auschwitz and the towers were manned when working parties of prisoners were out of the camps during the day. There were, of course, guard towers around the camps themselves.)

'We must be up to the outer guard perimeter.'

The driver nodded, but said nothing more for the time being.

Behind the engine, the nine cattle trucks contained about 520 Jews from one of the ghettos, situated in large towns and cities in Poland. They were packed around sixty persons to a closed cattle truck. Ventilation came from a single tiny window set up high towards the roof of the truck, and that was covered by barbed wire. Whole families, couples and individuals tried to cling to life and their sanity as the truck swayed to the endless

21

drumming of the rail joints on the wheels and the occasional judder when crossing points.

A section of an old oil drum was the only sanitary convenience and most tried vainly to keep as far from it as possible, as it had long since filled to the top. A few people had slumped to the floor, or as near to the floor as the press of bodies would allow. Some of these were dead, usually the sick and old people. Some were unconscious; some were too exhausted to stand any longer.

Conversation was negligible. What was there to say? No one knew where the train was going, only that they were to be 'resettled' in another camp, in 'the East'. However, they had been travelling mainly south.

Suddenly the train sounded its steam whistle three times for three seconds.

Josef Sussman lifted his eight-year-old daughter Rebecca to the wired ventilation space and asked, 'What can you see, child?'

'Only fields and trees,' she replied after a few seconds.

Just then a wooden guard tower flashed into her limited field of vision and then was gone again.

'I saw a guard tower, just then,' she told her father, 'I think we must be getting near to wherever we are going.'

In another place not too far away, another man named Josef heard the same far-off train whistle and sighed, because he knew what it meant. SS Obersturmführer Dr Josef Mengele rose to his feet from the seat at his laboratory at Auschwitz. He left the slide he was studying in the microscope and rubbed his eyes.

'Helga!' he called to one of the nurses who assisted his medical research in the laboratory. 'Telephone Scharführer Leun for my car!'

'At once, Herr Doktor,' replied Helga.

Dr Mengele looked out of the window to see if any rain was falling or likely.

It was May 1943, the weather was fine and he discarded the idea of a greatcoat. Taking off his immaculate white smock coat, he hung it on a peg and put on his tunic, belt and pistol. Lifting his cap from the peg, he set it on his head and checked his appearance in a mirror. He knew that some of the ladies

22

considered him good-looking. Indeed, with his family background, schooling and education to his present position as a doctor, he prided himself on looking neat and tidy and displaying fine manners, when he felt like it.

Mengele felt torn from his beloved medical research to go and meet another incoming train, because someone 'high up' in Berlin not only urged on his research, but also gave him the facilities to carry it out. More importantly, it kept him from service with perhaps a Waffen (armed) SS division fighting the Russians. On the Eastern Front, with its dangers and privations, he could be usefully employed with the unending streams of wounded to attend to, but he much preferred to remain where he was. True the place had an infernal stink of the crematoria, from the smoke that drifted over to Auschwitz I camp from Auschwitz II camp at Birkenau, a few kilometres away. At least here in this domain, he was one of the 'Princes over Life and Death' – quite literally.

Putting on a slightly larger sized white smock from the pegs over his uniform, Mengele strode from the room and out of the door of the laboratory. Scharführer Leun, his driver – and bodyguard, if he ever needed one – held open the door of the Horch car. Mengele got in and sat in the back seat. Glancing around, he noticed no one. Any few prisoners not already at work, passing in the vicinity, miraculously managed to disappear as soon as they caught sight of the white smock. It was not wise to linger in this area of Auschwitz and fall under the gaze of Mengele, 'The Angel of Death'.

Mengele relaxed for the relatively few minutes that it took his driver to exit the various guard checkpoints of the Auschwitz I complex and drive to the ramp of the Auschwitz town railway station, which was where incoming trainloads of Jews finally stopped. (Later in the war, the railway line was extended into Auschwitz II camp at Birkenau, where trains could be unloaded, but not until 1944.)

In the steam train, the driver had approached another set whistle point and had sounded two steam whistle blasts of three seconds each. His train was expected, but the whistle routine indicated, to those who listened, the general time of the train's arrival.

As the train ate up the last kilometre or so, rows of barbed

23

wire became visible some few hundred metres from the railway tracks, strung between concrete posts and with wooden, or more solidly built, guard towers manned by the SS guards at regular intervals. In the distance billows of smoke came from some sort of industrial complex with several squat brick chimneys, and overall a horrible indefinable stench lingered.

The train slowed down to a crawl and the fireman dropped off the side to wait until the engine and trucks had fully passed. Pulling a long metal lever, he heaved the points over, so that the train could reverse into its destination.

He waved his arm over his head from side to side and the engine driver sounded the steam whistle to give one long last blast and pushed the drive lever over to reverse. Slowly the engine pushed the trucks a short distance back the way they had come.

The gradual, slow puffs and bursts of steam from the pistons sounded like sobs, as if they knew what scenes of tragedy were to befall most of the people they were carrying. Clanking slowly round the curve the train reversed off the main line at the points. When the engine passed, the fireman rejoined the driver, as the train backed towards a special siding to one side of the main railway station. The Jews in the cattle trucks were slightly pleased that the journey at last seemed to be ending.

The train backed slowly on to one of the sidings and stopped with a final hiss of steam. Nearby a similar train of cattle trucks stood on another siding, but without an engine. The incoming engine would be shunted to couple up with those other trucks and take them away in due course.

As the train stopped, orders rang out by mouth and loudspeaker and, as if in a long running play, the 'cast' of guards and prisoners began to present the penultimate scene in a huge deception. From the cab the driver and fireman watched proceedings, but not too obviously, as there were SS officers scanning the area and giving orders. They would only see this scene of the 'play'.

At a furious pace, prisoners, dressed in blue and white striped garments, pushed box-like steps up to the edge of the still wired closed doors of the cattle trucks and guards stepped up with a prisoner to each door. At a given signal, the SS guard cut the wire strands with wire cutters and pushed up the

24

bolt. The prisoner then pulled the door completely open and guard and prisoner stood each side of the door.

A loudspeaker crackled and a voice announced in Polish and German: 'You have arrived at a new resettlement camp. I am sorry to learn that feeding arrangements during your journey had broken down. You will soon be given hot food, drink and accommodation. Please get down from the trucks and line up in fives quietly. Leave any luggage in the trucks and it will be sorted out and taken to your dormitories for you. If anyone is sick and cannot walk to the camp barracks, then we have lorries to assist you! A doctor will see you shortly. When that time comes, state your *Beruf* (occupation), if you are asked.'

The Jews started to climb down from the trucks, exhorted by the guards to be quick, but even then prisoners or guards were prepared to help lift down a child or aged person to the raised section of ground alongside the rails. It was not really a platform; it was exactly what the prisoners referred to it as – a ramp.

At the edges of the area stood SS guards with dogs on leashes, to prevent people from wandering off. Everything seemed to be anticipated, there were gangs of prisoners to unload any dead bodies on to low-wheeled carts, gangs to unload any belongings, gangs to empty the toilet drums and clean the trucks out. Here and there another category of prisoner, wearing stout boots, peaked caps and dark jackets, organized the men in their groups. An armband on their arms proclaimed their status – *kapo* – boss, prisoner overseer. They also carried wooden clubs and used them to encourage their charges to greater and speedier efforts.

Dr Josef Mengele arrived on the scene, standing out in his white coat amongst a small group of SS officers. He had not always worn his white coat for 'selections', but now he wore it as a badge of office. Although outranked by the camp commandant, Mengele's word or wishes were law in the camp. There were whispered rumours amongst the SS guards of Mengele having influence at the very highest levels in Berlin.

Making his way to a small table, situated perhaps ten metres from the front of the line of incoming Jews, he sat on the edge of it and swung one leg gently. It was a pose the guards had often seen him adopt. A guard and a prisoner clerk sat at the same table, but behind him, to record various details.

Relieved from his driving duties, Scharführer Leun strode along the lines, looking at the Jews. Most of them did not return his gaze. It was unwise to look at an SS man directly in the eyes, unless you were being addressed, because a guard could interpret any look as insolence, if he wished. Leun had an important task to do – a task that always accompanied Dr Mengele's 'selections' on the ramp – Leun was looking for twins. He looked for any twins, old or young, of the same sex, or from both sexes. He used a prisoner named Braun to assist him. Braun had sharp eyes and caused less of a disturbance pushing through the rows of people than Leun would have done.

Someone high up in the SS in Berlin was very interested in twins. This research work, into why twins occurred and what could be learned from this, had been passed on to Dr Mengele. Now the SS had located him at Auschwitz and he had a laboratory and nursing assistants. He also had a post-mortem room and highly qualified Jewish doctors to assist him, at an even more restricted location within the camp complex: in one of the crematoria buildings in Birkenau, an area off limits to everyone not directly employed there, including the SS guards. Thus Mengele had for months now an almost unending supply of twins delivered literally daily.

Whilst Leun and Braun went looking for twins in the column of Jews, Mengele nodded at an SS rottenführer (corporal), who stood at the head of the first row of five people. They happened to be a man aged seventy-two, a man aged twenty-nine, two boys aged sixteen and a woman aged sixty-eight. The rottenführer turned the people in the row to the left, which was the side that the train was standing, and then led each five up, one behind the other towards Mengele.

Mengele himself seemed detached from what was going on and merely flicked the tip of the riding crop that he held in his hand to his left or right. He whistled gently as he sat there, favouring tunes from operatic works. Right, left, left, left and right went the end of the crop. Although the Jews could not know, the tiny gesture had indicated their fate for the five – death, life, life, life and death. The people were separated and moved to the left or right respectively.

The right column with the old and very young would go directly for 'special treatment', which was a euphemism for the gas chambers. The left column would go to the barracks of the camps to live and work for a while.

The left column was further divided into columns of men and women. As the left columns were assembled, the guard at the table would ask each person *'Beruf?'* (occupation) and the clerk would note this down in a book, along with that person's name. Each successive row, seeing how the preceding row had turned and walked forward to the doctor in single file, followed on and needed little supervision. Guards at the edges of the rows encouraged them to step forward a pace, as each row went forward to 'see' the doctor.

Occasionally Mengele would ask a question – 'How old are you mother?' – when age seemed indeterminate. Sometimes there were cries of mothers separated from children. Mengele would calmly ask if the mother wished to go with her children and, gentlemanly, allow the woman to step to the right-hand column (and go to their death together). This would be followed by profuse thanks to the good Herr Doktor, who would nod and smile benignly.

The sick who couldn't walk to the camp barracks, the old, young children and mothers with children were helped up into lorries, which drove off after being filled.

They waved gaily to their relatives and called 'See you later' as they were driven off towards the smoking chimneys for their special treatment. Although these unfortunate people were not to know it, there was only one way they would exit the camp. As one of the prisoners spared to work observed, it was 'up the chimney'.

As the respective columns were led off on their way to barracks, or to the special treatment, the prisoner work gangs carried on tidying up the trucks and their contents.

Although mainly Jews themselves, these prisoners had the bonus of some of the food that they could 'liberate' from the belongings which had come in the trucks. They would not be able to open all the cases, but they would immediately be allowed to eat, or save, what food they could find. In the process any valuables had to be handed in, or the prisoners would risk a bullet, if they were discovered.

The prisoners of Auschwitz eagerly sought this type of work. Other fortunate prisoners would later sort all the contents of the suitcases and baskets after they were delivered to the Kanada warehouses near Auschwitz I camp (later in the war, within Birkenau). Thus they would get their share of food and possibly risk palming a gold coin or precious stone.

Having had them moved some distance from the ramp, Mengele surveyed Leun's haul of twins. There were four sets, comprising two boys aged twelve, two girls aged eighteen, a man and woman aged thirty and two women aged forty-six. Mengele studied them closely for some minutes. One of the older women asked when they would see their relatives again.

Mengele smiled and told them, 'Quite soon', which calmed them. The interpreter explained to them, that, as twins, they would have special privileges and not have to work. The good doctor was interested in studying twins for a research paper and they would now be led to their living quarters. A guard escorted them away on foot.

Dr Mengele walked back to his car, preceded by Leun, who held the door open for him.

The various columns and groups of people were gradually dispersed. The left women's column were led off to barracks in Auschwitz II – Birkenau. The men from the left column were escorted to Auschwitz I camp, a couple of kilometres away.

The Auschwitz extermination operation had developed into the largest, most efficient death factory the world had ever seen. However, the main function of the Auschwitz camps and their many sub camps was to provide labour for many local industries. The results of this train's arrival with 520 persons – was eight twins, 190 selected for work and 322 eliminated by gassing (including the family of Josef Sussman).

Near Auschwitz, another train whistled. Trains arrived at Auschwitz every day, sometimes many times a day.

In his barrack block, prisoner Josef Sussman tried to sleep as he wondered when he would see his wife and family again. By contrast, in a different location, the 'selected' twins thought that they were quite fortunate.

The following day was a day like any other. Trains arrived, people were selected, some were reprieved to work and some went to the gas chambers. Prisoner work parties left the camp for various tasks, some were beaten and some died. The smoke rolled endlessly from the crematorium chimneys at Birkenau. Life and death co-existed side by side.

In his laboratory, Dr Mengele studied new orders from Berlin. No new work on the research into why twins occurred should take place. Research should concentrate on experimental surgery to alter the appearance of twins of the same sex, to look facially the same. In addition, this was to be achieved without obvious scarring of the faces.

He acknowledged receipt of the order to Berlin and prepared to 'clear the decks'. Twelve sets of twins of different sexes were removed from the adjacent 'hospital' ward. These included the man and woman aged thirty years, from the previous selection process. Those twins were sent to Block 11 in the Auschwitz I camp and briefly placed in cells.

After arrangements had been made, they were taken one at a time up to the courtyard of the mini-prison, where a concealed guard shot each emerging prisoner carefully through the back of the neck, with a silenced pistol. Strangely, Dr Mengele could not bring himself to have the very young child twins killed. They were kept in a separate barrack, with a view of having them trained as messengers. Mengele informed Leun, by phone, that only twins of the same sex were required from now on.

'Helga, Renate, Gudrun, Johan!' he called to his nurses, and explained the new orders from Berlin. 'What are your first ideas?'

As usual Helga was the first to make an observation. 'Herr Doktor,' she began, 'I think that we should make accurate measurements with calipers of both twins for the record. We should then photograph each twin from a fixed position, so that perhaps one photograph of the same size can be placed upon the other, to help to identify differences. X-rays may also be of assistance.'

'Excellent Helga,' breathed Mengele. 'Those were the principles going through my mind also.'

'How about dental differences?' asked Johan, the only male nurse.

'Yes! Yes!' enthused Mengele. 'That is a less obvious area that cannot be overlooked. You have done well. Has anyone else any suggestions to offer?'

29

Renate and Gudrun shook their heads.

'Right then,' ordered Mengele, 'let us get started. Work in pairs. We have calipers. Let one measure and the other record. Each set of twins should be marked A and B and after each set is measured, let the other check the measurements of the first. We will need to ensure that we are measuring from exactly the same area of the face on each one. I will leave you to discuss the details, whilst I requisition the X-ray equipment and anything else we will need.'

'We will need more anaesthetic, disinfectant and morphine, Herr Doktor,' Helga offered.

'Yes! Yes!' replied Mengele. 'I will see to it straight away.'

Mengele sat at his desk, considering the practical side. He was a qualified doctor and surgeon, but he lacked in-depth experience of surgery, certainly recently. After reflecting on the problem, his thoughts turned to the eminently qualified Jewish doctors who did autopsy work for him over in Birkenau, in the Crematorium III building. They would be useful, and maybe a trawl through existing prisoners and incoming ones would help. He was an impulsive man for action. He told his staff he would be visiting Birkenau and summoned Leun to bring his car round immediately.

At Birkenau, several Jewish doctors worked methodically on the corpse of a twin, which lay on the autopsy table. It wasn't an autopsy to determine cause of death; the lethal injection was all too clearly the cause of most dead twins arriving there. The doctors dissected the body looking for abnormalities and recorded their findings meticulously. At the unexpected arrival of Dr Mengele, they stopped work and stood at attention to await instruction.

Mengele regarded his team in silence for some moments. 'A change of plans, men,' Mengele announced. 'Get rid of this corpse!' He noticed a look of fear cross their faces and continued, 'Don't worry. No one has done anything wrong. We are now ordered to do research on twins of the same sex. Berlin particularly wants to see how identical we can make two twins facially. Do any of you have experience on facial surgery of a minor kind, which might be termed cosmetic?'

30

To his immense relief two doctors indicated that they had had such experience and inwardly Mengele felt himself calm down.

'Fine! I think I will move you all over to the main Auschwitz camp to assist me, starting tomorrow. When you arrived here, were there any colleagues with you that had similar experience?'

The question provoked one reply with a name from one of the doctors, 'Dr Weissman, Herr Doktor.'

'When did you arrive here in the camp, do you remember?'

'January 21st 1943, Herr Doktor,' came the reply.

Mengele gestured at Leun, who wrote the name down with the date.

'Now then! Clear up here and then rest until tomorrow. Do not speak to the *Sonderkommando* (SK) about leaving. If any SK men come to you tonight with a burn, or some ailment, treat them as usual.'

The doctors nodded and Mengele and Leun swept out of the room and returned to the car.

'Drive to the main administration office back at Auschwitz,' Mengele ordered Leun, and sat back in the seat.

Leun drove off at a furious pace. Although Mengele was in a hurry, he was forced to tell Leun to slow to a more suitable speed, as he was thrown about in the back by the uneven state of the road and the potholes.

Arriving at the main administration building of Auschwitz I, Leun and Dr Mengele entered the building. The few SS guards on duty snapped to attention and the various prisoner clerks who had been seated at desks rapidly stood up and looked as alert as possible.

Dr Mengele addressed the SS scharführer in charge of administration. 'I am looking for the present whereabouts of a male inmate named Weissman, who arrived here on January 21st '43. He was a doctor by profession.'

'What was his first name and date of birth, Dr Mengele?' the scharführer enquired.

'How many Weissman doctors actually arrived on January 21st, do you think?' Mengele snarled, to cover his haste at not asking at least the doctor's first name when he was still in Birkenau.

The scharführer bawled out instructions to the clerks, 'You!

31

Over there! Check the W files for January 21st arrival '43 for a Dr Weissman. Sturmann Wolf, get your clerks to check the records of the dead.' The room was almost silent as pages of registers were hastily turned to find Weissman alive or dead.

After perhaps a minute, a clerk indicated an entry to the scharführer, who pushed him aside to see the entry better.

'Here it is, sir! Weissman, Salomon, date of birth 4/11/08. Prisoner Number 857016, Barracks 17, Road Building Gang.' He turned to Wolf, busy consulting the list of the dead, 'Anything, Wolf?'

'No, sir,' Wolf reported, 'Nothing to indicate his death.'

Leun anticipated his master's wishes and moved to the register entry to note the details on a piece of paper.

Mengele observed this. His gaze swept the room and he told the waiting guards and clerks to resume their work.

Leun drove Dr Mengele to Barracks 17. By that time of day, the work gangs would be returning, or would have returned. A few prisoners were in evidence near the entrance to the barracks, although they disappeared as the car drew up outside. Leun opened the door of the car to allow Mengele to get out, then hurried to the door of the barracks and held it open, whilst Mengele entered the hallway. The barracks were constructed in brick and had two floors, besides an attic and cellar.

Leun tugged a whistle from his pocket and sounded three piercing whistles to alert the prisoners, then shouted out loudly, 'Ältester!' for the block elder to attend. There was a scuffling of feet and two elders quickly descended the stairs and stood to attention before Leun and Mengele.

'I beg to report sirs, Ältester Schupp, Barracks 17 with 157 *Häftlinge* (prisoners),' the first block elder announced.

'I beg to report sirs, Ältester Bucher, Barracks 17 with 138 *Häftlinge*,' echoed the second block elder.

Leun read details from his paper. 'We are looking for a Salomon Weissman. He arrived January 21st '43. Date of birth 4/11/08. He was a doctor by profession'.

'I do not know such a man personally, sirs, but I will quickly check my men,' the first elder stated. He and the second elder, who nodded agreement then ran up the stairs to make enquiries.

Leun and Mengele could hear it from below.

'Attention! Silence there! Stand still and listen! Two officers are seeking a particular prisoner. Is there a Salomon Weissman here, who used to be a doctor and arrived January 21st '43? I say again, Salomon Weissman, come forward!'

For some seconds nothing happened and then from the top floor, a man pushed his way towards his ältester at the doorway.

'I am Salomon Weissman. I arrived in January '43, but I do not know which day. I used to be a doctor.'

'Good!' breathed the ältester, thankful that he had satisfied the request. 'Come with me to see the SS officers. Stand to attention at the foot of the stairs and do not speak until you are spoken to!'

The ältester descended the stairs rapidly. He was better fed and in better shape than Weissman, who descended as quickly as he could without tripping over.

At the foot of the stairs, the ältester announced, 'Sirs, I beg to report that I have found the inmate Salomon Weissman, who arrived in January '43, as you ordered.' Bucher indicated the inmate standing to attention behind him and moved slightly to one side to give Dr Mengele a better view.

Mengele studied the man's face for a few moments. As usual for prisoners, their eyes did not meet, because the inmate was not looking directly at an SS man.

'Are you Salomon Weissman, formerly a doctor, born on 4/11/08?' Leun enquired.

'I am, Sir!' replied Weissman.

'Show me your tattoo number,' ordered Leun.

Weissman moved a few feet towards Leun, rolled back his left sleeve and lifted his left arm to chest level, so that Leun could examine it.

Leun moved slightly to create a better light on the arm and read off the numbers 857016. He nodded at Dr Mengele, who had been standing in silence.

'It seems like today could be your lucky day, Weissman,' Dr Mengele said quietly. 'I may find your experience useful to me. I already have several doctors working for me. One of them mentioned your name. You will have better clothing, food and will be able to keep clean. I trust that you will prefer that to road building?'

'Certainly sir! You can be assured of my best efforts,' stammered Weissman, hardly able to believe his luck.

Leun wrote a message to release Weissman S, Barracks 17, Häftling 857016 from the road building gang and transfer him to the Medical Block, and gave it to ältester Bucher.

Having stood in the hallway for some minutes, both SS men were aware that Weissman, not surprisingly, stank. They did not want his stink in the car and they did not want the delay of Weissman trotting behind the car.

Leun then suggested a compromise. 'If I open a car window a few inches, this man should be able to stand on the running board of the car, Herr Doctor.'

Dr Mengele nodded agreement and the three of them left the barracks.

Inside Barracks 17, the inmates felt a great sense of relief after Mengele departed. They had suspected his arrival indicated a selection was about to take place.

With Weissman clinging to the side of the car, Leun drove steadily and carefully to the medical block. The sight provoked as much interest from those prisoners who witnessed the event as a bride and groom going to church on their wedding day. It was something never seen before.

Upon his arrival at the medical block, which was outside the prisoners' camp but not far away, Mengele introduced Weissman to Helga the nurse as a new assistant. He would be working with other assistants who would be arriving from Birkenau tomorrow. He instructed Helga to get Weissman fresh clothing and to allow him to get cleaned up. Then he should be shown where he would sleep and given food with the patients (twins) at meal times.

Helga showed Weissman to a bathroom with a real bath. Weissman stared at it, because it was the first he had seen since his arrival at the camp.

'Take some time to scrub yourself clean. Here is soap and a bristle brush. I suggest that you try to clean yourself, empty the water, swill the bath out and refill it with fresh water and carry on. I am sure that Dr Mengele will prefer a clean assistant tomorrow to a grubby one. There are towels. Leave your dirty clothes in the bin and I will get you fresh ones.'

She paused to think for a moment and an idea came into her head. 'Do you have lice?' she enquired.

'I don't think so, *gnädiges Fräulein*,' answered Weissman.

Helga half smiled at the polite terminology, it was some time since she had been addressed as 'gracious Miss'. 'Call me Nurse Helga,' she ordered. 'Take off your clothes!' She examined him for lice and appeared satisfied that he had none.

'That seems all right. Carry on and get clean,'

'Thank you, *gnäd* ... Nurse Helga,' Weissman corrected himself.

Helga went to a cupboard and got clean clothing and real pyjamas. She reasoned, if the twins had pyjamas, then the live-in assistants would need pyjamas too. They would also need shoes. Doubtless Dr Mengele could supply something.

She returned to Dr Mengele. 'I have examined Weissman and he appears to have no body lice, but we must ensure that these others do not bring lice with them to infect the ward.'

'Indeed, you are quite right as always, Helga,' beamed Mengele. 'I can confidently leave that matter with you to deal with. One other thing: although these men will be prisoners and may make mistakes, they are not to be beaten. Tell this to the other nurses and orderlies. They will be treated as special prisoners with privileges.'

'As you order, Herr Doktor,' replied Helga and left the room. She returned to the bathroom. Weissman was already in the bath and the water had certainly changed colour. He started to get up, but she told him that there was no need to stand to attention unless Dr Mengele or a nurse addressed him in the work place. She left clean clothes for him.

'When you are finished, clean the bath out and find me,' she ordered.

'Thank you, Nurse Helga,' said Weissman politely.

Helga left him in the bathroom and Weissman relaxed a little more in the comfort of the hot water.

She told her nurse colleagues, as she encountered them, about the other new assistants.

Her colleagues showed no real surprise. They had all been at Auschwitz long enough for little to surprise them.

Weissman reflected on his change in fortunes. A few hours ago, long hours of manual work, trying to avoid being beaten by a *kapo*, and poor food. Forced to live cheek by jowl with hundreds of others. Having to attend roll calls twice a day and endure selections at any time – an endless nightmare! Now, as he lay luxuriating in the hot water of a second prolonged bath, scrubbing his feet with a stiff brush, he noticed that he had started to hum a tune. The only music he had heard for some time had been the camp band. They played music for work gangs to leave for or return from work, or for some other occasion like a hanging.

Dr Weissman was beginning to come alive again, just as if he had been in suspended animation for months. However, he cautioned himself to remember his place and not be over-confident. Assistant to Dr Mengele or not, he was still a prisoner and would need to prove his worth.

Having bathed himself and dressed in his new clean clothes, he cleaned out the bath and put his old clothes into the bin.

Weissman looked for Helga, but she was not to be seen. He was wary of knocking on closed doors or blundering into areas that might be denied to him, so he stood at the bathroom door.

Shortly a male orderly appeared and Weissman spoke to him. 'Excuse me, sir. Can you please tell me where I can find Nurse Helga? I have just arrived here today.'

The orderly conducted Weissman to where Helga was at work, and left him. Weissman stood at attention until Helga looked up. She cast her experienced eye over him. He looked a different man.

'Let me see your hands,' she instructed.

Weissman extended both hands palms uppermost towards her. She examined them and then turned them over to examine the backs.

'Satisfactory,' she exclaimed; then she noticed his clogs.

'Your shoes will be too noisy in here. I will get you a pair of slippers and we will try to get you more appropriate shoes tomorrow. Come with me.' She took Weissman to a cupboard and gave him slippers, then went to another store to issue bedding to him. She conducted him to the small ward, which was empty of patients. 'You will sleep here. You can choose your bed. Tomorrow, other assistants will arrive here to work with you. At 6.30 p.m. the evening meal will be served. You will eat with the twins, in the ward, until further notice. I realise that you have no watch, but there is a large clock on the wall of the main ward. Put down the bedding and I will give you a quick tour of the establishment.'

Helga conducted Weissman on her tour. 'Main ward with beds for twenty patients, patients' toilets, kitchen, food store, clean utility room, dirty utility room, instrument sterilization, instrument store, operating theatre, surgeons' and nurses' dressing rooms, staff toilets – male, staff toilets – female, bathrooms one, two and three, treatment room, laboratory, Dr Mengele's office, Dr Mengele's sitting room, nurses' sitting room, orderlies' sitting room, store room for any deceased patients. The boiler room is down those steps. Any questions?'

Weissman shook his head.

'For the time being you are to remain inside. Tomorrow I will speak to Dr Mengele about exercise for you. Should any prisoner have reason to come here on an errand, you are not to discuss your work with them. You may go now to make your bed. Come into the ward for the meal and then stay in your room until tomorrow. You will be awoken at 6 a.m. and there is no involvement in the main camp roll call for inmates here.'

Weissman nodded his understanding and left the ward to make up his bed.

The following day at mid-morning, the other doctors arrived from Birkenau. The male nurse Johan showed them inside, issued them with bedding and took them to the small ward, where Weissman was already installed. He rose to greet the newcomers, amongst whom he recognized Dr Zacharius.

'Hello there!' said Weissman. 'I am pleased to meet you. My name is Weissman. Dr Zacharius, is it really you? Do I have you to thank for my being here?'

'I gave your name to Dr Mengele as a surgeon who has experience of working on people's faces to repair them after car crashes, or to provide cosmetic surgery,' explained Zacharius.

'*Prima!*' replied Weissman. 'Anything would be better than what I was doing, forced to build roads. How about yourselves?'

For a few seconds there was silence and then another doctor answered, 'Friend, we have been working on projects classified as secret, even from you. Please don't ask questions about it.'

'I apologize for my lack of tact, doctors. We must wait here until Dr Mengele calls us to instruct us. Meanwhile, please make up your beds. You seem a great deal cleaner than I was when I arrived.'

After about one hour, Dr Mengele arrived back from the

'ramp' after making a selection. Helga informed him that the new assistants were present and he asked her to assemble all the nurses and orderlies on duty in the orderlies' rest room, with the new assistants, in ten minutes.

Everyone assembled as instructed and waited. Dr Mengele opened the door to find them all standing, as there was insufficient seating. He also remained standing and addressed the meeting.

'Ladies and gentlemen, I have received instructions from Berlin. As some of you already know, our task is to experiment in ways of making two twins even more facially identical in appearance. This will probably involve operating and my new assistants already have experience in this field. Any operation is to involve the minimum of scarring. We have also begun to measure the heads of twins to determine the size of any physical differences. Photographs and X-rays may also be used. I have looked at the files of my new assistants and made a decision. From now on for communication in here you will be Assistant One, Two, Three, Four, Five and Six.' He pointed at each man in turn, 'I will get numbers to sew on your clothing and gowns in due course. The assistants will mainly be working with the nurses, who are Helga, Renate, Gudrun and Johan here. The orderlies will mainly be working with the nurses, whom they know already, and may not be in contact with the assistants much.

Let me be direct with all of you. This work keeps you and me from less pleasant duties. Numbers One to Six, it is keeping you alive and in comparative comfort, and it keeps me from the Russian Front. We must all be aware that things can change, and rapidly. We will all need to work hard and together. Please dismiss and resume your duties. Numbers One to Six remain here, and you also Helga.'

After the departure of the others, Mengele spoke to Helga and Numbers One to Six.

'For the benefit of Helga, here are some instructions for the rest of you to observe. Your clothes, laundry and food will be arranged here. Roll calls are not your concern any longer. You may not leave the building unless it is time for exercise, which has yet to be arranged. You will be fixed up with what toiletries you need and more appropriate footwear. Your contacts will mainly be the nurses. You are important to this task, but you must continue to remember your position as prisoners. Other privileges, such as books, may become available in the future. Now, tell me your numbers again.'

The men sounded off their numbers one to six. Weissman was Number Six.

'Fine! Nurse Helga will be your main contact with me, if my duties take me elsewhere. Address her as Nurse Helga. Any questions?' There were none, and Mengele left Helga to instruct them.

Later, the new assistants were shown around by Six, and returned to the ward to meet the patients. It was strange to see nothing but sets of twins in beds pushed closely together. The males were separated from the females by a series of screens and there were slightly more male twins than female. The usual clipboards with papers at the foot of the beds were absent, because the twins were all as healthy as their living conditions prior to Auschwitz allowed them to be.

Chapter 3

In Berlin, during August 1943, Adolf Hitler promoted Heinrich Himmler to be Minister of the Interior, in addition to his other duties. After a month or so, it also meant a move for myself to the Ministry of the Interior building in Moltke Strasse, not far from the Reichstag building.

By the end of that year, Himmler would have seventeen SS fighting divisions of which seven were tank divisions, besides all his men in the Sichertheitsdienst or SD, the Gestapo, the SS Reserve troops and the Totenkopf Verbände (the death's head units that guarded the concentration camps).

I had also been promoted to obersturmführer (lieutenant) for my work to date. I rarely saw Himmler these days and had my orders given in written form. Himmler wanted reasoned answers or solutions to hypothetical scenarios.

A particular question I remember being asked was: if we have small groups of men who wish to escape detection, possibly not on their own territory, how can they obtain food and survive, if actual currency is not available or acceptable? After some thought, my solution was that the men should be provided with gold rings to barter with.

When Himmler eventually read that, busy as he was with other things, he gave a secret order for one thousand gold rings to be put aside from the concentration camps and sent to Hohenlychen, north of Berlin. The rings and any other gold and precious stones would normally have gone to a special account in the Reichsbank. Naturally I had no knowledge of that, and the fact only came to light some years later.

I spent a leave visiting my parents and my sister Annaliese at our house, near Stettin on the von Eichwald estate. The war had not been going well and on December 26th came the news that the battleship *Scharnhorst* had been sunk in the Atlantic,

40

which put a dampener on Christmas celebrations. My parents were both well and Annaliese was doing well at school. She was now a member of the senior section of the BDM (League of German Girls), now she had turned fifteen.

I used my time relaxing, reading, walking and looking up old friends. I occasionally went to the cinema and liked to sit watching the boats on the sea near the harbour.

One day, after I returned to my parents' house, Annaliese took me aside with a smile and a twinkle in her eye.

'Erich,' she confided, 'Lotte wants to see you during your leave.'

'Lotte who?' I enquired teasingly.

'You know very well who I mean,' giggled my sister. 'Lotte Durner, of course. She is nearly eighteen years old now and says that she has to leave soon for essential war work. She asked me to let you call on her before you leave as well.'

I remembered Annaliese's friend as a giggly older girl who had usually been around with my sister when I was still at school. She lived in an apartment near the harbour with her parents.

'OK!' I replied, 'I will look her up tomorrow, if you wish. Does she still live in the same place?'

'Yes, still the same old place. She has not moved. Shall I ask her to expect you at ten?'

'All right', I feigned a sigh. 'Anything to please my little sister.'

'Not quite so little as I was, dear brother, nor is Lotte, I think you will find.' Without further explanation, she left the house and I sat in a chair to await my parents' return.

At 9.45 a.m. the following day, I arose, washed, shaved, and dressed in my best uniform. Outside Lotte's apartment, I paused, straightened my tie, adjusted my hat and knocked on the door. For a few moments, there was silence and I thought no one was at home, then the door was pulled open and there stood little Lotte. Only she was no longer little and the passage of time since I had last seen her, had transformed her from a giggly schoolgirl to a shapely young woman with, in barrack parlance, 'a lot of wood in front of the door'.

Lotte looked at me and grinned, 'Your mouth is open, Herr Obersturmführer,' she breathed.

I closed my mouth with embarrassment and fumbled for words. 'Fräulein Durner,' I stammered, 'I hardly recognized you.'

Lotte gently grasped my arm and pulled me inside the apartment. 'You too, Herr Koch. What a fine figure you are in that smart uniform and already an Obersturmführer, working directly with Reichsführer Himmler, I believe.'

I coughed. 'I don't exactly work with him, I am one of the people that works for him. There are many others, you understand.'

'Nevertheless, Herr Koch, it is a great honour for you and also an honour for me to have such an important person here in my apartment. Please take a seat.'

I sat down in a chair and Lotte sat on a sofa opposite, crossing her shapely legs.

'Annaliese tells me that you are shortly to leave on essential war work.'

'Yes, I am,' Lotte replied, and paused for a few seconds. 'Herr Koch, have you ever heard of Lebensborn?'

'I cannot say that I have,' I replied.

'It is semi secret,' she continued. 'Not a State secret, you understand, but something not widely broadcast to the public. Lebensborn is an organization to increase the population of true Aryans by producing babies from suitable young women and from selected partners from the military, but mainly the SS. The object is to produce healthy Aryan babies for the Reich, outside normal marriage. In this way we can increase the purity of future generations. I have been selected to apply. It is not obligatory, but I consider that I may best help the future of Germany in this way.'

'Indeed!' I replied, totally surprised. 'What will they think of next? I suppose that it is a good idea, but as you say, so revolutionary to conventional thinking that it has not been made public.'

'You are entirely right,' said Lotte, and stood up and crossed the floor to gaze out of the window. After a few seconds, she continued, 'I have known you for many years, Erich, what I am about to say may shock you, so be prepared. I need some help

42

and I have decided, in confidence, to ask you. Annaliese does not know, nor will I tell her.'

'Ask away, Fräulein Durner,' I stammered, 'I am sure nothing you say will shock me.'

Lotte still gazed out of the window and seeming to arrive at a decision in her own mind. 'The simple fact is, Erich, that I am a virgin. I wish to be "broken in", before I go to Lebensborn and I am asking for your help in this.'

She turned from the window to look at me. After a moment she giggled and smiled at me. 'Erich,' she breathed, 'your mouth is open again!'

I sat stunned for a few moments and then collected my thoughts. 'Of course, I will be honoured to help you, Lotte, but where will we go?'

'I have thought of that,' she replied. 'My uncle has a wooden cabin along the coast a few kilometres. We could go there by bicycle tomorrow, if you agree.'

'Yes! If that is your wish, then we will go tomorrow,' I said, trying to sound as normal as possible.

'It is my wish, Herr Obersturmführer. Now, if you will take an order from me, come here!'

I stood and walked over to Lotte, with my hat held in one hand. She took my hat and flipped it on to the sofa and put both arms around my neck. She had a pleasant perfume and looked up into my eyes. I gazed at her creamy skin with a pinky tinge to each cheek – what the Führer said was a peaches and cream complexion.

I stroked her blonde hair and held her tight, feeling her breasts against my chest, and kissed her on the lips. After that initial kiss, Lotte wriggled more closely against me. I kissed her again and found myself stirring.

Lotte looked up into my eyes dreamily, 'Do I shock you, Erich?'

'No,' I replied without much conviction, 'I think I have always been attracted to you, but time and circumstance have never taken things further.'

'Do you find me attractive, Erich?' she asked.

'Of course I do,' I answered.

'Do you find me desirable, Erich?'

'Believe me, I certainly do,' I told her.

'We have been taught certain things, but without practice the theory is nothing,' she continued. 'Are you sure that you find me desirable?' she asked, as she kissed me passionately.

'Definitely, most desirable,' I told her, as I tried to steady my breathing.

'Then stand still for a moment, Obersturmführer,' she breathed quietly. She unclasped her hands from around my neck, leaving her left hand on my shoulder. She slid her right hand down over my chest and down the outside of my leg. Moving her hand inwards, she brought it up the inside of my leg, until her palm could feel the hardness of my maleness. She looked up into my eyes again, ignoring the growing pinkness of my face.

'Now I believe you,' she said softly. She reached behind her for my left hand and lifted it to her right breast and held it there. 'I think that we will both benefit tomorrow,' she murmured and kissed me once more.

I distinctly remember walking back home rather stiffly afterwards.

The following day I put on warm casual civilian clothing and made a snack. I got two bottles of wine from the cellar and a corkscrew and set off to Lotte's house on my father's old bicycle.

Lotte awaited me at the street entrance to the building. She still looked very attractive despite a heavy overcoat over her white blouse and a long billowy skirt which she could cycle in easily.

She led the way out of Stettin and we cycled north along the coast on a road which was not restricted to military personnel. After a few kilometres, she pulled her bicycle over into some trees and stopped.

I did likewise. 'Why are we stopping?' I enquired.

'I am making sure that we are not being followed. I have told no one about this, but sometimes BDM girls and Hitler Youth boys follow people around to see if they are up to no good.'

We waited for some minutes, but saw no one. Lotte proceeded on her bicycle and, after a few more kilometres, turned off the road down a track. The area was forested and after a while, we began passing wooden shacks set in the trees.

She pulled up at one of them and we parked our bicycles against the wall. Lotte unlocked the door and we went inside. The curtains were closed and it was relatively dark, until she opened them. There was a sitting room/kitchen and a bedroom with two single beds at the rear of the shack. It was surprisingly warm inside, despite the cold time of year.

Lotte explained that her uncle had insulated the walls well to withstand the coldest temperatures outside, so that in normal times the shack could be used all year round, if required. There was no electricity, but there was a pump for drawing water. Lotte drew a bucket of water from the pump, lit the spirit stove and put the galvanized bucket upon it to heat.

'We could do with hot water to wash with later,' she explained.

I brought in the food and wine from the bicycle pannier and put it on the table. Despite being a virgin, Lotte led me to a bed. She seemed very knowledgeable and that helped considerably.

After the ensuing period of passion, Lotte became a real woman – a process that she demanded repeated several times.

Even passion has its drawbacks, on the way back, she found herself so deliciously sore and tender that she had to stand to pedal her bicycle, rather than sit, all the way back to Stettin.

I saw Lotte several more times, but the day soon dawned when she left for 'essential war work'. Her final observations to 'her Erich' were that she did not know when and how the war would end. A bomb could find either of us by chance, but somehow she had the feeling that I would survive. I waved her off from the railway station with my parents. My own leave would end in two days and I had to return to Berlin.

Over the same period Reichsführer Heinrich Himmler had visited Wewelsburg to meet with his generals, the SS obergruppenführers. He liked to indulge in practices that were based on the Knights of the Round Table, and indeed he had an immense round table at the castle with places for the 12 others, besides himself. Beneath the largest tower (of the three) was a crypt, in which it was intended that the insignia and ceremonial trappings of his 'Knights' should be burnt to ashes, as they fell, in battle or by age, and stored there.

After indulging in various ceremonies and exchanging Christmas presents, the obergruppenführers departed from Wewelsburg. Himmler remained for a while, contemplating the future, in whatever free time was not taken up with paperwork.

One evening, he decided to see Kaminski personally in his room. He instructed the guards to thoroughly search Kaminski and to conduct him to Himmler's own room at the castle. Himmler examined his pistol in its holster, before Kaminski arrived. He had two seats prepared at either end of a four-metre-long table. A tray with various types of alcoholic drink and glasses had been placed near the door end of the table.

The guard escort knocked on the door and opened it. Kaminski bowed to Himmler, and Himmler, who was standing, indicated that he should take the seat near the door.

Kaminski acknowledged with a 'Thank you, Excellency,' and took his seat.

The guards walked about ten paces down the corridor and waited.

Still standing, Himmler addressed Kaminski. 'Herr Kaminski, I must apologize for your stay here. I trust that you are comfortable and you are being looked after. Please help yourself to the drinks in front of you, if you wish. I myself will refrain, if you don't mind.'

Kaminski poured himself a measure of vodka and raised it to the Reichsführer, 'Good health, Excellency!'

Himmler smiled and nodded. He continued, 'I am told that you understand and speak German well, Herr Kaminski?'

'Indeed, Excellency,' replied Kaminski.

Himmler paused moved to his chair and sat down. He glanced at Kaminski, then wrote a short message in capital letters on a blank piece of paper. He rose from his chair and placed it on the table near Kaminski, although just out of reach, and withdrew to the other end of the table once more. Kaminski awaited instruction.

'Take the paper, Herr Kaminski. Read it, memorize it, ask no questions, and burn it in the fire.'

Kaminski did as he was told and burnt the paper afterwards in the open fire.

As he straightened up, Himmler addressed him again. 'Take as long as you wish for this prediction. When you are ready, tell

46

the guard that you have an answer for me. Write it out and I will send a courier to collect it. Is that understood?'

'I understand, Excellency,' answered Kaminski.

'The meeting is then ended,' Himmler stated rather abruptly. He reached for a handbell and rang it to summon the guards.

'May I be permitted to request warmer clothing, Excellency? The weather is very cold at the moment.'

'Of course, my dear Kaminski!' Himmler replied in a much warmer tone. 'It is our fault for overlooking such things.'

The guards knocked and entered and stood at attention. Himmler ordered them to take Kaminski back to his quarters, arrange warm clothing for him and ensure his comfort whilst he was the Reichsführer's guest.

After they departed, Himmler examined the fireplace for any unburnt paper and summoned an aide to make arrangements to return to Berlin.

Back in his own quarters, Kaminski considered the message he had memorized. He turned it over in his mind as he paced up and down his room. The message was brief: 'WOULD THE NEW VENGEANCE WEAPONS BEING DEVELOPED ALLOW GERMANY TO WIN THE WAR?' He himself obviously had no knowledge of such weapons, yet, at the same time, the question must be extremely important for Himmler to give it in person under such secrecy.

Kaminski again spoke to the guards, to remind them of how essential it was to have no interruptions, noise, or disturbance to his concentration. He would start tomorrow, but would need the warmer clothing before then, if possible. He would call for food when he wanted it, but otherwise, normal mealtimes were to be suspended. He was still a prisoner, but he was in a position to demand conditions for his work, on the pretext that Himmler wished it to be so. It gave him considerable satisfaction.

Before his evening meal was served, a guard brought him warm woollen socks, thick trousers, pullovers, gloves, scarves, a greatcoat. They also gave him a fur hat which had flaps that could be unfastened to cover the ears by fastening the tapes under the chin. It was a real prize and something that could suit him well for his trances. The guard remarked that it had been a gift from Himmler's Finnish masseur, Kersten. He had brought two such hats all the way from Finland. The guard neglected to say that the hat had formerly belonged to Heydrich (who had been assassinated), but it seemed a good fit and Kaminski was well pleased.

After his evening meal, Kaminski was allowed to exercise by going for a walk with two guards. They were both young men. One was convalescing after being wounded in 1943. He was in fact a Latvian from the 15th Waffen SS Division Lettisch, which had only been formed in '43.

Kaminski was allowed out of the castle and they walked around the now empty buildings of the village and along the street. The night was cold and there was a frost. The sky was clear and covered in many stars. As Kaminski paused to gaze at the sky, he thought he saw a shooting star for a moment – surely an omen of something for someone, he mused.

All too soon he had to retrace his steps to the castle and up the slope towards the sentry post at the outer wall. Back in his room, he read for a while and then undressed for bed. He left his socks on and his underclothes and put pyjamas on over the top. Although he had a blazing fire in his room, which occasionally spat sparks and made crackling noises, he intended to let it die out during the night, because that was exactly the sort of noise he did not want to distract him when he was concentrating.

Kaminski was warm and slept well. The fire crackled, spat and finally died before morning.

As the morning light filtered through the windows, Kaminski arose to make preparations. He dressed warmly, using the clothing provided, and went to the door. It had a flap in it at about eye height and he opened it (it had not been locked) to speak to the guard outside. As usual, there was a guard on the other side of the door.

'Good morning,' he hailed the guard, who got to his feet and acknowledged the greeting. 'This morning I am to start my work for the Reichsführer. As before, I must have no disturbance or noise, and I will call for food as I need it.'

He had noticed that the small hinges on the wooden flap squeaked slightly as he had pushed it ajar.

'You must understand that the slightest noise can interrupt

my concentration,' he continued. 'Please have these hinges oiled and ensure that there are no guards, who may fall asleep and snore outside this door.' The guard looked as if he would protest, and so Kaminski carried on, 'I rather think that all our heads depend on the results of my deliberations.'

The guard digested this piece of information and gave Kaminski a slight bow. 'I will convey your wishes to my colleagues and get someone to collect some oil,' he said.

The guard went along the corridor and passed on Kaminski's request to his colleagues, then returned to his post at the door. Presently another guard came along the corridor with a small can of oil, two cushions and slippers for his colleague. One guard oiled the hinges and tested the flap by swinging it to and fro, so that it could be opened to check Kaminski in his room without noise. The other guard put a cushion on his seat and the other one on the floor in front of the seat. Bending down, he pulled off his jackboots and put the slippers on. His colleague departed with the oil can and oiled the door at the far end of the corridor also. At the door, the guard sat down quietly on his cushioned seat, with his slippered feet resting on the cushion on the floor. The stone paving of the castle floor was cold to the feet, but by insulating his feet from direct contact with the floor, he should remain comfortable.

Kaminski shut all the blackout curtains and the heavy drapes over each window, until the room was practically in total darkness. Feeling his way in the room, with which he was familiar, created no problem. He felt his way to the table and picked up the fur hat and untied the ear flap fastenings. He pulled the fur hat on to his head, pulled down the ear flaps and fastened them under his chin loosely. Feeling for his comfortable armchair, he sat down, felt around his shoulders for where he had placed a scarf and wrapped it loosely around his face. From the coat pockets, he removed gloves and put them on. He placed his arms flat on the arms of the chair and assessed his comfort.

Something was not quite right with the coat. He rose and pulled off a glove, felt for the cushion at the rear of the chair and rearranged it to support his back. That accomplished, he slid back into the chair so that the seat of his greatcoat would not be disturbed, and put on his glove again.

Assessing his comfort again, he felt warm and relaxed. He listened, but could hear nothing. He sat back in the chair and let another cushion support his head. He steadied his breathing and concentrated his thoughts on Himmler's question. At first his closed eyes 'saw' pinpoints of dancing light, but then he progressed to absolute blackness.

After a while, the first hints of grey came into his consciousness, which developed into a swirling cloud that became lighter and lighter in colour, although he could distinguish nothing else.

Suddenly he was in daylight, and travelling at an incredible speed over countryside that he neither recognized nor had the time to examine. He knew that in these visions he had no control and merely had to remember what he saw and try and interpret it afterwards.

With a roar, something like a shooting star shot past him through the heavens with a fiery tail and receded into the distance. After a while, at the limit of his vision, the fire appeared to stop, an object fell to the earth below and there was an explosion.

He zoomed down towards the ground and in a clearing ahead stood an object like a pointed cigar. As he drew nearer, it caught fire at the base and shot into the sky and disappeared. Once more, he zoomed up into the sky himself and moved at an incredible speed to see the roofs of a small town come into view. As he drew nearer the town, there was suddenly an explosion, which flattened a number of houses from no apparent cause, although after the explosion there had been another smaller bang.

Back in the sky, he was amongst masses of huge aeroplanes as they roared on in formation. Suddenly at a tremendous speed another group of tiny flying objects appeared trailing smoke and fired at the huge aircraft and then disappeared again. Other aircraft appeared at fast speeds and fired on the huge aircraft, some of which caught fire and fell to earth. The small aircraft were apparently propelled by God himself, as there were no propellers to be seen.

The scene moved on over the sea. At first, looking down Kaminski saw only the waves. Then he saw a multitude of ships together, both naval fighting ships of all sizes and merchant transports. Suddenly the guns of the naval ships opened up a

50

thunderous barrage towards the shore and, like water beetles, tiny craft made their way from the merchant ships to the shore.

He skimmed closer to the waves. Up ahead a pipe stuck out of the water, with a float at its head. As he drew closer, he could hear the 'animal' snorting breath as it travelled beneath the surface. Farther off two warships were racing towards the pipe that they could not possibly see at that distance – it was uncanny.

He was conveyed over the land once more. The ground was littered with burning vehicles and buildings and the noise of battle. He was shot up high into the air, and as he turned his gaze around, he could see advancing fire in the West and also in the East as the two conflagrations moved towards each other. The fires met and died down. He found himself zooming over seas of ruined buildings. He saw many dead bodies, soldiers and civilians. He saw people shoot themselves. He saw people shot by others. Prisons were full. People were hanged.

In isolated places, a few people waited in hiding. Here and there in the countryside there were flags flying – Russian flags, American flags, British flags – there were no Nazi flags anywhere.

Kaminski felt the energy draining, the experience would shortly be ending. The sky clouded and grew dark. After some moments he could see no more. He waited whilst his astral spirit returned to his body in its own good time.

He slowly came to consciousness and removed the scarf. He opened his eyes to see only darkness and removed his gloves and flexed his fingers. He felt under his chin and untied the ear flap fastenings and pulled them upwards. His ears felt strangely warm, but he could hear nothing. He felt the chair arms under his hands and rose to his feet. The blood flowed more strongly to his legs and he remained motionless until more feeling had returned to them. He felt in front of himself and found the table. Once more re-orientated, he moved towards where the door should be and felt its stout wooden panels.

He cleared his throat and called out, 'Guard! What time is it, please? Only open the flap about a centimetre, because I am in darkness in here and sudden light will hurt my eyes.'

For a few seconds Kaminski heard nothing and then the inspection flap was opened about a centimetre. He screwed his face up from the light and looked away.

Outside the door, the guard consulted his watch.

'It is half past four in the afternoon, Herr Kaminski.'

'What day is it?' Kaminski enquired.

'January 4th,' the guard replied.

Kaminski reflected. As far as he could make out, he had been 'away' for over seven hours. As normal feeling returned to him, he blinked at the light, removed his hat and took off his greatcoat.

'Guard!' he called. 'Please unlock the door and take me to the toilet, I am desperate.'

The guard stood, unlocked the door and pushed it inwards gently. He saw Kaminski still had his eyes partially shut and led him by the arm to the toilet.

After he had relieved himself, Kaminski was led back to his room. Before the guard left, Kaminski seemed in brighter spirits and requested, 'May I please have a hot meal, as soon as something can be prepared. The Reichsführer also promised a bottle of vodka for me.' In fact Himmler had said no such thing, but Kaminski banked on the guard not questioning something attributed to the Reichsführer.

Kaminski felt his way to a window and opened the drapes and blackout curtain. It would soon be dark. He lay new logs and kindling in the fireplace and started a new fire to warm the room.

When his meal arrived, with a bottle of vodka, Kaminski realized that he had guessed correctly. He enjoyed the food and savoured the vodka. He rapped on the wooden door flap and proffered a glass of vodka to the guard when he opened the flap. The guard accepted, and toasted Kaminski's good health.

Kaminski politely nodded and smiled. He returned to his chair and sat looking into the firelight flames reflectively. As he got up to poke the burning logs with an iron poker, he could not help noticing that the fireplace had a fair-sized chimney.

I had scarcely arrived back in Berlin on January 4th 1944, to resume duties on the 5th at the Ministry of the Interior, than I was despatched as Himmler's special courier to Wewelsburg to collect another prediction from Kaminski.

This time I was flown down by Fieseler Storch light aircraft from Tegel airfield, to an air base a few kilometres west of Wewelsburg. From there, I was collected by a guard and driven to the castle. On the way, I noticed the guard's unusual insignia and asked him where he was from. The guard indicated that he was from the 15th SS Grenadier Division Lettisch. He was a Latvian, who had been wounded last year on the Eastern Front during the fighting near Kiev.

Arriving at the castle, I had a meal in the mess and was taken to see Kaminski privately. The guard withdrew down the corridor to wait. Kaminski appeared in good spirits and, as before, asked me if I wished to read the papers. I again politely declined, and Kaminski put his written predictions in a large envelope that he sealed himself and signed across the sealed edge.

I put the envelope into my briefcase and enquired if there was any message to go with the papers. I was relieved that there was none on this occasion. Taking my leave of Kaminski, I left the room. The guard locked Kaminski's door once more.

As I was saying goodbye to the commander of the castle guard, I asked why there were foreign SS men amongst his detachment. The commander told me that the Reichsführer liked to see representatives of his foreign SS legions from time to time. He also added that although I might not believe it, he had even seen a British citizen, who had been helping to recruit prisoners of war for the Britisches Frei Korps, a Mr Emery (Amery) he thought his name was.

I returned to the airfield by car. On the way I spoke to the driver, not the Latvian soldier this time.

'I understand, Rottenführer, that you see a few foreign SS men here from time to time, and even an Englishman, I hear.'

'That is correct Sir,' the rottenführer replied. 'I saw him myself and could hardly believe my eyes.'

'Do you know why he was here?' I queried.

'I don't know sir, but there was a rumour that the Reichsführer wished to know more about Britain and that the gentleman was actually helping him "brush up" his English.' (Amongst the high-ranking Nazi leaders, Heinrich Himmler was one of the few that had some grasp of the English language.)

I was surprised, but said nothing further. At the airfield, the same pilot awaited with the Storch. I checked once more that I had Kaminski's letter secure and climbed into the plane. After the usual pre-flight checks, the pilot was given clearance to take off and gunned the engine of the light aircraft. The flight to Berlin Tegel would be uneventful, unless bad weather occurred unexpectedly. The towns and fields moved slowly below the aircraft, as I reflected on my master's new interest in the English language.

Hundreds of miles away, in a part of the British Isles occupied by Germany for several years, it was bitterly cold. Not only was it winter, but the fierce winds swept in from the sea over a small island, codenamed 'Adolf'. This small island boasted one difference to Guernsey and Jersey. Alderney had a concentration camp on it, run by the SS. The Sylt camp was a sub camp of Neuengamme Concentration Camp, which was situated east of Hamburg. Like all other concentration camps (unlike extermination camps), it had a commercial function. The Alderney sector of the SS Bau Brigade was concerned with the building of bunkers, gun sites and fortifications upon the island.

The SS camp commandant did not usually get directives straight from Berlin, but in January 1944, he received the instruction to release twenty prisoners from his work force to return with a few specialist guards to the mainland (France), en route for Duisburg in Germany.

He chose Rottenführer Schmidt and a few of the SS guards, who were Croats. The commandant was further instructed that prior to their departure, the selected twenty prisoners were to be excused all work and have double food rations. No further explanation was given, but he speculated that the men were being rested and given a special diet for some sort of secret operation.

Several days later, after darkness had fallen, two lorries transported both the prisoners and their guards down to the small freighter *Franka*, at the harbour in Braye bay. After a few hours, the *Franka* sailed in convoy with the harbour escort vessels to Cherbourg in France. Once arrived, the prisoners entrained and were taken by cattle truck to Duisburg, which is near the Rhine, north of Cologne. Having arrived at the camp there, they were again rested, except for physical training

54

exercises, which they had to do each day. The guards also had to undergo physical training, although not with the prisoners.

At Auschwitz, life and death proceeded in monotonous regularity. Dr Mengele had made progress with his experiments on the twins using the skills of his prisoner doctor/surgeons. He had made them alter the face of one twin slightly to be the same as the other one. This was effected through surgical operation under anaesthetic. The problem was not the operation itself necessarily. It was the scarring afterwards and the risk of sepsis which were the major concerns. Mengele needed to reduce the post-operation effects, and the anxiety nagged at him and made him unpredictable.

The twins who had not yet been operated on had now been moved to an annexe, at Helga's suggestion, so that they didn't get anxious or frightened at seeing their fellow prisoners after operations. The twins in the annexe were able to lead a more or less normal life and were not confined to bed. They dressed and exercised daily in a restricted area. They were issued with playing cards and board games like chess, and even had a record player with a limited supply of records to divert them.

Naturally they asked about the other members of their families from time to time, and were usually pacified by being told that they would be together again soon. The twins remained oblivious of the daily cycle of harsh working conditions, meagre food, beatings and death which were familiar to the ordinary prisoner of Auschwitz I Camp. It was as if life had miraculously provided them with a safe oasis in a barren desert of death and decay. Illusions at Auschwitz existed. It made the terrifying reality more palatable.

The Britisches Frei Korps had been moved to barracks in Hildesheim, south of Hannover. Early attempts at recruiting further members by parading at prisoner of war camps had been met with catcalls, jeers and derision.

The German officers in charge of the Frei Korps then decided on a different course of action. They arranged that several Britisches Frei Korps men would arrive at the administration offices of a prisoner of war camp, outside the prisoner compound. Individual prisoners of war would be called for from within the camp and then directed, seemingly carelessly, to the 'wrong' room to receive mail, or a Red Cross parcel. In the 'wrong' room, they would find several SS soldiers laughing and joking and would be invited inside. They would then discover the SS men were British or Commonwealth former prisoners who had thrown in their lot with Germany to fight the Communist menace from the East. Faced with this scenario and without their colleagues for support or counsel, this did succeed in swelling Frei Korps numbers slightly.

Some prisoners did opt for the 'better' life, but others refused. The prisoners who did accept were transferred to the Frei Korps barracks without returning to their huts. During the next prisoner roll call, German guards removed the personal effects of the departed prisoners from their huts and these were sent on to Hildesheim.

In their barracks was a portrait of the Duke of Windsor, the former King, who had actually met Hitler at Berchtesgaden, before the war. The B.F.K. were encouraged to regard him as a fellow rebel and the rightful King of England.

Their main effect on the morale of British and Commonwealth prisoners of war could not be measured. On occasions, outside working parties of POWs would come across a couple of lorries carrying SS troops, temporarily delayed by some 'mechanical hitch'. It must have been bewildering to see and hear those SS troops whistling or singing 'It's a Long Way to Tipperary' or other British songs. The more observant prisoners could even see that these healthy SS men had Union Flag emblems on their arms and appeared to be British. If, as prisoners of war you are led to believe that your side is winning the war, it was mind-boggling to find the enemy had seemingly plenty of your own countrymen fighting on his side already.

Yet, in the same way, thousands of Russians had taken the same route out of their prisoner of war camps. In total some 800,000 Russians would serve or fight for Germany, during the war. That was more than any other 'enemy' nation provided for the German war machine.

* * *

Far from the Britisches Frei Korps in Hildesheim, Heinrich Himmler was at his own eastern headquarters, named Hochwald. Hitler had his own headquarters nearby, called Wolfsschanze or Wolf's Lair to the east of Rastenburg. Seated alone one evening in January 1944, Himmler read the contents of Kaminski's sealed prediction report.

He could recognize and interpret most of the things that Kaminski described. The 'shooting star' with the fiery tail was a V1 rocket. The small 'pointed cigar-like thing' was a V2 rocket. The small aircraft trailing smoke were the rocket-powered ones, and the ones without propellers were the new jet planes.

Sooner or later the Allies would have to invade France, Belgium or Holland, and that would need a huge naval operation preceded by bombardment of shore fortifications and guns.

Himmler did not correctly interpret the 'animal' breathing underwater through a snorkel. However, he did correctly surmise that if Allied shipping were able to develop their radar to identify and attack submarines by the radar sighting of periscopes, then the future for U-boats looked grim.

When the Allies got a foothold in the West and the Russians continued to advance from the East, they would inevitably eventually meet. The military forces of these countries would probably occupy Germany. Unless the Allies fought the Russians, then there could well be retribution for those held responsible for the conduct of the war. Particularly for those involved in the secret operations which would come to light, like the 'Final Solution'.

Himmler, paled, shivered slightly, took off his glasses and rubbed his eyes. Kaminski was a remarkable man, he mused. Some of the things that he wrote could be anticipated or guessed. Other things described accurately must be beyond his personal knowledge and could only be described if he was able to 'see' certain events in the future in some way.

Himmler screwed up the sheets of paper and the envelope. He lifted the lid off a stove and dropped the papers into the flames. For a moment, he watched them blacken and curl. He started to poke at the burning sheets with an iron poker, to ensure that all the information was destroyed. Afterwards he replaced the lid of the stove, which was provided for heating, and put down the poker.

He seemed lost in a reflective mood, as he paced up and down his bunker office. Heinrich Himmler had come a long way in a comparatively short time, from relatively humble beginnings. He had researched, collected and collated men's secrets and shortcomings over many years. These files, including even one on Adolf Hitler, lay under his personal lock and key in Berlin and/or Wewelsburg.

Germany would lose the war, he reflected, despite the best endeavours of its scientists and military men. The 'writing was on the wall'. Nevertheless he wished to survive, and had been told by Kaminski how he could do so. 'No one looks for someone who is already known to be dead'. What mattered now was to commence the long process, stage by stage, of ensuring his own survival in the time left, using the resources that he had available.

In those times Himmler had agents who fed back information to the SS in almost every organization, military or otherwise, in the Reich. It followed that if he had such people, then other organizations or individuals, such as Martin Bormann, who was the Nazi Party Secretary, could have their own agents amongst his senior SS staff. Therefore Himmler determined to prevent any information leaks by doing nothing via his senior men, but to involve either one or two junior officers such as ... who?

As he deliberated, he thought of Koch as a young intelligent junior officer who could perhaps do his master's will without necessarily being aware of the real purpose. Furthermore, by signing orders which resulted in the executions of four British POWs, Koch had already unknowingly been compromised. Himmler smiled momentarily. His cunning mind began to quickly think of various possibilities, but not in any great detail. As he began to run over a mental list of tasks and objectives, he realized that Koch alone could not achieve all that might be necessary.

He picked up the telephone and phoned for an aide to attend him in his office. Within perhaps a minute Brandt had arrived and stood at attention before Himmler.

'I have decided to give young Koch one or two tasks,' explained Himmler. 'Please write down the following.'

Brandt sat down, got out a pen, and looked up when he was ready.

'Order Obersturmführer Koch to make a list of any SS officer, or NCO of German or Austrian origin who has experience of flying an aeroplane, including navigation by night and day, or naval experience, including navigation of ships. Make it clear that any circumstances, such as being dismissed from the Luftwaffe or Kriegsmarine, are not a problem for this enquiry.'

'How do you wish me to inform Koch in Berlin?' enquired Brandt.

'Send the order with the urgent mail that goes on the courier plane tomorrow,' answered Himmler, and he indicated that Brandt could go.

Himmler stood for a few more minutes thinking and then prepared for bed. He slept well that night, far better than was usual for him.

At that time advancing Soviet troops were already inside the former border of Poland. The Allies were advancing up the length of Italy. Germany was making huge efforts to accelerate the development and production of new wonder weapons including V1 and V2 rockets, mostly in secret underground locations in Germany, since the Peenemünde installations were bombed by the RAF in August 1943.

Chapter 4

After receiving my orders, I thought about the task. Although seemingly complex, the questions would not be too difficult for the clerks in the administration department of the SS Personnel File Archive. (This was naturally a time before the advent of computers.) By a process of cross-indexing, lists could be compiled quite speedily. (For example, SS officers, or enlisted men with knowledge of the Spanish language, or experience of mountaineering.) In fact the SS was such an umbrella type of organization, that there would almost certainly be SS personnel who had the experience for any type of specialist work required.

Women largely staffed this department. I had little difficulty in getting co-operation after I presented the officer in charge with a personal order signed by Himmler.

Card indexes detailed men in alphabetical name order. The cards were contained in specially designed trays which enabled the cards to be flipped open at any point. The details could then be read without having to pull the card out of the tray. The format of the cards gave basic details such as: family name, other names, nationality, date of birth, address and blood group. Next followed SS number, rank and division or administrative body. Specialist experience was also listed briefly. Wounded personnel had a yellow tag on the top of the file, which was removed if and when the person returned to active duty. SS men killed in battle, or by other means (such as bombing), had their cards removed from the main index.

It was relatively easy therefore to organize the ladies to work in pairs. One would read the first card, looking at specialist skills only. If that matched what was being sought, the lady would read off name, initials, nationality, SS number and skill to her colleague, who wrote it down. After each fifteen minute period, they changed over tasks. It was comparatively quick and easy. For example, seeing flying experience and seeing the nationality was Belgian did not come within the criteria sought and the next card would be turned and scanned.

Nevertheless, the process was time-consuming, but after a further twenty-four hours Himmler passed me an order amendment. Now anyone above the rank of hauptsturmführer (captain), or older than thirty-five years of age was to be excluded from the search.

I had already decided, that if the list looked quite large, then I would exclude *Reichsdeutsche* (Germans living outside Germany) SS men from the final list. This would then leave only Germans and Austrians on the list.

After about one week, I had a list of some sixty men's names and details. For some further days, I sat in an office within the personnel archive reading each man's file and making notes. I had about twice as many men with naval experience as those with flying experience. Further reading indicated the men who could navigate, and thus the preliminary list was then reduced to twenty-four. Seven of these were flyers, the remainder naval. The list included three men thrown out of the Kriegsmarine (navy), but no one had been thrown out of the Luftwaffe (air force). I had my final list and notes typed and sent to Himmler. What he wanted them for, I had no idea.

One of the problems that beset Heinrich Himmler was severe cramps of the stomach. He had been a patient at a clinic at Hohenlychen several times and had returned there whilst I was conducting my research. Naturally, such things were kept quiet on a 'need to know' basis. So, as I despatched papers, presumably for Himmler in his Hochwald eastern HQ, they were actually diverted to the Hohenlychen clinic, north of Berlin.

Himmler had literally been laid low by the stomach cramps many times. He had tried various 'quack' remedies to little or no avail. The best treatment seemed to come from Felix Kersten. He was a Finn who had studied massage, designed to help various complaints. Although Kersten was a large man who liked his food, he seemed to have a strange power to alleviate pain by the use of his fingers. Just as some large men seem to be able to exhibit a delicate touch for the keys of the piano, Kersten's finger ends seemed to be able to 'see' underneath a patient's skin and to diagnose and apply the appropriate pressure and manipulation to provide relief.

In fact Himmler had offered Kersten a high-ranking SS position to keep him near to him, but Kersten had declined. But Kersten's pain relief was so effective that Kersten could request favours from Himmler including the release of prisoners, and Himmler would usually agree.

Himmler sat in his day room at the Hohenlychen clinic, where he was recuperating. He possessed the ability to run a series of ideas or projects through his mind and regularly updated them. He had a good memory. He had made a decision in his own mind at the beginning of 1944 and was determined to act upon his gut feeling and Kaminski's predictions. The possessor of almost unlimited power and resources he did not find it too difficult to put an idea into reality.

He read the files of the men whose details I had forwarded to him. The naval men seemed the most interesting; especially those slung out of the navy. Before the war, his former right hand man – Reinhard Heydrich – had been a former naval officer, who had been cashiered from the Service. Heydrich had many talents, particularly organization, until British agents assassinated him in Prague.

One of the naval men seemed quite promising for what Himmler had in mind. Wolfgang Humbert, a former junior U-boat officer, who had previously had good service reports. He had fallen foul of the authorities by attempting to steal the garrison's paymaster chest from Trondheim in Norway. Where was Humbert now? Himmler read further in the notes – Moabit prison in Berlin. It seemed that Humbert had been accepted into the SS and had risen to the rank of scharführer (sergeant). Humbert had tried to carry out some similar criminal act near Smolensk, whilst in the SS. Not exactly successful, but it did indicate a man with greed for money, who might also be ruthless and daring – a man who could be useful to him.

Himmler summoned an aide and issued rapid orders.

'Have Müller (the Gestapo Chief) investigate the case of this Wolfgang Humbert. Tell him to create new evidence to implicate someone that was in Smolensk at the time and is now dead. Get on to Judge Freisler and organize Humbert's charges being dropped in the light of new evidence which will be passed to him. Humbert himself is not to be told of this. Then arrange for Müller's men to collect Humbert from Moabit prison and install him as a special prisoner in Sachsenhausen concentration camp, where the commandant will await my further instruction.'

The aide hurried away to carry out his master's bidding and Himmler stretched his limbs, feeling better than for many days. He began to pace the room and run over other ideas in his mind. Calling for another aide, he issued orders for a return to Berlin as soon as possible.

After returning to the Ministry in Berlin, he was updated on developments needing his attention. He gave instructions accordingly and dealt with a mountain of paperwork. As the afternoon progressed, his thoughts returned to the long-term future. Turning to a large map of Germany, he considered certain areas with the aid of a magnifying glass. Then he called for me to come to his office.

After I arrived, Himmler told me to stand at ease and look at the map.

'A hypothetical question, Koch,' he stated, waving the magnifying glass at the map. 'If Germany were to be defeated and occupied, what territories do you think that it might lose to other countries, as happened after the last world war?'

I considered the geography of the map. 'Here in the East, Reichsführer, in the unlikely event of defeat, Germany could lose land to Poland from East Prussia. In the South, I do not see borders changing necessarily. On the French border, the Alsace-Lorraine area may again be ceded to France, and there could be interest in the Saar region by France. It would largely depend on how any agreement was carried out. For example, America or Russia might not agree to territorial gain for France, just because the land was adjacent to their own.'

Himmler mused for a few moments.

'What about our northern coastline on the West and in the Baltic?' he asked.

I again thoroughly scanned the map before replying.

'I do not see any obvious territorial change happening. These countries – France, Belgium, the Netherlands and Denmark – have all been defeated and occupied by our troops. I cannot see the Allies giving territorial land there. It would lead to bad feeling for years in the future, as in South Tyrol.' (After World War One South Tyrol was given to Italy.)

Himmler hesitated for a moment or two and then pointed to Emden on the West Coast of Germany, near the border with the Netherlands. 'How about this area, Koch? Do you think the Netherlands would want it?'

'I can't imagine why,' I replied firmly, 'It is a marshy area with little value. It does have the port of Emden, with its small population, and that is about all. I would think the Dutch have enough problems of their own already in trying to keep their land drained and usable, without taking on more of the same. This whole area up to Hamburg is a marshy area criss-crossed by dykes, and apart from the rivers and ports themselves is of little use to anyone else, as far as I can see. In addition, if Germany was defeated and occupied by the Allies, then they would need control of the ports in order to bring ships with supplies over here, both for their own people and presumably ours.'

'You are very perceptive, as always, Koch!' Himmler stated. 'In case you are wondering, I always like to try and envisage all possibilities; a bit like watching both ways when crossing the road. Thank you for the benefit of your advice. Please return to your normal duties and send another aide to me.'

I saluted and left the room. After a minute or so another aide knocked at the door and was told to go into the office. Himmler rapped out a few terse instructions to the aide (he had several).

'Get in touch with the SS Bau Brigade at Duisburg. They have a *kommando* of prisoners from Alderney who have been transferred there and rested. This is what I want them to do' – he outlined his instructions – 'now go and draw up the orders and submit them to me for signing. Top priority, understand?'

'At your orders, Reichsführer!' replied the aide, who saluted and almost ran from the room.

Himmler smiled to himself as he turned his attention back to the map. He believed in getting things done through delegation, yet in a way that his subordinates could not see the whole picture, just their own jigsaw piece.

Moving to the telephone, he ordered the operator, 'Connect me to the commandant at Sachsenhausen KZ!' (concentration camp).

The operator confirmed the instruction and Himmler put the phone down to await the connection to the concentration camp.

After a minute or so, the phone rang and Himmler picked it up. At the other end was a nervous, breathless commandant wondering why Reichsheini wished to speak to him.

'Ah! Commandant,' breathed Himmler quietly down the telephone, 'how are things in sunny Sachsenhausen? Is everything in order? Tell me, how are my "money men" doing?'

'Everything is running smoothly Reichsführer,' gasped the commandant, vastly relieved that Himmler seemed to be asking about his group of forger prisoners, who were involved in the production of various currencies including British banknotes.

'One small thing, Commandant,' Himmler carried on, 'I am sending you a special prisoner in the next few days named Wolfgang Humbert. He is to be treated the same as other prisoners for food, clothing, work and roll calls, but he must not be physically harmed. You will therefore need to tell your guards and whoever is his barrack *kapo* (foreman/overseer, but still a prisoner). He is not to be questioned, or told that he is getting favourable treatment. Understood?'

'At your orders, Reichsführer!' spluttered the commandant. 'May I be allowed...?'

Himmler put the phone down. He chuckled to himself, 'No! You may not!'

After a few days, Humbert was collected from a cell in Moabit prison and taken to the administration block. He was made to stand in a room. Already there were two other prisoners, who looked the worse for wear. It was forbidden to speak, unless spoken to by a guard. After perhaps one hour, all three men were hustled outside to a covered lorry. They were made to sit in silence and look only ahead. Humbert was used to taking orders and so he did not find this too difficult.

A few minutes later the lorry lurched off and stopped, presumably at the prison gates, for papers to be checked. Those in the rear of the lorry could not see outside. The lorry travelled for perhaps an hour until it finally stopped and the prisoners were hustled into a nearby door. Inside a similar administrative block to Moabit were SS guards and a few prisoner clerks dressed in their blue and white pyjama-like striped shirt and trousers.

Details of the prisoners were noted and then they were bustled into a store to be issued with their own striped clothing. Just before issue, a rottenführer stepped forward and asked, 'Which one of you is Humbert?'

'I am, sir!' answered Humbert quickly.

'Then this is your uniform, Humbert!' He tossed it over. 'All of you change quickly and follow this guard to your block. Do not speak to any guard unless spoken to first. Hurry up! Get a move on! This place is not a sanatorium!'

The three men rapidly pulled off their clothes and pulled on their 'stripes' and clogs. They shuffled as fast as they could after the guard. Around a wide-open area were green painted wooden barrack buildings.

A few other prisoners were to be seen. It seemed that they glanced at Humbert for longer than the other two new prisoners. Humbert also noticed that all the other prisoners had coloured triangles of cloth sewn to their shirts. There were red ones, green ones, black ones, some were brown. Some prisoners seemed to have two triangles stitched one over the other to make the six-pointed Star of David. Humbert had noticed that when he put his own uniform on, he had a large red triangle on both the front and back of his uniform. It was many times larger than the other triangles and had a white spot on it in which a large letter S was marked. Surely it is not S for schiessen (shoot) he thought? I cannot be the only condemned man here.

The three newcomers were allocated bedspace, two men to each of the three tiers of the bunks of the barrack room. They were shown where they could wash in the mornings or after work and where the latrines were. After that the block elder gave them a brief synopsis of camp life and what they should and should not do. Humbert became depressed, and he had only been there for a few minutes. Excused work until next day, Humbert had plenty of time to reflect on his misfortune. He was told that he was in Sachsenhausen KZ, north of Berlin, and that it was no sanatorium, which was something he had no difficulty in grasping.

Within a few days, he had seen things that he could not have believed would happen. Prisoners were beaten, sometimes hanged, worked until they dropped, fed with small amounts of bread and a liquid that was laughably called coffee at breakfast, and soup for a midday meal. Most prisoners could not survive this regime. Some even committed suicide at night, hanging themselves from the rafters of the barrack room.

Roll calls were held in the early hours of each day. The bodies of any night time deaths had to be present at the roll call with the living, for the numbers to tally. Yet, so far Humbert thought himself lucky, no actual blows had fallen on him – by pure chance, he believed.

Once a guard with a stout stick seemed to be going to strike him, but relented at the last moment. Other prisoners did not seem to want his company either. They perhaps sensed that the man with the unusual insignia on his clothes was special, as the S on his clothing actually indicated to the guards *Sondermann* (special person).

After only a week he had lost weight, he was permanently tired and he wondered how long he could continue before he collapsed.

Out of the blue, one day he was ordered to the gatehouse and he hurried over with apprehension. Pulling off his cap and standing to attention, he reported to the guard on duty at the gate, who indicated that he should enter the office. Inside, he was shown into the presence of Obersturmführer Hartmann, another of Himmler's aides. Hartmann played very well the part that he had been instructed to play by Himmler.

'You must be the former Scharführer Humbert?' Hartmann enquired.

'Yes, sir,' said Humbert, as he stood at attention before the SS officer.

'Humbert, I am one of the aides of Reichsführer Heinrich Himmler. Our master gets to know almost everything. In particular he always has an interest in his brave successful soldiers, as well as those who let down our SS brotherhood, like you, you miserable worm!'

Humbert visibly paled as he contemplated Himmler's personal interest.

'Someone suggested to the Reichsführer that the prisoners

here should know that they are sharing their barracks with a former SS Scharführer!' Hartmann stated, observing Humbert closely.

Humbert was desperately trying to maintain control of his bowels, an indication of his extreme fear. A cold sweat broke out on his forehead. He considered that, if he was allowed to speak, his words should be well chosen.

'On the other hand, I myself have reminded the Reichsführer that sometimes in the worst of men, something useful can be found and used, if the circumstances are right.'

Humbert sensed a glimmer of hope. 'Permission to speak, sir?' he requested.

'Permission granted,' answered Hartmann.

'I admit that I have let down the SS and I am ready in any way to try and make amends and serve my country,' Humbert blurted out.

'But you would say that, wouldn't you, Humbert! Anything to save your skin.' Hartmann exclaimed indignantly.

'Surely, sir, with my experience in the navy and the SS, I should be of more use to the armed forces than as a prisoner in here?' Humbert offered.

'That is a matter of opinion, Humbert. In what way would you be prepared to serve?' demanded Hartmann.

'In any way sir! Ten days in here would make the most habitual criminal into a law-abiding citizen for the rest of his life,' Humbert pleaded.

'Maybe, but perhaps you should be left here for a few more months and be transferred to the road gang?' Hartmann said threateningly.

Humbert was desperate and suddenly a spark of inspiration came to his racing brain. 'Sir, after a few more months in here, I would probably be dead. The Reichsführer is a great leader; surely there is some way in which I could serve him in a more useful way alive. He has enough soldiers, but perhaps my naval experience may be put to use in some way for him?'

Hartmann made no reply. He sat down on the edge of a table, regarding Humbert in silence. Humbert could hear his own heart beating rapidly and was aware of the damp sweat of fear on his forehead. Time seemed to have stood still as he waited at attention for a reply.

Suddenly Hartmann turned his head and called out sharply, 'Guard!' It made Humbert jump.

After a few moments a guard entered and clicked his heels as he stood at attention.

'Take this prisoner away!' Hartmann ordered curtly.

Humbert's heart sank and he began to move towards the door.

Hartmann called out behind him, to the guard, 'And get him cleaned up and given some civilian clothes. I want him back here in thirty minutes!'

'At your orders, Obersturmführer!' replied the guard.

Humbert felt that he had been transported to Heaven. He took some deep breaths and the spark of life in his inner self began to grow brighter. Given the benefit of soap and a hot shower, he rapidly scrubbed at the accumulated dirt on his skin.

Like a butterfly emerging from a chrysalis, he began to perceive his former self, as if he had been occupying someone else's body. Yet at the same time his instinct urged caution, he was balancing on a tightrope and one false move would likely be fatal.

As he dried himself on a towel, the guard brought him a razor and clothes. He gazed at his pinched face as he lathered up to shave and make himself more respectable. The guard passed him a comb and hairbrush, and after he had shaved, he tidied his hair as much as he could. Looking at his reflection in the mirror, it struck him that his hair had not been cut upon arrival like the other prisoners', but that seemed a lifetime ago. People learn to bury the bad times in the deep recesses of their minds, after a change for the better.

A new man presented himself to Hartmann twenty-five minutes later. A man who clicked his heels, saluted and stood to attention with his head held up – a paler version of an SS scharführer, but with some semblance of a military bearing.

Hartmann filled in various release forms for the KZ administration and led Humbert to a waiting car outside. Humbert decided that it was a good idea to be discreet. Instead of asking questions, he would keep his own counsel. The driver drove them north. As the journey progressed, Humbert relaxed a little. He watched the passing scenery of fields, trees, farms

69

and villages, like a man reborn. After the stagnation of Sachsenhausen, the very air that he breathed seemed like champagne.

After a while Hartmann broke the silence. 'I am taking you to a clinic at Hohenlychen, in the district of Uckermark. There are mainly wounded men recuperating there. You will discuss what you have recently experienced with no one, if you wish to carry on living. You are SS Scharführer Humbert again and you will be left to regain your strength for a few days.

'The Reich has need of SS men with naval experience. You will shortly be sent to a secret training unit of the Kriegsmarine (navy), although you will remain in the SS, and train alongside naval personnel. There are already a few SS men training there for specific tasks. You will not talk to them, nor will you be used operationally against the enemy, unless the Reichsführer approves. He doubtless has his reasons for this – whatever they may be. You are not to leave the clinic, and any attempt to do so will be treated as desertion. We may have travelled some distance from Sachsenhausen, but there is an equally nasty place quite near to the clinic named Ravensbrück KZ. It is mainly for women concentration camp prisoners, but there is a camp for men there also. So watch your step, Humbert!'

'You can be certain of my highest endeavours and loyalty, sir!' protested Humbert. 'I will be pleased to undertake the training that you speak of.'

'Rather you than me!' answered Hartmann, 'You "fishmen" find the sea your element, but I prefer to keep my feet on dry land.'

Humbert nodded and made no further reply. They continued towards Hohenlychen, where Humbert was booked into Professor Gebhardt's clinic, given a room, pyjamas, dressing gown and toiletries and, most welcome of all, a hot meal.

Hartmann warned Humbert that he would remain under observation, and left for Berlin to resume his duties.

At that time of the war, the German Navy had a group of seamen of various ranks who trained together at various locations. As a shortened version of their full name or title, they were known as K-Men (Kriegsmarineverband).

The German Navy started to train K-men as frogmen, after seeing successes by the Italians. They eventually moved on to train with explosive motor boats, human torpedoes, and finally midget submarines. It was dangerous work.

Nevertheless, just like the navy's U-boat arm, there was never a shortage of volunteers. Trials with German midget submarines were started. They had discarded the concept of the British X-craft midgets, which had attacked the *Tirpitz*, for their own midget submarines, which could fire one or two torpedoes.

In Berlin, Himmler had been to see a man named Braun, who worked with Hitler's photographer, Hoffman. A long time ago, Braun had been used to take and modify photographs of Adolf Hitler. These showed the face without hair or moustache and were used in eventually locating three men who could and did 'double' for Hitler.

Now Himmler wanted to utilize the same process for himself and Martin Bormann, the Nazi Party Secretary, who was probably Hitler's closest confidant.

Getting the photographs was not difficult, but subsequently finding men similar to Himmler or Bormann was much more difficult. Martin Bormann was almost unknown in Germany generally, except in Hitler's immediate circle.

Fortunately, the armed services and all branches of the SS had card indexes of personnel with photographs of all individuals in their files. Given basic features of the human face such as nose, lips, ears, face shape – round, narrow, etc – then it was relatively straightforward for clerks to quickly look at photographs and compare them against the image that they were looking for.

Although Himmler's photograph was regularly in magazines and newspapers, he was usually photographed in uniform and with a hat on. This, combined with his glasses and moustache, tended to portray an image to the public. Remove from a photograph the background, the hair, the moustache and the glasses, then fill in the area under the moustache with an ordinary hairless upper lip, and the resulting image was not immediately recognizable. Perhaps Himmler's fortune was that he had a fairly ordinary face.

71

In order to cloud the water further, another face was used in the index checking, which was actually that of a soldier who had died in Italy. This was of no practical use and was merely used to see if the clerks could in fact locate similar-looking personnel in their files.

The work was done in relays, whereby one team of 'checkers' started to look for personnel similar to the first image. After they had finished one drawer of cards, a second set started to look in the same drawer for the second image, and then the third and last set started to search for the third and final image. In this way, each team only looked for people like one photograph that they had to compare against.

It took a long time, but without removing anything from the files, lists of names were eventually drawn up, to be submitted. It was quite easy to disguise the whole exercise under the heading RASSENFORSCHUNG (race research). A suitably briefed SS officer, with credentials indicating that he was from the Race Research Department, then visited the various locations of the personnel files indexes one evening at the finish of work. Given access to the card drawers, he could work in peace after the clerks had gone home. He wrote down a list, as instructed, of the details of each man named by the clerks in their earlier search. He wrote down against each name: age, date of birth, home address, present location, rank, height and any special skills. This list comprised in total several hundred people, but the list for the Himmler image was initially about seventy people.

At Himmler's request, the lists were passed to me to trawl through initially. I was given the dates of birth and told where both Himmler and Bormann grew up. I was instructed to reject anyone ten years younger, or ten years older, than Himmler and Bormann on the lists. I would then look at other details to establish which persons were closest to Himmler and Bormann and arrange these in a list, so that Number 1 started with the closest comparison, etc.

Against each entry, height and home area were noted. Naturally a Bavarian would have a different accent than a Pommeranian and a two metre tall 'Himmler' would hardly be convincing against the real Himmler's height of 1.73 metres. Himmler was a Bavarian from the Munich area and aged forty-three at that time. Bormann was also forty-three, but came from the Harz Mountain area of central Germany. He was also stouter than Himmler.

Having made a list, I was also authorized to make evening visits to the files and actually look at the photographs themselves. From these visits, I amended my list to give the names of those most closely resembling the Reichsführer Himmler and Reichsleiter Bormann. The factors that I considered were resemblance, age, home area and height – in that order. The lists for each man were thus changed and a 'top ten possibles' emerged. Himmler gave orders that each man was to be photographed and medically examined. This would allow other factors such as build and any deformities or wounds to be recorded. Any front-line men on the list were temporarily, or permanently, pulled back behind the lines.

This produced surprising results – for example the Number 1 contender for a Bormann double had a club foot and had to be placed much lower down the list (but not discarded altogether).

Himmler studied the results in privacy as they arrived. Bormann lookalikes had their details passed to Martin Bormann himself at the Reichschancellery. It was decided that the top five 'Himmler lookalikes' should be filmed walking, saluting, and reading an extract from a speech. For this purpose, they were brought to Berlin and steps were taken for them not to meet each other.

They were briefed on their possible future appearance in a propaganda film and they were given a run-through of what the film makers expected them to do. Basically they had to walk along a corridor towards the camera, pause within two metres of it, come to attention and give the Nazi salute, and pass into a room beyond to read the speech extract whilst seated at a desk.

This was run through without a camera, until the film maker was satisfied. Then the sequence was filmed using two cameras, one in the corridor and one in the room. The corridor and room had been specially prepared, so that there were no mirrors or glass in which the actor could see any reflections.

Finally the actor was dressed in officer's boots and a black full-length leather coat. As he stood in the corridor for another take, the director put clear glass rimless glasses on the actor and asked him to keep still. Unseen, an assistant placed a peaked hat on the actor's head, which the director adjusted. Finally, to complete the make up, the director applied a false moustache to the actor and told him to run through everything as before and remain seated at the desk after reading the speech extract.

Everything went to plan and, as the actor sat at the desk afterwards, the assistant came in behind him to remove hat and glasses, which were placed in a cardboard box. The director removed the moustache, apologized for any discomfort and made general pleasantries as he helped the actor off with the coat and boots.

Eventually several short clips of film joined together were delivered to the Ministry of the Interior for my attention. Each actor had his name given on a clapperboard, so that he could be viewed normally and dressed to look similar to Himmler. The Ministry had a projection room and Himmler ordered me to preview the film sequences and give my opinion on whom I thought was closest to Himmler himself. He also got me to order the projectionist to set up the film, show me how to work the projector and then leave. I then locked myself into the room, started the projector and turned off the lights.

The pictures flashed before me in quick succession. I watched the film, stopped the projector, rewound it and watched the film again, several times. I decided that actor 1 and 4 seemed the closest to the Reichsführer in appearance. In fact actor 4 seemed very promising. His name was Heinrich Hitzinger, a scharführer in the GFP Secret Field Police. He not only had an uncanny resemblance to Himmler, he even had the same initials, HH.

I made my report to Himmler in writing, removed and kept the film and carried on with my tasks. Himmler was once again in Rastenburg and did not return for some days. When he had viewed the film, he also agreed that actor 4 looked the best 'double', with Number 1 as an alternative. I had nothing further to do with this project and never saw Hitzinger again until 1945.

Hitzinger was contacted once more and told the 'good news'. He was to undergo secret training to learn how to represent

Himmler convincingly, for use as and when required. In return, he would be well paid, kept away from the fighting and bombing and have an easy war service. As an alternative, he was told that refusal would result in him being sent on an 'Ascension Day Kommando' on the Eastern Front (a suicide mission). Not surprisingly, Hitzinger chose the former.

His previous unit was advised that Hitzinger had been transferred to the Eastern Front. His former comrades thought Hitzinger must have got into trouble to be transferred. They never saw him again. Some time later, his old unit and the SS Personnel Bureau were informed of Hitzinger's death on the Eastern Front. Heinrich Hitzinger now officially ceased to exist, although he was alive and well.

Hitzinger was kept at a secure house north of Berlin. He was no longer allowed to move freely and was effectively in protective custody. Here he was medically examined. His blood group was checked and was found to be the same as Himmler's. Hitzinger was measured with both tape and callipers to establish how he varied from Himmler himself. Most importantly, his teeth were examined and his dental details were recorded. Heinrich Hitzinger had one more tooth in his mouth than Himmler did – it was perfectly healthy, but was removed by an SS dentist within a few days.

Himmler gave instructions for the SS Personnel Dept to 'post' Himmler's present dentist elsewhere. This was not the same man as had removed Hitzinger's tooth. Finally, Himmler had his own dental records changed to agree with those of Hitzinger, and this included substituting X-rays of Hitzinger's teeth for Himmler's. Fortunately Himmler had no dental problems and had no need to see a dentist for the foreseeable future.

Hitzinger settled down to a diet of being taught about Himmler's background, relatives' names and dates, identifying other major SS and military persons from photographs and films and receiving lectures on Nazism to indoctrinate him further. He also had to listen to speeches by Himmler, watch films of him and practise his mannerisms, walk, salute and so on. It was time-consuming, but Hitzinger proved a good mimic. He could look and act the part quite well, but his grasp of 'who was who' from photos etc was taking longer to absorb. His teachers were patient with him.

He differed from Himmler in one main way physically. Hitzinger was slightly plumper in the face. In height and build they were similar enough. Himmler now had a close double and planned to create an even closer match.

Chapter 5

At Auschwitz, Dr Mengele's team had succeeded in making minor surgery to make one twin look even more similar to the other. Slight alterations were made to facial bones in some cases. In others, the face could be slimmed down by the removal of a small strip of skin. The remainder of the skin was then stitched together very carefully, in areas such as creases in the skin, so that any resulting scar would be less obvious.

This was all done under general anaesthetic. The Jewish doctor surgeons did the actual surgery, whilst Mengele allowed them to demonstrate what they could do. As this meant several Jewish doctors had sharp scalpels in their hands during the operation, an SS orderly observed from a window in the adjacent room. The orderly held a Walther pistol in his hand in order to protect Dr Mengele if necessary.

The doctors were intent on the operations and nothing happened. The main difference was the experienced surgeons used finer needles and thread to do the actual stitching together of flesh. This part of the operation was done much more slowly and carefully than a doctor might normally stitch up a wound in a hospital.

In Berlin, however, nothing surgical was contemplated with Hitzinger at that time. He continued to learn his role, under the guidance of his tutors.

At the same time, near Emden, rottenführer Schmidt of the SS Bau Brigade arrived from Duisburg. He was on the opposite side of the river to Emden and further from the river mouth. He shivered as he explored the area on this bank of the Ems. It was marshy ground, thinly populated, with just a few small villages and hamlets and farms in between.

Some isolated farms were run-down and neglected because their owners had undoubtedly been conscripted into the armed services. The remaining women and children could often not carry on alone. In other cases, the death of the owner meant that other members of his family had to move to relatives, as there were no prospective buyers for the farms at the time.

Schmidt had made his way down several farm tracks to explore the possibilities. Finally he found an abandoned farm, with the farm buildings close to the river yet screened from the coastal road by trees. The farm buildings included a dilapidated boat-house and dock with lock gates. This would allow a water level to be preserved within the boathouse dock, irrespective of the height of the river, as it was affected by the tides. It was exactly what he had been ordered to look for. The wood of the lock gates looked in good condition. The boathouse was quite large containing a central dock with some four metres of dry land around it, within the walls. The dock was ten metres long and five metres wide.

Schmidt found a broken length of wooden ladder a few metres long. He carefully lowered it into the water at various places around the perimeter of the dock to ascertain its depth. He made a few written notes, returned to his motorcycle and rode to the nearest village. A check with the local Burgermeister (mayor) indicated that the farm owner had been killed in the invasion of Crete. The man's wife had gone to live with relatives in the Black Forest, near Freiburg.

After reporting his findings to the SS Bau Brigade in Duisburg, he was told to await an engineer, who would arrive in a few days. Schmidt had found accommodation locally, whilst he waited. He was glad of the free time, but becoming tired of the locals, who wanted to pump him for news of the war. Perhaps they thought every soldier was in the front-line. He did not wish to explain that he was just a concentration camp guard for prisoners on building projects. However, it was far better than the bleak wind-swept island of Alderney, where he had been based.

The engineer duly arrived and made his own investigations and report from the location that Schmidt showed him and passed the details back to Berlin by telephone from the village. There was nothing particularly sensitive about building dimensions, etc. He was told to wait for fresh orders, which would be phoned. Next day, Berlin informed him he was to stay there with Schmidt and act on the instructions being sent to them via the camp at Duisburg.

At Duisburg, the former Alderney camp prisoners were assembled with their guards, together with various building materials and tools, loaded into three lorries, and driven off to meet up with Schmidt, after written orders had been received from Berlin.

The lorries arrived at night and Schmidt met them on his motorcycle and led them off the road to the farm buildings. The lorries could be easily hidden in the barns, for the time being. The prisoners were unloaded and soup (brought with them) was heated and distributed with bread. A guard rota was drawn up. The prisoners were told that escape attempts would result in their death on capture, besides that of some of their comrades. Their lives were therefore reliant on their fellows. With the availability of plenty of straw, prisoners and guards not on duty settled down for the night, in different parts of the barns.

The next day the lorries' contents were unloaded completely and two lorries departed back to Duisburg.

The engineer was up early, making his own calculations to interpret the orders which had been received from Berlin. Initially, the water-filled dock was covered with wooden planks and a small moveable scaffolding structure was erected on the planks. The engineer could now closely examine the wood of the boathouse roof to assess its condition. He found one patch of rot in one beam, which was later replaced. At the same time, two guards erected signs adjacent to the road, which indicated that entry to the farm was now officially barred.

They did not expect 'visitors', but to preserve a degree of secrecy, the prisoners had been issued with ordinary work clothes, as opposed to the usual pyjama-like striped uniform.

Over a period of days, the planks were removed from over the dock and the dock itself was drained. The water was pumped from the dock into the river outside the lock gates. This continued until the water that remained in the dock was too shallow for the pump.

Some prisoners had to descend into the dock and empty the

remaining water by filling buckets, which their colleagues at ground level hoisted and emptied. The remaining mud and debris stank, but now the hard work began, as it was scooped out of the dock base to increase its depth to five metres. In addition the dock length was cut away and excavated to give a length of thirteen metres, which took it close to the end of the boathouse. This involved strengthening the sides of the dock with braced wooden shuttering to prevent them collapsing into the excavation. It was quite difficult. Metal sheet piles were used at the lock gate end.

The work was exhausting, but fortunately the prisoners had benefited by being 'rested' beforehand. It was found better to tip the spoil from the dock length extension into the mud at the bottom of the dock, so that this drier soil helped dry out the mud a little. Nevertheless good progress was made. All eyes were on the engineer as he periodically dropped a line to the mud level to calculate the depth of the excavation. When he gave 'the nod', the workers could have a rest.

All excavated soil, rubble and mud was carefully removed from the boathouse. It was put into one of the barns, to allow it to dry out more, with a view to putting it on the fields of the farm later. It was absolutely forbidden to tip the mud into the river, which gurgled a few feet away. Any tiny leaks in the lock gates had been sealed with hot bitumen to keep the water out.

Finally the engineer was satisfied with the dimensions of the excavation and called a halt to work for that day. The prisoners had food and were left under guard to chat or sleep, as they wished. The next day concreting started. They had brought a large commercial concrete mixer with them and the prisoners were well experienced in this work. They had been used to building concrete bunkers and gun emplacements on Alderney, which is why they had been chosen for this work.

Mixed concrete was conveyed to the boat shed by a chain of metal barrows and tipped into the base of the dock. Two prisoners, actually standing in the dock base, moved the concrete mix around with shovels to give a fairly uniform level to the base. At six measured locations, a twenty-centimetre-long threaded bolt was pushed into the still soft concrete with the open threaded end vertical. After this was completed, the prisoners in the bottom of the dock were hauled out and the concrete was allowed to dry.

Whilst it dried, the prisoners assembled wooden shaped fixtures of stout wood to the engineer's specifications. There were three of them and they appeared to have no obvious purpose.

After the concrete dryness had been tested, a few days later, the prisoners installed more wooden shuttering, one section at a time, around the three sides of the dock (other than the lock gates), and into the space between the layers of shuttering, further concrete was poured. This was done gradually, so that the concrete could set between each half-metre of height being added. Concrete was also used to strengthen the section underneath the lock gates.

Finally, after the space of some days, when all was judged ready, the shuttering was removed and any air pockets in the poured concrete were patched. The work force was then sent back to Duisburg under guard, leaving just a few guards at the site to wait until the concrete strengthened.

It was several weeks later when two lorries returned with crates and another gang of prisoners. They were soon put to work. Outside, near one of the barns, some prisoners mixed concrete and poured it into small mould shapes that were set on a 'skin' of metal on the ground to create slabs like paving stones, but slightly thicker. They were also inset with lifting lugs. The other prisoners started to dig holes around the edge of the dock on both sides, at least one metre back from the dock edge. These cavities were as directed by the engineer. Most were only about one metre deep, but at least three were two metres deep. Some prisoners thought that they looked like graves, but fortunately they were not.

These rectangular cavities were also lined with a skim of concrete, so that they resembled small empty concrete boxes set in the dock surround inside the boat-house.

So far their presence had not noticeably come to anyone's attention, either from the road, or from ships and patrol craft on the river. In fact by keeping an unobtrusive watch on the river, work was stopped and the concrete mixer was stopped, when a patrol craft was in the vicinity. A fence also shielded the prisoners from being seen from across the river whilst working. No lights visible to either road or river were shown at night.

The engineer had kept his superiors informed of progress every other day throughout the project. One afternoon, two lorries arrived with further materials and guards from the Bau Brigade's parent concentration camp of Neuengamme, near Hamburg. Their guard commander passed Schmidt and the engineer new orders. Basically the engineer had to explain what he had already prepared to the new guard commander, and then return in the same lorries to Duisburg.

The new lorries had their contents unloaded, mainly wooden crates and a few large drums. Schmidt had his men give a hand with storing them in the barns. He made a final roll call of his prisoner charges and handed over to the new guard commander. Schmidt then got his guards and all but five prisoners on the lorries, together with the concrete mixer, and departed.

As the lorries rolled out to Duisburg, leaving one remaining at the farm, the new guard commander opened his sealed orders. These gave reference to the numbered crates which he had brought with him, and the drums. The prisoners were made to open the wooden crates and transfer their contents to the concreted cavities which their chief guard indicated. These 'bits and pieces' largely meant nothing to the prisoners. The metal drums were carefully rolled out to the deeper cavities and carefully hoisted in to lie on their side. Thin shims of flat metal were placed over the cavities.

Next the pre-made concrete slabs were carried out between two men, who held them by a metal peg inserted into the carrying lug at each end of the slab. The slabs were light enough to be carried by one man, it merely made it easier to use two men. The guard commander could see that as the prisoners covered each hole with one or more slabs, the next cavity was exactly one or two slabs away.

After covering each cavity, the guard marked each slab that covered it with a letter in chalk. Thus, as they progressed, the prisoners gradually slabbed the whole three-side flat surface surround of the central concreted empty dock. When this was completed, the prisoners were led off for a meal in a barn. The guard commander remained and drew the internal slabbed area accurately. His plan showed the location of each slab that

82

covered a cavity. Thus anyone with the plan could determine which slab covered cavity 'A', etc. The contents of the cavities were listed separately.

After his own meal, the guard commander had the chalk marks washed and scrubbed off the slabs. Sand was brushed in between each slab. The concrete mix had deliberately included a sprinkle of dirt and soil to give the concrete a 'less than new' look.

More concrete was mixed by hand, but in much smaller quantities than previously had been used for lining the dock. The new concrete was used for making a lip to the dock between the dock sides and the first row of slabs. Into the lip, a number of small hinged metal rings were placed around the edge in the wet concrete.

After this had dried, the wooden fabrications made by the previous gang, were taken to the boathouse and placed in the base of the dock in specific positions, according to the written orders. The wood was drilled to correspond with the threaded bolt positions and then they were placed over the bolts. Washers were added and the wooden assemblies were bolted down to the concrete dock floor. The rigidity of the wooden structures was checked and all loose rubbish was removed from the dock. The whole of the dock interior, base, all the wood and the dock sides were then painted with a dark blue paint, almost black.

After the paint was dry the next day, the guard commander with a colleague slowly raised the 'paddles' of the lock gates to let river water into the dock. The water roared as it poured into the dock, swirling around the wooden structures in the base and foaming slightly. It took some time to fill, but finally the level of the water inside reached that of the river outside the boathouse. Closing the paddles once more, the guards swung open the lock gates to ensure that they functioned properly. Apart from an initial inertia, before the lock gate bitumen sealant gave way, the gates functioned without problem. The two guards then closed the lock gates completely and walked off to collect their food.

They returned an hour later and the water had settled. Peering into the water, the guard commander thought that he could still distinguish the wooden shapes beneath the surface.

This had been foreseen, and they returned to the barn where they had stored the crates and pulled out four loosely woven hessian sacks containing something lumpy. The sacks were not particularly heavy and the two guards carried two sacks each back to the boat shed. A guard tipped his two unopened sacks into the water at equally spaced points along one dock wall; his colleague did likewise on the opposite side.

It was the dock designer's 'secret weapon'. Germany was a country with many oak trees. Oak bark is rich in tannin, the raw material to tan a raw animal skin into leather. The sacks contained oak bark chippings. As they were tipped into the water, they would begin to release tannin into the water like huge teabags and thus make the water cloudy. Moreover, the cloudiness would remain in the water, unlike dirty water with soil in it, which would eventually settle if the water was left undisturbed.

Work being over for the day, the dock was left until high water. The guards let a little more water into the dock through the paddles and closed them again. Moving to a certain concrete slab, they lifted it via the lugs, lifted the metal shim and left the handle for operating the paddles inside the cavity. They also stuffed two more sacks of oak bark chippings into the concrete cavity. Replacing the metal shim and concrete slab, they dusted a little sand around the slab edges.

Various bits of 'dressing' were placed in the boat-house: an old piece of tarpaulin, a few ropes hung on the walls, the broken ladder on one side, with an empty rusty drum from a barn. A couple of old boxes were brought from the farmhouse and a few well-worn and weathered rubber tyres from the farm buildings. The tyres were hung from the metal rings around the dock edge with old pieces of rope to look like boat fenders. Best of all, an old wooden boat, with a hole in the bottom, was carried in from the riverbank and left on the dockside, as if long abandoned. The whole scene was meant to look scruffy, unused and dilapidated and in that the creators succeeded.

The following day, the drier mud and soil from the excavation, which had been stored in a barn, was dug out and transported to an adjacent field. The field had been ploughed some time ago, but the mud and soil would soon 'weather' after a little rain.

Finally, the prisoners were made to tidy away all signs of

their stay at the farm buildings. All rubbish and remaining building material was loaded into the back of the canvas-covered lorry. The straw was turned in the barns and the guard commander made a last check. Then everyone climbed into the lorry and they drove back to Neuengamme Camp, near Hamburg. Neither group of prisoners or guards ever returned to this site near Emden. Similar gangs of camp prisoners were engaged in many odd constructions around Germany. Therefore nothing was noteworthy about this one.

The plan of the location of the hidden stores was sent off to the Ministry of the Interior in Berlin. The orders also instructed the guards to despatch the two metal pegs for lifting the concrete slabs to Berlin by parcel.

The recipient in Berlin stored plan and pegs as per his own orders. He also sent off a letter to the widow who owned the farm, to inform her that the area had been requisitioned for essential war work. No changes would be made to buildings, nor would people be billeted there. Nevertheless, for the time being her former home had to remain 'off limits'.

Whilst the modification of the boat-house dock had needed a small number of men, the German war machine involved many millions of men and women as the war progressed. Heinrich Himmler had been keenly encouraging and monitoring the progress of the Vengeance weapons during this period. Launch sites for the V1 rockets were built along the northern coast of France facing England.

On June 6th 1944, the Allies landed their armies in Normandy and six days later the first V1 'flying bomb' exploded on English soil. It was a mere pin-prick by comparison.

It was a chaotic time. Initially the Germans thought that the Normandy landings were a ruse and that the main landings would be in the Pas de Calais area. Divisions of desperately needed tanks were kept back by Hitler in Northern France, instead of being deployed to Normandy.

Later in June 1944, German K-men deployed their first new naval weapon against the Allied ships supplying the Normandy beaches. This primitive weapon was basically a live torpedo slung under another, in which the operator sat under a perspex cupola. The Neger had a range of thirty kilometres and a speed of three knots. It achieved little.

Losses amongst the K-men were high. The original Neger could not dive and was a sitting target if spotted. Luckily for Humbert, his K-man training did not yet involve going on actual operations.

Gradually other naval weapons were developed for the K-men of the Kriegsmarine.

On July 20th 1944, a group of plotters failed to blow up Hitler with a bomb, placed by von Stauffenberg under a table at Hitler's eastern headquarters at Rastenburg. He witnessed the explosion from a distance and flew to Berlin to start the Coup to seize power, along previously agreed lines. Hitler was hurt, temporarily deafened, but largely intact. A phone call from Hitler convinced army officers that he was indeed alive and the plot fizzled out quickly.

Several officers, including Stauffenberg, were immediately executed by firing squad the same day. Hundreds were arrested. Some, including Field Marshal Rommel, committed suicide.

After 'show' trials in August, the chief remaining conspirators were hanged in Plötzensee prison. Families of other conspirators were held in prison, or in concentration camps, as a lesson to others.

Even with the Hitler bomb plot as a priority for Himmler, he managed to leave enough time in his busy schedule to give me orders to identify up to ten Britisches Frei Korps men who were brave enough for a special mission. This proved to be difficult, as many BFK men did not have the stomach for fighting. After some time, I identified six men and they were separated from their colleagues and sent for special training. The SS also had *Kommandos* and these BFK men were trained in the niceties of swimming underwater and using breathing apparatus. They were also trained in parachute jumping. One was killed during training, leaving just five in the 'special' group. Further training and 'toughening up' continued in many types of military establishments.

* * *

In September 1944, some K-men, including Humbert, started training on the new Seehund (Seal) two-man midget submarine, which could fire two externally carried torpedoes. They were based at Neustadt on the Baltic coast. This was by far the best underwater weapon developed by Germany beyond experimental stages. Himmler had been aware of the testing of prototypes for some time and had copies of evaluation reports.

The Seehund midget submarine was 12 metres long, with a beam of less than 2 metres. It had both a diesel engine and an electric one and could travel at 7 knots with the former, or at 3 knots with the latter. It had a range of 1,000 sea kilometres and had two major advantages over many larger U-boats. It could dive to around 10 metres in 4 seconds and had proved to be almost unaffected by depth charges. A bit like trying to squash a grape pip between your fingers, the Seehund tended to be shot out of harm's way by depth charges.

As with all new German submarines at this time, it had a built in schnorkel device, so that it could operate on the diesel motor whilst almost entirely submerged at periscope depth. The tiny periscope was effective, but was fixed. It could be rotated but not lowered.

The main controls were in tandem, as one crew member sat in a low chair behind the other. Either could operate the submarine, if required. Conditions for the crew were primitive. They could be shut inside during an operation for two or even three days at a time. Breathing apparatus could extend the duration of time submerged. Whilst under operational conditions, they could neither stand or lie down and in particular there was no toilet fixture in the craft. In addition, the single hatch was the only means of entry or exit.

The two conventional full-sized torpedoes were carried externally at the sides under metal curved rigid 'flippers' and attached to the craft by hooks. Firing the torpedoes singly or together was accomplished by pointing the craft at the target, or sufficiently in front of the target's course, activating the torpedo motor and simply unhooking them from inside, which released the torpedoes at the target. It was simple and it worked.

Besides the development of midget submarines, the main U-boat arm of the Kriegsmarine was developing U-boats which had much bigger batteries for their electric motors to propel them faster and longer whilst submerged.

It was thus envisaged that with the improvement of radar by the Allies, particularly for attack by aircraft, that these new 'electric' U-boats might be more effective than their predecessors, which could only travel at seven or eight knots whilst submerged. The type XXI and XXIII could dive and disappear in half the time of the earlier U-boats.

Germany had never built as many capital warships as the Allied navies. *The Graf Spee, Bismarck, Scharnhorst* and *Tirpitz* had all gone. Some of the remaining German larger warships were also damaged and in dock. Germany's main naval power was in submarines.

The Russians were advancing in the East. The Allies were advancing through Italy and had also landed on the South Coast of France. The Allied invasion of Normandy had broken through beyond Paris to liberate Brussels by early September 1944.

At about the same time, Finland who had been fighting on the German side made an armistice with Russia. The outlook was looking grim for Germany.

Himmler's Waffen SS troops had been fighting the Allies in Normandy, some months earlier. They had also been resisting the Allied paratroop drop at Arnhem, in Holland, fighting alongside troops of the regular German Wehrmacht (army). The attack was beaten off after days of heavy fighting, although many Allied soldiers were able to withdraw back across the river.

With the advance of the Russians in Poland, Himmler ordered that the gas chambers and crematoria at Auschwitz II Camp – Birkenau – should be blown up and all traces destroyed. These orders were carried out, but destruction was not total, particularly as some of the chambers had been underground. The crematory ovens at Auschwitz I were dismantled. The adjacent gas chamber had not been used for some time.

For the time being, the camp prisoners remained at Auschwitz, but plans were made for evacuation, both by train and by marches to other areas closer to Germany.

Dr Mengele remained at Auschwitz. No incoming train-loads of new prisoners meant no selections at the ramp for him to attend. One of the 'Princes over Life and Death' began to imagine that he would become redundant and forgotten. The prospect of being transferred to some field hospital, close to the enemy front line seemed a likely prospect.

Out of the blue, he received enquiries from Berlin concerning the progress he had made on making twins more facially identical. Berlin wanted to know if he could operate on a German to do the same sort of thing. Mengele replied that he and his team probably could perform such an operation, if he had details to study beforehand. If he was unable to see the 'subject', he needed large photographs and facial measurements of both persons.

Several days later, he received a telephone call ordering him to attend the SS headquarters in Krakow at the end of the week. On the appointed day, scharführer Leun drove Dr Mengele to Krakow. An SS sturmbannführer from Berlin met Mengele and conveyed him upstairs to an office.

'What I am to tell you and show you, Dr Mengele, is a matter of State secrecy. You are to discuss this with no one. Understood?' demanded the sturmbannführer.

'Of course, Sturmbannführer, I am used to working on projects which are classified as State secrets!' replied Mengele haughtily.

The sturmbannführer took large photographs from his briefcase and placed them on a table. He laid them out carefully, spaced apart and placed a typed list of measurements at the last photograph. He invited Mengele to inspect them.

Dr Mengele moved to the table and looked at the photographs and swallowed hard. The photographs clearly showed what appeared to be Heinrich Himmler, full face, without glasses, and further photographs half profile of the left and right side of the head and full profile of each side. This set, together with the written data, was labelled A.

Before Mengele could ask questions, the sturmbannführer placed other photographs, full face, half and full profiles, in the spaces alongside the first ones. These were labelled B. Mengele looked at them. They were also of Heinrich Himmler, but, if he glanced from A to B and back again quickly, there seemed to be slight differences between the photos.

'Is this the Reichsführer?' enquired Mengele.

'Is who the Reichsführer?' answered the sturmbannführer mockingly.

Mengele looked at the photos again for a few seconds.

'Is this the Reichsführer?' he asked, pointing to the photos marked A.

'No! That is not the Reichsführer!' answered the sturmbannführer, as uncommunicative as ever.

'Then is this the Reichsführer?' Mengele asked, pointing at the B photographs.

The sturmbannführer seemed to be enjoying himself. 'Who do you think it is, Mengele?' he demanded.

Mengele stammered, 'I think this is the Reichsführer in these photos marked B.'

'Why?' enquired the sturmbannführer.

'Well, because he looks like the Reichsführer!' Mengele answered, as he began to get annoyed.

'So! Dr Mengele, if this photo B is the Reichsführer, then who is this in photo A?' asked the sturmbannführer.

'A twin or double, I suppose,' replied Mengele in frustration.

'Why is it a twin or double, Doktor?' demanded the sturmbannführer.

'Because B looks slightly different to A. Both are very similar, but there are small differences, particularly here in the cheeks. Look B seems to be thinner in the face,' Mengele answered.

The sturmbannführer looked at Mengele quizzically for a few seconds.

'This *is* the Reichsführer Heinrich Himmler in photographs B. This a double in photo set A. The question is, Dr Mengele, can you get A to look closer to B, without obvious scarring?' the sturmbannführer asked, placing another list of measurements beside the B photographs.

Mengele looked at list B and compared it with A. He studied it in silence for two minutes or so. At length he told the sturmbannführer, 'Yes! I think I can. I believe that I could do it!'

'The Reichsführer will want a better guarantee than your

belief, Herr Doktor, he will want your assurance. Can I give him that?' demanded the sturmbannführer.

'Given appropriate medical conditions and my own work team and instruments, then you have that assurance!' Mengele exclaimed.

'I am sure that you will be held to that,' replied the sturmbannführer quietly. 'Will you take a schnapps, Doktor?' he asked in a more friendly tone.

The two men relaxed over a drink or two and began to make plans. Mengele was given the photos, lists and further verbal instructions.

When the sturmbannführer escorted Mengele back to his car, he listened for a moment. Far away he heard a distant rumble.

'Is that thunder I hear, Doktor?' he enquired.

'Sort of!' smiled Mengele. 'It is the sound of the approaching Russian guns!' As he drove away, he noticed that the sturmbannführer looked aghast.

Chapter 6

In battered Berlin, Himmler was busy. He had SS divisions fighting on both Western and Eastern Fronts. However hard they fought alongside the Wehrmacht, they were gradually being forced back towards the borders of Germany itself.

He was involved with the preparation of a large thrust that Hitler had decreed in the Ardennes to recapture Antwerp in Belgium. His SS tank troops would be in the thick of the fighting there. A few American-speaking German soldiers would be used in captured jeeps to create confusion in the lines principally held by the Americans, in what would become the 'Battle of the Bulge'. He considered using some of the Britisches Frei Korps men, but discarded the idea.

I was working on a plan to hide small groups of soldiers in enemy-occupied territory, in order to attack the enemy as and when required. This was known as operation '*Werwolf*'. I concluded that the best idea was to devise a way of hiding the groups in a small underground base, in a wooded area. The obvious problems would be a water supply and sanitation, if such groups were to avoid detection.

I eventually hit on the idea that near isolated villages, water was usually piped from a large tank covered in earth, from the highest ground point nearby. If a bunker was built in a nearby wood, then a simple pipe could also be installed just under the ground surface from the water tank to the bunker. Dependent on the sites selected, the distance might only be 200 or 300 metres for such a temporary pipe. I considered other problems and eventually made a sketch with a short report, which were sent up to Himmler's office.

After Himmler had time to read the report and think about it, he dictated a few further notes to a secretary and then I was ordered to search for suitable sites in various parts of Germany.

There were to be 400 of these *Werwolf* bunkers in locations from the former Polish border in the East to the Dutch border in the West. I could not search alone, because the area and numbers of sites were too large, so I was ordered to consider sites at three areas – between Emden and Wilhelmshaven, between Bremerhaven and Hamburg and in the area west of Neumünster, which is north of Hamburg and towards Denmark.

This work took me some time, and the weather at that time of year did not help. Eventually I located three sites which I thought would be suitable and made my report back to Berlin. Himmler decided to make a start in the West and several *Kommandos* of prisoners from the SS Bau Brigade were sent out by lorry from either Duisburg, or Neuengamme camps to begin the work. The prisoners, as usual, were not allowed to see where they were going and wore civilian clothes. I had chosen isolated locations and the guards could ensure more privacy by placing the usual 'barred area' signs on nearby lanes and tracks, and keeping watch.

The following description details the construction of one of these *Werwolf* bunkers. The precise location of the sites was given by map co-ordinates and denoted by measurements from the edge of the wood involved. The actual bunker sites were always away from any path or track and the lorries involved were hung with camouflage netting to hide their outlines. The work mainly took place in the daytime and prisoners and guards slept in a farm barn away from the bunker site. The farmer who owned the barn was paid for this. The farmer's house was far enough from the site so that he could not see where his barn 'guests' went each day.

Great trouble was made to cut away the surface of the ground within the selected wooded area intact and temporarily store it nearby. The surface was frozen, but deeper down the digging was easier, and by laying tarpaulins on the ground at the finish of work, the ground could still be dug the following day. The 'spoil' from the digging was loaded on to the lorries that had brought the *Kommando* there and taken away daily, except for a small amount which was kept. It was simple to get rid of, because there were many bomb craters around the larger towns and on, or near Luftwaffe airfields.

As the work progressed, sentries were posted near the work site at night, when work had finished.

Concrete was mixed some distance from the actual work site, so that no signs of it should be left in the vicinity of the bunker. The water for the concrete mix was brought by a lorry which carried a water tank. The prisoners built a reinforced concrete rectangular four-sided room under the ground surface. It was initially open to the sky, and a section of water pipe with a tap was installed in the wall facing the water tank, which was located in a field nearby. Various things were incorporated in the bunker from Himmler's own notes, although the guards and work force knew nothing of his involvement.

One evening, as darkness fell, the prisoners were made to dig a shallow channel and lay a thin insulated pipe fifteen to thirty centimetres beneath the ground to the edge of the water tank. Whilst some were doing this, others made a small covered shelter adjacent to the hump of the earth-covered water tank. After this was set up, two prisoners dug into the earth. In the dim lights of torches, which were thus shielded by the shelter from being seen outside, the grassy turf was carefully removed and set aside.

Eventually the prisoners dug in as far as the side of the tank, which was made of metal. A special bore was used to cut through the tank. When it was withdrawn at a given signal, a narrow jet of water shot out of the hole. A prisoner quickly capped this by using a mallet and a piece of wood to bang in a specially shaped metal bung with a valve.

This bung was threaded at the end protruding from the tank. After being inserted into the side of the tank, the threaded end of the pipe being laid was connected and tightened. The valve was turned on and the connection inspected for leaks. All was well, no problems. A guard shone a torch towards the wood and another guard called down to the bunker. In the excavation, a prisoner hung a bucket under the tap and turned it on, when told by the guard. After a few gurgles of air being expelled, the tap poured water in a steady clear stream and it was turned off.

The water tank earthwork was carefully covered up again and the pipe channel was refilled with earth and covered with turf. Footprints were also erased as the gang made their way back to

94

the bunker site. Work having progressed to the satisfaction of the chief guard, they finished for the night.

The 'roof' consisted of a relatively thin layer of reinforced concrete poured on to wooden planks which were held up from below by further pieces of wood to stop them sagging in the middle, before the concrete dried. An area for an access hatch was left in the roof area where indicated on the plan. Several ventilation pipes were also inserted into the roof area.

The roof access hatch was designed around a domestic metal drain cover, which was concreted to fix it in place fifteen centimetres below surface level, with a fourteen centimetre vertical metal strip surrounding its edges. A similar strip was welded to the rectangular metal drain cover and metal lifting rings also welded in position. The cavity created above the drain cover, within the vertical metal strip was filled with earth and grass. The concrete roof was then re-covered with earth from the original excavation, and landscaped with the turf that had been retained, so that the roof was not a flat area.

A large fairly flat rock partially covered with moss, which had been brought with the work *Kommando,* was also landscaped into place adjacent to the hatch. It was to help locate the bunker hatch entrance and also served to lay the hatch on, after it was pulled up (or lifted up, if there were people inside the bunker), so that its weight did not mark the grass or ferns.

One air vent was disguised as a rabbit hole, although, where the hole curved out of sight, a wire mesh kept any real rabbits out of the vent. The turf was also put back except around the other vent pipes, taking care to blend in the edges carefully with the surface that had been relatively undisturbed.

Before they finished this operation, a lorry was sent off to collect and load the items detailed for the bunker. When it returned the prisoners spent the next few days installing them in the bunker.

These items included: a metal ladder, to be eventually fixed beneath the hatch, pieces of wooden bunks for four people, heavy storage batteries and lots of marked wooden crates – all sized to go through the hatch. There was a bicycle frame and bicycle parts, including one bicycle wheel without a tyre, an air pump, a chemical toilet, drums of kerosene and a pump for pumping out water, etc. Various instruments were attached to the walls.

Within the bunker, two prisoners constructed a simple table and assembled several wooden bunk beds. Two others assembled parts of a cupboard made of heavier wood; this was wooden backed and attached to the wall, as detailed in the instructions. Yet others put together a kerosene oven/stove with the associated pipework up through an air vent, which would take the fumes away. A chimney of pipes was fitted together and put inside a dummy tree trunk from the Berlin film studios. This 'tree' assembly was fitted over an air vent pipe on the surface, so that the kerosene fumes could be taken away by the wind about four metres above ground level.

The tree trunk looked just like a tree hit by lightning. It came on a metal base and was bolted down to the concrete roof of the bunker. Earth and turf was laid around it and slightly up the sides. It looked very realistic.

At another vent pipe another dummy tree was used, so that it looked in keeping with its dummy neighbour, although it was not an identical tree. In fact it contained a narrow periscope which led down into the bunker beneath. Unlike conventional submarine periscopes, this was similar to that on a midget submarine, very basic and only a thin pipe with mirrors. It was set so that it could be raised or lowered a few centimetres only. It could view the area on the surface around the bunker through 'woodpecker holes' in the 'tree'. These were located about four metres from the ground. The chimney and periscope were sealed in the dummy trees, so that rainwater could not enter, and small drainage holes were set into the 'trees' near their tops, to allow any rainwater to drain out.

Finally, after completing most of the bunker interior installations, a small concrete 'shelf' was installed about one metre below the hatch. It was partially supported by horizontal metal bars on the top of the metal ladder, which was attached vertically to the side of the shelf, and was designed so that a person crouching on the shelf and straightening up could open the lid from inside the bunker, as the hatch was pushed upwards overhead. Alternatively the hatch could be replaced above one's head by gradually crouching down on the shelf as it was lowered into place.

It also meant that in an emergency the people entering the bunker could safely jump into the open hatch cavity and close the hatch over them.

Finally, the chief guard inspected the interior of the bunker and raised the periscope to viewing height. He peered out at the four viewing points and, after satisfying himself, lowered it again to the built-in stop. He checked the water tap. It worked, and he turned it off and left the bucket underneath the tap. Glancing around, he checked that all relevant parts of the installation were above the surface of the floor and away from the walls.

Shouting up to a guard on the surface, he was lowered down a last crate, which he placed on top of the others. He then climbed out of the bunker by the metal ladder and supervised the hatch cover being placed in position carefully, with adjacent grasses lifted out of the way so that they did not interfere with the seal. The lifting rings of the hatch were carefully buried just under the surface of the soil in the cover after being measured from the rock. These details were then marked down on the plan by the guard.

He walked around the wooded area, even into areas where they had not been, to ensure that no prisoner had thrown any item away. He found nothing, and made his way back to the prisoners. The concrete mixer was loaded on to the back of the lorry and all signs of the bits of spilled concrete or odd bits of gravel were swept up and put into sacks. When all was tidied up, the lorries, with guards and prisoners aboard, drove away from the site and collected their road guards and signs. They then drove back to their camps.

Germany had many areas which were not heavily populated. It was felt that there was little chance of these 'works' being discovered, unless perhaps an aircraft crashed in that area of the wood by chance. The locations were certainly off the beaten track for any foreseeable fighting with the enemy.

Over a period of time, after prisoner *Kommando* work gangs completed similar work in various parts of Germany, the individual marked plans eventually arrived at Himmler's headquarters in Berlin. They were duly filed, amongst the Reichsführer's papers. The selection of (mainly) men for future possible *Werwolf* operations behind enemy lines was unobtrusively begun.

* * *

97

In the middle of November 1944, a sedative was administered to Heinrich Hitzinger's food. After a short while, he became sleepy and his face was covered with bandages to conceal his appearance. Two male nurses were summoned and the 'patient' was taken in this state, under conditions of extreme secrecy, to an airfield north of Berlin.

He was carefully loaded into a Junkers transport plane that had been waiting on standby and within a few minutes it took off. Himmler did not have control over the Luftwaffe, but his intelligence system was such that he knew things which were to the detriment of many people, including members of the armed services. It needed little persuasion for the appropriate air force officers to write the orders for the aeroplane movements, without Himmler's direct involvement being visible.

A few hours later, the Junkers descended after an uneventful flight to an airfield near Katowice in Poland. After the engines were switched off, an ambulance backed up to near the side door in the Junkers' fuselage. Two SS medical orderlies unloaded the 'patient' into the ambulance, under the watchful eyes of Dr Mengele.

The ambulance drove off towards the Auschwitz I Camp. Dr Mengele accompanied the patient to check his respiration. Shortly afterwards the Junkers was refuelled and flew back to its home base.

At his 'hospital' outside the Auschwitz camp, Dr Mengele had his own nurses and orderlies take over the care of the patient. They carried the still sleeping Hitzinger inside the building on a stretcher and set him on a couch in Dr Mengele's own room.

Leaving Helga to check on the patient's condition, Mengele gathered his nurses and the Jewish doctor surgeons together into the sitting room to brief them.

He asked the assembly to make themselves comfortable. Some nurses chose to sit. The doctors for the most part leant against the walls.

Mengele began, 'Ladies and gentlemen, the day has arrived. We have in a few hours to perform our most important operation of our time here. It is an operation where there is no room for mistakes. It must succeed. I have no need to tell you what failure might mean to ALL our futures. To you doctors, I repeat my guarantee that nothing will happen to harm you. If this operation turns out well, you will be evacuated with other prisoners from the main camp to other camps within the Reich, within a few days. Number Six, you have studied the photos of the patient and another person, are you satisfied with what you have to do?'

'I am, Dr Mengele,' replied prisoner doctor surgeon Number Six. 'I feel confident that we have a good chance of success.' If he recognized the person in one set of photographs, he chose to remain silent.

'Very well.' retorted Dr Mengele, 'I suggest we all get some rest for a few hours, until the patient's last meal has been digested. We do not want any possibility of choking under anaesthetic!'

Mengele left the room. The nurses and orderlies talked quietly. The 'Numbers' asked permission to step outside to get a breath of fresh air, which was granted to them. The Jewish doctors stood outside in the fading daylight, trying to ease the tension in their bodies. They were lost in their own thoughts of their pasts and what they dared to hope for the future. They stood or walked a few steps in silence. Their eyes were open, but they took no notice of their immediate surroundings. As medical men, they were aware that their own pulse rates had already speeded up and strove to take deeper breaths to calm themselves.

Although there were other prisoners in barracks nearby, there was comparative silence in the camp. It was as if it too was waiting.

At length, Number Six, who seemed to have become the leader of the Numbers, led the way back inside the building. The doctors all showered and scrubbed up, changing into sterilized gowns, trousers, caps and face masks and placing wooden clogs on their feet.

The nurses and orderlies had undressed the patient and dressed him in an operation gown and cap. He was carried into the operating theatre and placed up on the operating table under the large light.

Outside, in another part of the building, an orderly started up a generator, just in case there was a breakdown in the electrical power, so that they could switch to an alternative source.

The nurses laid out the sterilized instruments and swabs in the operating theatre and stood in readiness. The Jewish doctor surgeons entered the theatre. Each had a large number between one and six embroidered on the chest area of his gown. Dr Mengele entered the theatre two minutes later, scrubbed up and gowned. In order to make him immediately identifiable, should there be any problem, his gown had large runic SS insignia on the front and back.

'In your own time, Number Six,' requested Mengele.

Number Six asked Number Three to administer anaesthetic to the patient, who had been showing signs of the sedative wearing off. Number Three did so and waited, whilst he observed the patient's breathing. After a few minutes he lifted the patient's left eyelid and nodded to Number Six.

Number Six had already delegated tasks to other Numbers before the patient had even arrived and they positioned themselves to assist him. Trolleys of instruments were moved closer to the patient's head, and nurses were gently eased out of the way for the Numbers to group around the head area. Mengele could only watch a few feet away.

Six elbowed himself some more room and announced his requests and his own moves aloud, as if he was back in a teaching hospital.

In fact, after a while all the Numbers became so engrossed in what they were doing that they quite forgot Mengele, the passage of time, their surroundings, or where they actually were.

Time passed slowly for Dr Mengele. He realized that he was completely governed by the skill of his Numbers to do a job that he had neither the skill nor experience to do himself.

At length Six stood back for Two and Four to complete the tiny stitches. They took great care with every stitch to ensure the same tension on the thread. Number Five counted the swabs and instruments.

Six examined the efforts of the others and pronounced himself satisfied. Turning to Dr Mengele he announced, 'It is finished, Dr Mengele!'

Mengele drew closer and stared at the face with its tiny stitches.

'Are you sure that there will be no scarring?' he demanded.

100

'I am confident that unless the patient interferes with his wounds, that the scars will be almost invisible,' replied Six.

'Very well then. Numbers One to Six come with me into the sitting room,' instructed Mengele.

The doctors followed Mengele with trepidation, peeling off their face masks. In the sitting room, a smiling Nurse Helga proffered a tray of poured drinks.

'Gentlemen!' boomed Mengele, with bonhomie. 'Please take a drink to our success!'

He seemed oblivious to the fact that he himself had taken no part in the operation, and now the Numbers had been elevated to 'Gentlemen'. It was unheard of.

The doctors seemed reluctant, perhaps suspecting poison.

Mengele said, 'It is all right! It is good schnapps!' and took a sip from a glass himself and handed the others round. Pausing for a moment to think of an appropriate toast, he exclaimed, 'Gentlemen! To the end of the war!'

The 'Gentlemen' all drank to that.

Mengele told the doctors to relax and went out to supervise the post-operative care of the patient with his nurses.

Hitzinger remained at Auschwitz for five days, although he was never told where he was, nor was he able to explore. He was not exactly pleased to have been operated on, but there was nothing he could do about it. Number Six looked in on him from time to time to check his progress. At Mengele's request, Six also wrote notes of future treatment and when the stitches could be removed.

Finally, Mengele had Hitzinger's face bandaged as before and they both went by ambulance to Katowice airfield. There, another Junkers transport aircraft collected them and were both flown to an airbase north of Berlin. Mengele and Hitzinger were taken by car to the clinic at Hohenlychen. They both remained there for Hitzinger to recuperate from his operation.

Dr Mengele did not return to Auschwitz. By early January 1945, the majority of the remaining prisoners in the camp were evacuated in a series of forced marches to other camps. These groups included Mengele's doctors.

These marches for the prisoners were literally 'march or be shot'. Many prisoners died en route. The doctors were generally in better shape, than many of the other prisoners and most of

101

them arrived at Mauthausen concentration camp, near Linz in Austria.

Mauthausen was no sanatorium and its main industry had been the adjacent stone quarry. Conditions were harsh and the death rate was high. There was a gas chamber, but only a minuscule version of the Birkenau installations. It was not an extermination camp as such, but prisoners died in numbers daily.

At a similar time of year, one of the K-men's Seehund two-man midget submarines left Ymuiden base on the coast of Holland. The Seehund made its way down the coastline, on the inner side of the German minefields, to the Scheldt Estuary off Antwerp, Belgium.

This area was the Allies' main waterway artery to its troops in Belgium and southern Holland. It was illuminated every two miles by buoys all the way across to Margate, England. The area had been a fruitful hunting ground for the Seehund midgets, but this particular midget was on a secret mission and, unless detected, was not to use its two torpedoes.

Arriving at the English coast, it made its way northwards on the inner side of the British minefields, passing from Suffolk to Norfolk. The midget kept close to the British coast, except north of Aldeburgh, near Lowestoft and Yarmouth, where the waters were too shallow close inshore. It was hazardous with numerous sandbanks, the possibility of being spotted by aircraft or surface shipping and the chance of mines breaking loose from their moorings. Radar stations were also scattered along the coast.

Weybourne (a village north of Sheringham) had deep water off its coast. In fact the British had once considered it a possible area for a German seaborne invasion and had extensively mined the beach and placed an army base nearby.

The Seehund travelled on, schnorkelling at periscope depth, with the forward crewman constantly taking observations through the periscope. Although it was not impossible, the most difficult thing to do was to look behind them. Here the forward crewman had to get out of his seat, turn the periscope and crouch behind it, facing the other crewman. At least that was preferable to the noise and heat of the engine only centimetres behind the rear crewman's seat. Conditions inside were cramped and primitive.

When daylight and sea mist allowed, they used landmarks as reference points. The lighthouses no longer functioned during wartime, but they made useful recognition points. The Seehund submerged and ran on the electric motor when they came near any of the known radar stations on the shore. Any radar contact might be mistaken for background 'clutter' by the radar operator, but the K-men took no chances. The voyage was long, boring and uneventful.

At last the long bank of shingle was seen, which denoted the approach to Cley-next-the-Sea with its windmill. The Seehund carried on until the commander spotted the Blakeney Fairway buoy, then submerged on its seaward side in the deeper water.

After an hour, the crew blew the tanks and approached the buoy on their electric motor. Darkness had fallen. The commander got out a small package in a waterproof rubber bag and opened the hatch. He stood on a metal step below the hatch and looked all round.

All was quiet, as expected, but for the movement of the sea. With hand gestures to the crewman behind him, he guided the Seehund on a course where the buoy would gently brush against his craft. As he approached and judged the distance, he ordered the motor to be cut. The Seehund glided in to 'kiss' the side of the gently rocking buoy, and the commander grabbed hold of it. It had no bell to ring and the commander wasted no time in fastening a rope securely to one of the buoy's struts. The other end of the short rope was threaded through a metal eyelet in the sealed rubber bag and knotted several times. Then he moved the rope down the metal strut to its base and lowered the bag into the sea.

The bag was heavy and whoever had sealed it had excluded most of the air. It sank a few feet below the surface and pulled the rope taut. The commander waited for a few moments in silence, then whispered to his colleague to reverse on the electric motor. He released his hold on the buoy as soon as he heard the motor hum. Taking a final look around at the darkened English coast, he blew it a kiss with his hand.

The mission was now over, but for the return trip. It seemed a long way, just to drop something for the SS. For some minutes the commander stood in the hatchway, letting the wind ruffle his hair. Bending down he called softly, 'Do you want to see the English coast, my friend?'

His colleague agreed, and for safety's sake the commander closed the hatch. The midget submarine began to rock while the commander returned to the front seat. His colleague climbed out of his seat and on to the step under the hatch. As the boat steadied, the navigator opened the hatch and gazed out at the blackness of the coast for a few seconds. The crew then set course east again along the coast. They would have to avoid the shallow water near Cromer, before the coastline turned south.

Early the following morning, a small fishing boat left from Morston, near the village of Blakeney, and set out to inspect the crab pots just off the coast. It was nothing unusual, but a bit earlier than most mornings. As was often the case, there was a slight sea mist. The boat's sole occupant drew near to the Blakeney Fairway buoy and carefully but rapidly lifted the roped bag into the boat. The rope was undone and thrown into the sea and the rubber bag was placed into a rucksack. The boat returned to near Morston about an hour and a half later with a crate of crabs from the crab pots.

As the return voyage of the Seehund progressed, the commander had to be careful of the many sandbanks in the area. Sandbanks have a nasty habit of being moved by storms and a depth of ten metres one day might only be one metre deep a few days later. As it progressed southwards the Seehund hit a section of sandbank at seven knots and became firmly grounded. The two crewmen did everything that they could to try and get off, without success. They sent a final wireless message to Germany and prepared to abandon their vessel.

Had they been in deeper water, they could have dropped their torpedoes, but if they dropped them where they were, they might not drop at all, or be rolled on, as their vessel rolled with the waves. The only advantage was that they were on the surface, as the tide dropped.

104

Finally the crew shot off several signal flares. They inflated a small rubber dinghy and attached it to the periscope. The navigator sat in the dinghy, whilst the commander activated a scuttling charge and rapidly got into the dinghy. They cast off from the Seehund and both paddled for the mainland as fast as they could. The crew were shortly rescued and made prisoners of war. Lowestoft was treated to a really loud bang as the Seehund, with its torpedoes, exploded with a roar soon afterwards.

Within a few days, a considerable distance away at Auschwitz in Poland, the Russian Army arrived. They found several thousand prisoners still at the camp, who had been judged to be too sick to move by the Nazis. In another area of the camp, the Russians found a number of Dr Mengele's child twins alive. They were filmed again and again walking towards the camera, down a corridor between two barbed wire fences, until the Russians were satisfied with the film shots.

Some time after the Auschwitz prisoner doctor group had arrived at Mauthausen KZ in Austria, Dr Mengele suddenly arrived by car. Possibly he had been reminded by Himmler to ensure that no witnesses of the operation survived. He stood in his car during the prisoners' roll call and asked for any doctors who were with him at Auschwitz to step forward. Some of 'his' doctors were present, but all stood their ground, as if suspecting that the invitation would end in their deaths. Fortunately they were not near the front of the assembled ranks.

A lengthy silence followed on the *Appellplatz* (roll call area) at Mauthausen. Despite the cold, more than one doctor felt sweat on his brow. Fortunately Dr Mengele departed without a further search for his doctors. His doctor 'Numbers' never saw him again. He returned to Linz by car and then back to Hohenlychen by plane.

At least one Jewish doctor who had been forced to perform autopsies on the bodies of dead twins within the Birkenau crematoria complex for Dr Mengele, survived the war, when Mauthausen was liberated. It was not Number Six.

* * *

On February 10th 1945, Himmler sent a messenger to meet Humbert the submariner at the Seehund base at Ymuiden in Holland. The messenger passed him sealed orders, together with two shaped pieces of metal. Humbert read the orders, which gave no indication of originating from Himmler, after the messenger had departed. Inside the envelope was a small packet, which contained a diamond. Humbert took it out and held it between two fingers. He hid the orders in a safe place and rushed into the town, as soon as he could, to visit a jeweller's shop.

'Is this real?' he asked the aged Dutch jeweller.

The jeweller took the diamond and put an eye glass in his right eye and examined the precious stone between the jaws of small tweezers. He moved it slightly and let out a slow whistle.

'Yes! It's real, *mein Herr*! Do you want to sell it?' replied the jeweller.

'Not at present,' answered Humbert. 'What do you think it is worth?'

The old man gave Humbert back the diamond, looked into the distance and rubbed his chin in thought. After a few seconds, he wrote a figure in pencil on a piece of paper and showed it to Humbert – who also gave a slow whistle.

'Thank you!' he called over his shoulder as he left the shop.

'Come back if you want to sell it!' the jeweller called after Humbert. He shook his head. One did not see a diamond like that every day.

Five days later Humbert was crewed with another SS man, trained by the K-men. They were to embark on a regular operational sortie with other Seehund midget submarine crews, to torpedo Allied shipping in the Scheldt Estuary approach to Antwerp. However, Humbert had not been allowed out on operations before. This was to be the first time.

After the Seehunds started to leave Ymuiden harbour, Humbert's had been, by design, the last midget to leave. Unknown to him, SS engineers, dressed as naval maintenance personnel, had made slight modifications to his Seehund before his departure.

106

Humbert turned to Krauss, the other SS man, and called out, 'Change of plans, Krauss. I am turning through 180 degrees. Here are written orders for us both.'

He passed the orders behind him to Krauss to read. This took several minutes and meanwhile Humbert took them northwards up the Dutch coast, away from their intended area of action. He kept a good lookout at the periscope, as the Seehund snorkelled through the sea at seven knots on the diesel engine.

Still watching through the periscope, he called out to Krauss behind him, 'No complaints then, Krauss?'

Krauss replied that not only had he no complaints, but it seemed that he was in luck!

The hours passed, with the occasional dive if a surface ship was spotted. Humbert remained on the seaward side of the Friesland Islands, until he sighted the island of Borkum and turned inland into the estuary of the river Ems.

As they approached Emden on the left of their craft, Humbert switched to the electric motor. This slowed the speed from seven to three knots and decreased the 'feather' wake of the tiny periscope. Moreover, the design of this tiny craft was such that if they wished to show less periscope or make a shallow dive, all they needed to do was to lean forward. In addition, both had some weights beneath their seats which could be moved to alter the trim.

Emden was passed submerged, as dusk was beginning. As the darkness fell, Humbert blew a little air into the dive tanks to raise them to snorkel depth again. The periscope revealed no shipping or patrol craft and Humbert studied the riverbank on their right for a boathouse situated on the river's edge, as indicated on his orders. At last, as he was avoiding a 'dolphin' (mooring platform) in the river, he saw a boathouse on his right. It was dark, but the moon was shining brightly.

Blowing more air into the dive tank, Humbert surfaced the Seehund. Getting out of his seat, he crouched on the metal stand beneath the hatch, switched off the lights inside the boat and opened the hatch, after the Seehund had stopped rocking.

He told Krauss to pass him a coil of rope from inside and climbed up to crouch on top of the hatch coaming, holding the periscope with one hand. Calling instructions to Krauss inside, he conned the vessel to the side of the bank, parallel with the closed lock gates of the boathouse. As he approached the bank, he ordered full astern for four seconds and had the electric motor turned off.

As lightly as he could, Humbert sprang on to the bank and grabbed at the Seehund's rear towing eye. He passed the rope's end through the eye and tied a small knot and tied the other end to a metal mooring ring. The Seehund swung in the current slightly, but was tethered. Glancing inside the boat shed briefly, in the moonlight he saw the concrete blocks that he was briefed to expect. At least he was in the right place.

He could see that the river water level was practically the same as inside the boathouse dock. As Krauss waited patiently in the Seehund, Humbert opened the lock gates of the boathouse. They could open to about 135 degrees from their closed position. With the gates fully open, Humbert called gently to his colleague, 'Krauss! When I give the order, make a short reverse burst on the electric motor.'

The midget rocked slightly, as Krauss indicated that he had understood the message. Humbert nipped over to where the rope moored the Seehund and undid it. Pulling on the rope, he walked sideways towards the open lock gates. Turning the lighter end of the Seehund was not difficult, but moving the whole vessel certainly was.

Eventually he felt confident enough to call to Krauss, 'Reverse now, Krauss!'

After a second or so, the Seehund surged towards him, which made guiding it with the rope easier. Humbert ran down one side of the dock and around the end, holding the rope and pulling on it to correct any deviation from the midget's course for entering the boathouse. He got the Seehund halfway in before the portside scraped a lock gate and slowed it.

Humbert ran around to pull it clear. He was sweating hard. He called again to Krauss for one second of reverse and the Seehund glided into the dock, so that he had to strain against the towing eye to stop it from bumping the rear of the dock too hard. Humbert pulled on the towing eye to get the end of the Seehund as near as possible to the dock edge and called Krauss to get out and help him.

'Bring those two metal tools that I showed you,' he called to Krauss.

Krauss emerged slowly as the Seehund rocked slightly. He shut the hatch for safety and gently sprang on to the dockside. The Seehund made a hideous scraping noise as it moved up and down the concrete and old tyre fenders of the dockside, caused by the shift of weight.

Humbert reached into his jacket for the orders. He consulted them briefly by shielded torchlight. Taking the metal rods Krauss had brought him, he went over to the slab indicated in the plan, inserted the metal tools into the lugs and lifted it. In the cavity underneath he found more rope, and lifted it out.

Humbert got Krauss to push the nose of the Seehund nearer his side of the dock, with the section of broken ladder left on the dockside. He looped his rope through the forward towing eye on the casing of the Seehund. Two ropes, one at each end, now secured the midget. Positioning the nose of the Seehund against one side of the dock with the tail diagonally against the opposite wall, Humbert closed one lock gate whilst Krauss held the midget in place. He then got Krauss to throw over the rope on the fore end to him, on the other side of the dock. He strained and pulled the Seehund forward slightly, then started to heave the nose round to the side of the dock with the gate closed. As it cleared the centre line, under Humbert's instruction, Krauss shut the remaining lock gate. The two men then centred the Seehund in the dock by using the ropes.

Next, under Humbert's instruction, they lifted several planks of wood from the far end of the dock and placed them across the dock width. They positioned them in front of and behind the tiny conning tower, pushing them towards the tower to ensure that the planks rested under the lip of the conning tower's splash barrier.

Humbert then walked along his plank and bent forward to open the hatch of the Seehund again. He entered slowly and carefully and shut the hatch. He switched on the internal lights and, after looking around for anything he might need, or that Krauss had left, he disconnected the batteries. In darkness he opened the hatch again and lifted two small weights, used for trimming the vessel, out on to the plank. Ducking inside the Seehund again, Humbert reached out to touch the familiar diving tank vent control and opened it gently. Almost simultaneously, he climbed quickly and carefully from the

Seehund on to the plank and secured the hatch. He picked up the weights, raced the few steps along his plank to the dock side and kicked each plank a few inches away from the tower splash guard. The moonlight shone on the water and Humbert moved carefully on to the lock gates centrally with the forward end rope. Krauss had hold of his rope at the other end of the dock.

Krauss and Humbert thus held the submerging Seehund midget centrally on their ropes. They released more rope hand over hand as the Seehund became heavier with water and disappeared beneath the surface of the dock. As it finally became too heavy to be guided by the ropes, they let go of them. The Seehund gently descended the last two metres to sit in the wooden cradle (made by the prisoner *Kommando* earlier), with a soft booming noise. Even the periscope had disappeared under the surface, and although the process had produced small wavelets in the dock, the surface soon calmed.

Each man gathered a bundle of rope in his arms. Krauss waited whilst Humbert bent down and looped his rope under the hand bar of one weight and knotted it. Then he dropped the weighted rope down the edge of the dock to sink it. Krauss similarly weighted his rope and dropped it carefully into the dock.

'Well that appears to be that!' remarked Krauss, 'I did not think that I would be able to see this war out sitting at home. With an official pass invaliding me out, I can't go wrong! How about you, Humbert?'

'I have a few points to tidy up here,' replied Humbert. 'Then I will be off too.'

'What is all this about anyway?' asked Krauss. 'Why leave the Seehund here?'

'Your guess is as good as mine. I think that in our business, these things are on a "need to know" basis. If we are getting out of this war alive, I for one am not going to question it! Let's get some sleep if we can.'

Humbert and Krauss examined the buildings and found that it would be warmer in the hay of a barn than in the farm itself. They settled down to sleep after their exertions and did not awaken until 10.30 the following morning. Both men had a very quick wash from the almost freezing water of a farm tap, pulled the straw from their uniforms and combed their hair.

'Before you go, help me shift the planks out of the way,' Humbert asked Krauss.

Together they walked over to the boat shed and, taking the end of a plank each, they carried it down the sides of the dock to the end. They repeated this with the other plank. Gazing at the brown still surface of the water in the dock, there was no sign that the Seehund, or any other vessel, had ever been there.

Later that morning, Krauss waved goodbye to Humbert, as he set off to journey back to his home in Wiesbaden. Humbert warned him never to mention the mission, if he did not want to be recalled to active duty or posted to the Russian Front. Having bandaged his head in accordance with orders, Krauss was to act as if he was mentally unstable, if questioned by local officials, as stated in his discharge papers.

Humbert waited for a few hours to ensure that a curious Krauss was not going to return. He then lifted another slab and removed a battery-operated portable radio transmitter. At 3 p.m. in the afternoon, he broadcast in the open air the brief message 'The shark is sleeping'. He repeated this at intervals of forty minutes until, after the third try, the message was acknowledged. He put away the transmitter and consulted his plan for the location of other stores that he would need. He was ordered to stay at the site for up to one year, or until otherwise advised. He had the stores and provisions to do it, and a carte blanche covering order signed by Himmler himself, if he ever needed to fend off any enquiries locally, before the Allies had advanced that far.

In effect, with the Allies already occupying parts of Holland, he was being ordered to sit tight near the Dutch border until well after the end of the war. He was so inclined, because of the promise of more diamonds for his trouble. The one he had already was real and valuable, so he had no reason not to believe that he could obtain others. Humbert didn't care who paid him, if his services were valuable enough to be paid in diamonds. It was better than the prospect of possibly sitting in some prisoner of war camp, if he was captured, or losing his life on some suicide mission.

Humbert was, unknowingly, a tiny part in one of Reichsführer Heinrich Himmler's survival plans. Humbert and Krauss's Seehund was reported overdue from its mission out of Ymuiden and was eventually assumed to be lost through enemy action or accident. As far as the Kriegsmarine were concerned, both SS men were presumed to be dead. The Kriegsmarine reported this to the SS personnel department. The personnel department was later informed that Krauss was safe, but had been invalided out of the SS.

Chapter 7

In the middle of February 1945, Kaminski, the clairvoyant in Wewelsburg castle, made his move. He had been accumulating vodka in his room from his generous rations. He got the Latvian SS guard into the habit of drinking with him at night, although the guard always remained outside Kaminski's locked room.

On the night of his planned escape, Kaminski actually drank water, and succeeded in giving the guard so much vodka that he went to sleep in his seat. Kaminski knew the guard routines and he had another two hours before the guard was due to be changed.

He had prepared everything that he thought he might need and climbed the inside of the chimney in his room, trailing additional clothing below him with a series of belts and braces. At the top, he found that bars across the chimney top were sufficiently old and corroded to be forced and he got outside on to the roof of the castle.

He succeeded in moving to an area where a large metal drainpipe led to the ground, at the rear of the castle, without alerting the guards. He put on woollen gloves and donned an overcoat against the bitter cold. He had descended about five metres from the roof, when the section of drainpipe to which he was clinging suddenly gave way and plunged him twelve metres to the unforgiving rocks at the base of the wall. He was killed instantly in the fall.

His body was not found until a thorough search could be made at first light, after the Latvian guard had been found in a drunken sleep. The Latvian was placed under close arrest and the information was relayed to HQ in Berlin.

Himmler had more important problems to worry about and needed soldiers. He refrained from having the Latvian shot, and had him sent to the Eastern Front. He was killed in action shortly afterwards. Kaminski's death had tied up another 'loose end'.

One might wonder if the clairvoyant knew the time of his own death. Perhaps it was the one area never delved into, for who would want to know when they were to die?

In early February 1945, there was an extremely important meeting between the Big Three – Roosevelt, Churchill and Stalin – at Yalta. This conference decided on the post-war split-up of Germany, with zones of occupation, amongst other things. The Germans got to know of the conference decisions fairly quickly. Himmler then knew approximately which areas of Germany would be occupied by which Allied troops. This was an important factor in deciding where he would make for at the war's end.

In mid February, the Russian advance in the East had got as far as capturing Budapest in Hungary. In the West, the British and Americans were approaching Cologne in Germany. The area controlled by Axis troops was constantly decreasing.

On February 19th, Heinrich Himmler met Count Folke Bernadotte of the Swedish Red Cross for secret talks about possible offers of peace.

On March 5th Himmler privately agreed in principle to free all the Jews in the concentration camps. However, nothing actually happened.

During March, Himmler personally broke the bad news to me that all my family had been killed in an air raid on Stettin, with about a thousand others. Casualties were so bad that the dead had been buried in mass graves. He offered comfort to me, but apologized that he could not grant me leave to visit my parents' and sister's grave, due to the fighting. Himmler then made a remark which, upon reflection, I should have realized was very strange. He warned me to watch my own back, because others could be jealous of my position working directly for the Reichsführer.

I did my own grieving, but realized that I was one of thousands who had had relatives die. Himmler's brother Gebhardt was reported missing on the Eastern Front.

The Nazis still occupied and controlled Northern Germany, together with Denmark, Norway, Southern Germany and Northern Italy. The Americans advancing rapidly, had cut a swathe across central Germany towards Weimar.

On March 12th, Himmler was at Hohenlychen and agreed to surrender all concentration prisoners alive to the Allies.

By March 16th, Himmler was ill at Hohenlychen and could no longer command Army Group Vistula. A German Army general wanted Himmler to go to Hitler to convince him to seek an armistice.

I carried on working, when the incessant bombing of Berlin would allow it. On April 7th, I was passed a written order from Reichsführer Himmler to go to Munich in Southern Germany, where I would be given further verbal orders. The only remaining way to get there was by plane, because the Americans were in central Germany. The next day, I was flown down in a light aeroplane that flew most of the way at treetop height to an airfield near the village of Eschenried, north of Munich. The pilot had managed to avoid coming to the attention of Allied aircraft.

An SS scharführer met my plane, conducted me to a car and drove me to the nearby town of Dachau. The name Dachau is chiefly associated with the wartime concentration camp, on the eastern outskirts of the town. The scharführer drove, without conversation, to the external administration buildings of the camp. I was conducted to quarters and told that the commandant would see me at 09.30 hours the following morning in his office. I had a meal in the mess and slept fitfully.

The next morning I rose, washed, shaved, dressed and breakfasted and presented myself at the commandant's office. It was April 9th 1945. The camp commandant greeted me warmly and informed me that I was there to witness the execution of a prisoner, who was to be shot on the Reichsführer's orders. I had never seen actual combat and I think I blanched slightly at this news, but nodded my assent.

Within a few minutes the commandant conducted me outside and around some buildings. As we turned a corner, we happened to bump into an SS photographer complete with camera.

'Ah! Stachel!' ejaculated the commandant, 'Just the fellow, I need!'

Turning to me, he announced, 'Obersturmführer Koch, it is not every day that I receive a representative of Reichsführer Himmler here in Dachau. Please indulge me in my hobby of photography and allow my photographer to take a photograph of us both.'

Out-ranked by the commandant, I could hardly refuse.

The photographer got us to stand together and, unseen by me at that time, a man was brought out between two guards on stone steps behind us. Thus, as it was intended, when the photographer clicked the camera shutter, the photograph deliberately included the face of the man standing on the steps, behind the commandant and myself. The photographer took a couple of photographs and hurried away.

Walking out of the administrative area, the commandant paused near the steel barred gate of the gatehouse, the main entry to the camp. He walked towards it, under an archway, and pointed out to me the metal inscription set in the gate, *ARBEIT MACHT FREI* (work brings freedom). He spoke of the large numbers of prisoners in the camp and the difficulty in feeding them. Supplies were constantly being halted or destroyed by Allied aircraft.

Behind my back, two guards escorted the man already photographed, farther down the lane outside the camp wall. As the commandant turned back to me, an SS man ran up to us and saluted. He gave the commandant a paper and waited. He read it, frowned and told the SS man that there was no reply, and to dismiss.

The commandant led me about 200 metres down the lane at the side of the camp wall of the concentration camp. He paused at a gateway on the left in a wall parallel to the camp wall. He held up an arm to pause our walk. Almost gently he confided, 'Obersturmführer Koch, there appears to be a change of plan. You are ordered to execute the prisoner yourself!'

'What!' I exclaimed somewhat indignantly, 'But I have never fired a shot in anger. Still less shot someone!'

He proffered the order which he had just received.

I read the words, '*To Commandant Dachau KZ: Obersturmführer Koch is hereby ordered to carry out the execution of prisoner JOHANN MÜLLER himself by shooting him with a pistol. (Signed) Heinrich Himmler Reichsführer SS*'.

The commandant appeared genuinely sorry for my discomfort. He advised me, 'It is simpler than you think, Obersturmführer. In a moment, in this yard, you will see the prisoner, who has his back to you. As you approach, withdraw your Walther pistol and click the safety catch off. The prisoner's guards will force the prisoner to his knees. He will be on the lip of a ditch. Place your pistol quickly against the prisoner's neck here' – he indicated a point on his own neck. 'Hold your pistol at this angle and fire once. The body will fall forward into the ditch and a guard will check for any sign of life. It is normally foolproof and requires no second shot. I take it your pistol is loaded? Are you ready?'

I mentally tried to slow my racing heart and nodded to the commandant. He led the way and we stepped a few paces into the yard of a building, which had been screened by the wall. To the right of the path, I saw two guards with a man dressed in ordinary civilian clothes between them. He had his back to me and appeared resigned to his own imminent death, although I did not see his face. I lifted the flap of my holster and drew my pistol, flicking off the safety catch and holding it pointing downwards at my side.

The two guards forced the prisoner to his knees and the commandant quickly intoned, 'In the name of the Führer Adolf Hitler, you are condemned to death for treason.'

I had positioned myself to the immediate rear of the prisoner and I could hear his breathing becoming faster. Sweeping up my pistol, I moved the barrel to within two centimetres of the prisoner's neck, adjusted the angle of the pistol slightly and pulled the trigger.

The pistol recoiled in my hand as the prisoner fell into the ditch before me. As I re-holstered my pistol, a guard stepped down into the ditch and checked the body. The prisoner was quite dead.

The commandant gently placed a hand on my arm to lead me away. As we rejoined the lane outside, nausea overcame me and I had to run to one side and vomit on to the ground. He was not surprised. He told me it was often the way.

As we walked back up the lane towards his office, the SS photographer came out of a shed near the execution site with his camera. Unknown to myself at that time, he had taken photographs of me executing the prisoner. His camera needed no flash, or I would have seen it. The guards moved the body slightly and the photographer took a photograph of the face only and then again another photograph, showing the bullet hole in the back of the neck. This had all been pre-arranged. The photographer waited nearby for a decent interval to elapse, as the commandant and I walked up the lane, screened by the wall.

The second guard walked over to the building and shouted. Two prisoners dressed in the stripes emerged and ran over to the execution ditch and carried the body between them to the building. It was the camp crematorium. The body was cremated in one of the ovens at Dachau within the next two hours.

In the commandant's office, I signed the order for the execution being carried out, printed my name and added my number. Although I did not notice at the time, the form was offered to me in a way that I did not see the name on the execution notice. I was in a hurry and less careful than usual.

After a schnapps or two from the benevolent commandant, I was driven back to the airfield. As I left the car, the driver handed me a padded envelope. It was addressed to SS Reichsführer Heinrich Himmler and I was merely to act as the officer courier. I signed for the envelope and made my way to the flight controller's office. This time I had to wait a few hours and was flown back to Berlin in a Messerschmitt 108 two-seater trainer. The air turbulence did not help how I was feeling. Allied aircraft largely controlled much of the airspace in central Germany, in an area between Munich and Berlin, but I was lucky not to receive the attention of Allied fighter planes on either flight.

Himmler was not in residence in Berlin, when I returned.

On April 11th, the advancing Americans arrived at Nordhausen. North of the badly bombed town, they found the concentration camp of Dora-Mittelwerke. It was a small concentration camp, with a large adjacent industrial complex. More importantly, two huge tunnels had been driven into the hillside for two kilometres or more. They both had many side galleries. Here the Americans found the underground production lines of the V1 and V2 rockets. They were amazed at the technology.

This area was in the sector to be handed to the Russians, by the Yalta Conference. The Americans moved heaven and earth to remove the rockets and machinery back to their own lines for shipping to the USA. Within a short time they received the surrender of rocket scientists including Wernher von Braun. It was like many birthdays coming at once for the Americans.

On April 12th President Roosevelt died. Harry Truman, the Vice-President of the USA, succeeded him.

On April 14th, I was summoned by Himmler to see him at Hohenlychen. It took a great deal of time to get there, due to roads having been bombed, etc. When I reported to Himmler, I immediately saw that the Reichsführer seemed angry.

'Where were you on April 9th, Koch?' Himmler almost bellowed.

I quickly recollected and answered, 'I was at Dachau KZ, according to your orders, Reichsführer!'

'What orders?' exclaimed Himmler. 'I gave no such orders for you!'

Fortunately I still had the written order with me. Orders were often verbal and so I had kept the written order, as being more important. I felt in my pocket, pulled out some papers, located the correct one and proffered it to Himmler, who snatched it from my hand.

Himmler's eyes screwed up and he became angrier, but I discerned that the anger was not directed at me personally.

'It is a forgery, Koch!' he announced, 'I realize that you were not to know and I can now see why these photographs have mysteriously found their way to my desk.' He gestured at the desk to some large photographs and I stepped forward to look at them.

The photographs were about twenty by thirty centimetres in size. The first showed the Dachau camp commandant and myself. Behind my own face, I could see the face of another man in civilian clothes between two SS guards. I guessed from his size and clothing that he was the man I had executed. The next two photographs clearly showed me executing the prisoner with a pistol. In fact one photo had captured the moment of gunsmoke from my pistol and the body beginning to topple forwards. The last photos showed the same man, now dead, full-face in close up, and lastly the wound

119

in the back of his head. The photographs had been taken from very near the execution site. I recalled a small shed had been nearby.

I stood back from the desk and exclaimed, 'But the Commandant told me that you had ordered me to personally shoot this prisoner, Reichsführer!'

Himmler stood in silence for a moment, hands on hips, as if contemplating.

'Did he say the prisoner's name?' he asked quietly.

'The Commandant told me the prisoner's name was Johann Müller and he showed me an order signed by you, for me to carry out the execution personally!'

Himmler threw back his head slightly and snorted derisively. He seemed to calm himself and asked me, 'Do you know, who it really was?'

I naturally was both surprised and bewildered. I gulped, 'No, sir!'

Himmler continued, 'It was Georg Elser!' He tossed me a copy of the signed execution order of Elser, bearing my own signature, over to me.

He studied the expression on my face for a moment, as the name did not immediately signify anything. Himmler continued, 'Whilst you were still in your school years, Koch, on November 8th 1939 Georg Elser very nearly succeeded in blowing up Hitler and others by means of a bomb that he had made and planted at the Bürgerbrau beer cellar in Munich. Rather than put him on trial, by the mercy of the Führer himself he has been kept ever since in protective custody in Sachsenhausen and Dachau camps. Now, although you have undoubtedly been misled, you are the individual who personally executed the man that tried to kill the Führer! Germany might not mind, but the Allies might certainly be interested in a matter of weeks now. It may also explain why certain other document copies and photos were forwarded to me some time ago.'

Himmler went to his desk and removed a folder, which he shoved across the desk towards me. I took it and opened it. Inside was a copy of my order for the collection of the British prisoners of war, who had declined to join the Britisches Frei Korps, together with four copies of the named files marked NN and signed by myself with my rank and number. Photographs in the folder showed the four men alive and also their dead bodies, with a name on paper attached to each.

Himmler enquired, 'Do you know what NN means, Koch?'

'No, Reichsführer!' I replied.

Himmler explained, 'It means *Nacht und Nebel* (night and fog). It is a secret order for people to be made to disappear – a euphemism for clandestine death. My dear Koch, you have unknowingly been used by others to compromise yourself. If Germany loses this war, you could become a wanted man. If one copy exists, then there are doubtless others elsewhere.'

'But who would do such a thing, Reichsführer?' I enquired hopefully.

Himmler shrugged. 'Who indeed? Possibly Kaltenbrunner, or some minor officer who is jealous of your status.'

I looked glum. The wheel of fortune had dealt an unkind hand. Himmler let me reflect on my misfortunes for a few moments longer.

'Never mind, Koch!' he exclaimed. 'You have always been a hard worker and it is time I repaid you in part for your loyal services. I am going to send you on a secret mission. You will meet a few others there and you are likely to see this war out alive, if you follow orders. Things are at a critical stage, but I believe I can count on you.'

Himmler invited me to sit down. He briefed me for a long time, then dismissed me and made arrangements for my transfer to another location.

On April 15th, the British took over the Belsen concentration camp, situated north of Hannover, by arrangement, from the remaining small number of SS guards, who were then arrested. For the time being, other camp guards from the Hungarian Army, who served with the German forces, remained in the guard towers. There were some 40,000 prisoners there and typhus had a grip.

This was the result of the forced-march evacuations of prisoners from concentration camps farther east. Over the last two months particularly, large numbers of prisoners had arrived at the camp, literally on their last legs of strength. Bombing of nearby Celle had also affected supplies of running water to the area.

Belsen was situated in a remote area of heathland. In the

121

closing days of the war, despite the best efforts of British doctors and medical students rushed there, the inmates' death rate daily was huge. It took some time to bring it under control. It naturally affected the British troops, and the horrors were recorded on newsreels to be shown in cinemas.

The Allies perhaps formed the impression that all SS soldiers were evil murderers, although most members of the SS had never even seen a concentration camp. It would scarcely involve up to 900,000 men to guard a relatively small number of camps. Moreover, SS concentration camp guards hardly drove tanks in battle, or acted as infantry in their spare time. The confusing aspect was the very similar uniform of the SS Totenkopfverbände (camp guards) and the completely separate Waffen SS military divisions. Even regular German Army tank men also used the skull and crossbone insignia and their officers wore black uniforms. The difference was essentially the position of the eagle badge – on the right of the chest = Army, on the left arm = SS.

Some Allied soldiers subsequently shot small groups of Waffen SS men who had surrendered, in cold blood. The Russians also shot captured members of the Waffen SS in large numbers. There was often a witness or even a survivor of these incidents, and that only served to make other remaining SS forces more fanatical and brutal in the way they fought. Himmler was aware of the Allies' opinion of his SS men. His own survival plans were now at a quite advanced stage.

On April 20th, Hitler's fifty-sixth birthday, Heinrich Himmler paid his respects to the Führer, in the bunker under the Reich Chancellery in Berlin. At the time, the Russians were closely approaching Berlin. Himmler left his chief to his imminent end and he headed north, ostensibly to defend Mecklenburg from the Russians.

April 22nd brought a fresh meeting with Folke Bernadotte and an offer by Himmler to surrender to the British and Americans.

The British and Americans refused Himmler's offer of surrender, but they broadcast it on their radio and Hitler ordered Himmler's arrest the next day. Shortly before this,

Hermann Göring, the Luftwaffe chief, also wished to surrender and was arrested for a time by the SS in Bavaria. Himmler himself was a different prospect. He was in control of the very apparatus of arrest, and no attempts were made to arrest him. Himmler was now at the Northern German Supreme Headquarters at Rheinsberg, to the east of Hohenlychen.

Shortly afterwards Grand Admiral Dönitz, who was in overall charge of the Kriegsmarine (navy), arrived there to check on the actual military situation in the area. Himmler requested a conference with him. During the meeting, he broached the question that if Hitler ever became unable to carry on in Berlin and transferred power to him (Himmler), would Dönitz serve in an administration with him?

Dönitz told Himmler that his own priority was to try and save the huge numbers being evacuated from the East from the Russians. If and when a legally constituted government was formed, he was prepared to serve it.

By this time the Sachsenhausen and Ravensbrück concentration camps had both been evacuated. Near Hamburg, the Neuengamme concentration camp had also been emptied. All the prisoners were marched northwards towards the Baltic coast by their SS guards. Many died en route.

During the battle for Berlin in April 1945, about thirty members of the Britisches Frei Korps were involved in resisting the Russians. Their unit had been attached to the SS Nordland division, which now numbered a few hundred men, the majority of whom were Scandinavians.

Near Neuenhagen, to the east of Berlin, they encountered several Russian T34 tanks. They ambushed the tanks and destroyed two of them with Panzerfausts.

This group of SS men then withdrew into Berlin and fought to defend it. They joined with the French of the SS Charlemagne division. During the final battle for Berlin, many of the remaining SS fighting troops were non-Germans.

On April 30th, Adolf Hitler committed suicide, after marrying Eva Braun, in the lower level of the Reich Chancellery bunker. She took poison. Hitler broke a poison capsule in his mouth with his teeth, and simultaneously shot himself in the head with a pistol. At his wish, the bodies were burnt with petrol in the garden area outside the bunker's emergency exit.

After the Russians captured the area, they discovered one particular dead body, shot in the head. It had been placed with other bodies in an empty water tank outside the Führer bunker emergency exit. This body was dressed as Hitler would be and the resemblance was remarkable. In fact, one of the former bunker occupants, a senior officer, identified the body to the Russians as being that of Adolf Hitler.

The body was in fact either one of Hitler's doubles or a chance look-alike. The confusion for the Russians lasted months. They had bunker survivors in captivity swearing that Hitler shot himself in the head and his body was burnt in the bunker garden. They had the charred remains of a male body that had no signs of gunshot (nor a complete skull) that had been found buried in the bunker grounds and they had an unburnt body of 'Hitler'.

For many months the Russians could not be certain that Hitler was even dead. The Russians were very secretive. It is only many years afterwards that these events can be described chronologically as they happened. If the Russians had told their British and American Allies of the discovery of the body of a 'Hitler double', it might have made the Allies a little more careful.

In his will, Adolf Hitler appointed Grand Admiral Dönitz as the new Führer. Dönitz was in Plön, an inland naval training centre to the south-east of Kiel. The news astounded him, when he received it. He contacted Himmler, who was in nearby Lübeck, and requested him to come to Plön.

The news of Hitler's successor visibly took Himmler aback, but he offered his services as the second in line to Dönitz. The admiral refused.

Himmler was now officially without power, but actually he could still control many things. He left Plön after a short time.

By May 2nd, British troops entered the Northern German Baltic port of Lübeck. Also on May 2nd, all the German armed forces in Italy unconditionally surrendered and on the same day, Dönitz formed a government on paper, at Flensburg in Northern Germany, just beneath the Danish border.

The large city of Hamburg held out until May 3rd before surrendering to the British forces.

After discussions with the British, Dönitz ordered his

representative Admiral Friedeburg to accept the British conditions for surrender. On May 4th 1945, U-boat command continuously broadcast for twenty-four hours the instruction for all U-boats to cease hostilities.

Even this did not reach all U-boats. Close to the coast of America on May 5th, a U-boat attacked and sank a ship, but was sunk itself on the following day. The U-boat had been carrying the five Britisches Frei Korps men who had received special training. Their mission had been to kidnap the Duke of Windsor from the Bahamas. Thus another of Himmler's last-minute projects to buy time came to an end.

The surrender for the German armies in the Netherlands, Denmark and Northern Germany was signed on Lüneburg Heath on May 5th 1945. Field Marshal Montgomery received the surrender from Admiral Friedeburg and others.

On May 6th, Dönitz officially dismissed Himmler from all his posts – Minister of the Interior, Chief of Police and Commander in Chief of the Reserve Army. Himmler stayed in or around Flensburg with a large group of SS Officers and men, for the time being.

Within days, Colonel General Jodl of the German Supreme Command signed for unconditional surrender at General Eisenhower's headquarters at Reims, France. His colleague Field Marshall Keitel similarly signed unconditional surrender documents with the Russians in Berlin.

May 8th 1945 became Victory in Europe day.

Despite Dönitz's orders for German warships to remain intact, the bulk of vessels remaining were U-boats. Many of their captains believed that Dönitz might be under arrest by the Allies and decided to ignore the order. As a result a large number of U-boats were scuttled in the fiords of Kiel, Flensburg and elsewhere.

After they had gone, Himmler was without another of his means of escape, on a newer type XXI or XXIII U-boat. However, even with his armed SS guards, Himmler would have had great difficulty in taking over a large U-boat and getting the crew to take them where he wished. (Two U-boats did in fact successfully make their way to South America.)

On May 10th, Himmler sent out a few mysterious messages by radio transmitter. He then selected a small group of SS officers and bodyguards and left Flensburg in several cars. He did not tell the remaining SS members of his force that he was leaving. The group travelled across country towards the West Coast of this Schleswig area. As they approached the Elbe river estuary, they left the cars when fuel ran out. Moving on foot to the river, they contacted a fisherman, who was paid to take them by boat to the opposite side.

There was no reason for the fisherman to know the identity of his passengers. They had all affected a variety of non-military clothing.

Himmler and his group were now in a sparsely populated marshland, between Hamburg and Bremerhaven. The area still contained some German troops after the cessation of hostilities. Although there were some British troops there too, they did not have the resources to deal with such large numbers of potential prisoners.

In fact in some areas quite a number of German prisoners behind barbed wire in open fields starved to death. The Allies began to appreciate how difficult it was to try and feed masses of people at short notice. Their priority was to feed their own troops. German civilians also starved in some areas.

Over the next day or so, Himmler's group made its way, using smaller roads, roughly southwards about fifty kilometres. They were just north of a small town named Bremervörde. Himmler sent a few group members into the outskirts of the town to scout around. They succeeded in finding temporary accommodation in a farmhouse and the group moved in. Part of Himmler's disguise was a false eye patch and he had shaved off his moustache. He had also stopped wearing his well-known rimless eyeglasses and used more ordinary ones.

Further investigations of the town revealed the presence of British troops and a control post on a bridge over the river Oste in Bremervörde.

On May 20th, Himmler decided to take a chance. Two of the group approached the Bremervörde bridge checkpoint and were stopped by British troops. One of the two was a doctor. He claimed to be in charge of a group of sick servicemen. The British provided trucks to fetch the others. This group was transferred under arrest to Westertimke internment camp, not far away.

Himmler and two aides were not amongst this group when the British trucks arrived, they had in fact moved to a nearby tiny village. They spent the night in another house, whose occupant was away. During the evening, Himmler decided to use up some coffee that they had brought with them. He told his aides that he would make it and carefully added finely powdered sleeping tablets to their brew.

During the late evening, after the aides had gone to sleep, Himmler donned women's clothes from the house, leaving his own clothes there. He removed a bicycle from the hallway, exited the house noiselessly and checked that all was quiet. Mounting the cycle in the darkness, but aided by some moonlight, Heinrich Himmler, dressed as a woman, cycled about two kilometres towards another tiny hamlet.

After dismounting, he silently wheeled the bicycle to an isolated farmhouse, left it nearby and knocked on the door in the way of a pre-arranged signal. After some seconds, the door opened and he saw my familiar face once more. As arranged some weeks earlier, I was expecting him, but not in women's clothes!

Himmler hissed, 'It's all right, Koch, it is me!' He slowly lifted the women's scarf from his head. I goggled at my chief. Himmler looked so different without his moustache. Finally Himmler brought me out of my bewilderment, 'OK! Koch. Don't stand there all night. Let me in!' He brushed past me and entered the farmhouse.

Dr Mengele stood in the heavily curtained living room and Heinrich Himmler's double, Heinrich Hitzinger, sat asleep in an armchair. We all now wore civilian clothing. I had been there for some weeks with them both. During that time, Dr Mengele bragged about his operation on Hitzinger to make him look even more like Himmler. Indeed, Mengele was a very talkative man, but he had never described where he had actually performed the operation.

Himmler looked at Mengele inquisitively.

'Hitzinger is sedated,' explained Dr Mengele.

Mengele then launched into a charade, for my benefit, because at that time I did not know what Himmler and Mengele

127

had planned. I was just another useful part of Himmler's plans.

'I am sorry Reichsführer, but there is awful news. Since coming here, Hitzinger has developed severe stomach trouble, as Koch has witnessed. It has gradually been getting worse and I have examined his faeces. I diagnose stomach cancer. Not only that, but a terminal case. I can only alleviate the pain with morphine, but his death is only days off.'

Himmler's face was a picture.

'Oh no!' he moaned. 'Just when we were so close to using him. Are you sure that there is nothing you can do, Mengele? No operation or anything?'

Mengele remained stony-faced, 'I regret Reichsführer, that there is nothing that I can do for him,' he replied.

'When will he awake?' Himmler asked.

'Within an hour,' Mengele answered.

Himmler turned to me and after making a few pleasantries, asked me to go and get some sleep, as he would need me shortly.

Himmler and Mengele spoke softly together and about one hour later Hitzinger awoke and saw his own likeness opposite for the first time.

'My dear Hitzinger, this is dreadful news! How do you feel?' Himmler enquired.

'Not too bad at the moment, Reichsführer.' answered Hitzinger. 'The good Doktor gives me medicine to relieve the pain, but I am told it may only be a matter of days now.'

'So I understand,' said Himmler gently. 'We had hoped to use you as a double, whilst I escaped to carry on the fight elsewhere. You could then reveal that you were a double to the Allies. Now it seems that is not to be.'

Hitzinger stared at Himmler for about half a minute.

'There is one thing, Reichsführer, that I could still do,' he said softly. 'If I got myself picked up by the British hereabouts, I could reveal my identity as Heinrich Himmler to them. I could then or later commit suicide by throwing myself from a window, or attacking a guard to get them to shoot me. If I, as Reichsführer Himmler, was already dead, it would give you a better chance to evade capture and carry on the struggle.'

Himmler looked astonished. Hitzinger was proposing an even better idea than his original plan.

'My dear Hitzinger, it is out of the question!' he exclaimed.

'I have nothing to lose that I will not lose in any case, Reichs-führer. It will be my small effort for the continued struggle of those that fight for the Reich,' Hitzinger stated calmly.

Himmler seemed genuinely embarrassed. 'If there had only been more with your faith, Hitzinger, then Germany would not be in its present state. If you are determined to do what you say, this is what we could do.'

Over the next two hours Himmler gave Hitzinger a quick briefing about his aides, the general situation and his instructions. Dr Mengele gave him a glass phial of cyanide, which Hitzinger had to keep in his mouth at all times. It was small enough inside his mouth to talk, eat, or even drink with. At the appropriate time he was to bite hard on the glass, after he had revealed his identity to the British.

Mengele also gave Hitzinger a final dose of medicine containing morphine to deaden the pain of his stomach 'cancer', in a small bottle to take with him.

'Take this at the last possible minute, before you set off to the bridge checkpoint. If anyone asks, it is for your stomach cramps,' instructed Mengele.

Himmler shook hands with his likeness. It was an uncanny feeling. The close resemblance was remarkable, and no signs of scarring could be seen on Hitzinger. Mengele went upstairs to awaken Koch.

'We must exchange clothes now, Heinrich,' said Himmler softly to Hitzinger.

They exchanged clothes, and Hitzinger and Himmler's former appearances were transposed. Himmler gave him identification papers made out to Heinrich Hitzinger, who had been demobilised on May 2nd.

I was awakened and appeared from upstairs. Himmler, now differently dressed, identified Hitzinger in the woman's clothing. Himmler gave me instructions and a map. I led Hitzinger outside and collected the bicycle. I gallantly gave the 'lady' a ride on the crossbar back to the house indicated on the map.

Himmler and Mengele watched us go from a window.

'Are you sure that the arsenic dosage is not too high?' Himmler asked Mengele. 'Do you think that Hitzinger will go through with it and kill himself?'

'You may be sure, Reichsführer,' answered Mengele, 'as long as he remains in control and takes the poison before it can be taken from him. Although Hitzinger might not die just yet from the arsenic which I put in his food, he will not feel like wishing to live any longer once his "medicine" wears off. He has been effectively taught to believe in Germany's final victory. I think we can count on him carrying out his chosen mission.'

'Isn't science wonderful?' Himmler added quietly.

Himmler had actually planned to have his aides awaken to discover 'his dead body' (Hitzinger) and a suicide note. Thus Himmler would be dead and his aides could report it, if they wished. Now Mengele was saved the job of killing Hitzinger and moving the body to the other house. I was not aware of that original plan at that time.

A few kilometres away, I arrived with Hitzinger at the other house indicated to me by Himmler. I entered, and found Himmler's two aides still asleep. I recognized them as colleagues I had worked with and brought Hitzinger inside. Checking the bedrooms, I located Himmler's civilian clothes and disguise, where I had been told they would be. Hitzinger took off the women's clothes and redressed in the male clothing. Picking up the eye patch, he paused for a moment.

'Over the left eye,' I reminded him.

We both stood in the dark room and shook hands. Both of us wished each other well.

I then departed, carefully closing the door, and walked back quietly, the way I had come, back to Himmler and Mengele.

Early the following morning, Himmler gave Doctor Mengele his promised documents, instructions and introductions, along with a little money. These were to take him from Germany to Italy and eventually South America. Mengele also had some gold coins sewn into his civilian overcoat. He made his way on foot, choosing to go away from the Bremervörde bridge checkpoint. Ultimately, it is now known, he made it to South America.

Himmler awoke me and I was surprised to find Mengele had gone. He led me towards a wood across some fields. Ensuring that we were unobserved, Himmler took out a map and walked in from one corner of the wood and looked around, but found nothing. He led me over to another corner of the wood and again moved into the trees a certain distance. Looking around, he saw a flat rock and, after orientating himself, began to feel around in the grass on one side. After a while he detected one metal ring under the surface and then it was easy to find the other.

'You are young and fit, Koch. Get hold of those rings and give a good heave upwards,' breathed Himmler.

I did as I was told and, standing astride the area, heaved on the rings. At first nothing happened, then as grasses tore, a block of 'turf' was lifted, revealing an uninviting black hole underneath.

'Put the lid carefully on to the rock,' ordered Himmler. I did as instructed.

'We will leave it to air a bit, before I show you around. Do you remember this project, Koch? This is a *Werwolf* bunker. Welcome to our new home!'

Chapter 8

A couple of kilometres away, Heinrich Hitzinger dozed in a chair whilst Himmler's two aides slept in armchairs nearby. After a while, Hitzinger made himself a snack from the remnants of the food which the others had brought with them. At present his stomach pains had been deadened by Mengele's medicine.

The two aides finally awoke at about 10 a.m. and looked around rubbing their eyes. It was May 22nd 1945.

'You two have certainly slept well!' said Hitzinger, as he tried out his role as Reichsführer Heinrich Himmler for the first time for real.

'I am sorry Reichsführer!' blurted out the senior ranking aide. 'We seem to have let our efforts over the last few days catch up with us.'

'Quite so! We are all naturally very tired. I think that the first group must have crossed the bridge in Bremervörde safely by now. We have heard nothing, nor seen any signs of a search to worry about. I propose that we also go to cross the bridge in an hour,' stated 'Himmler'.

The two aides murmured their assent and gathered together a few belongings. Just before they set out, Hitzinger went into the kitchen and took the last dose of his stomach 'medicine'. He put the empty bottle down and pulled the poison capsule out of his pocket. He gazed at it for a moment and then put it into his mouth, under his tongue, and pushed it towards the rear. It was quite small and lay there easily.

One hour later, they set out towards the British checkpoint at the bridge. The two aides walked in front, dressed in long waterproof coats. The 'Reichsführer' (as they thought him to be) followed. They all wore civilian clothing.

The earlier group from Himmler's entourage had mentioned three others, who had been 'left behind' after they were

132

arrested, so the British soldiers in Bremervörde were still on the look-out for three men together.

As they drew nearer to the bridge, a patrol of British soldiers stopped the three men and 'Himmler' offered his papers. The soldiers arrested them and took them to the control checkpoint at the bridge. There they were searched for any weapons and their details noted. They were locked into a first floor room of the checkpoint.

The following day, the three men were taken to Kolkhagen internment camp near Barnstedt. That evening Hitzinger told his aides that he had decided to ask to see the British camp commander.

The British captain in charge of the camp granted this rather unusual request. When they arrived at his office, he saw two military looking men and a smaller older man. He decided to speak to the older man first, without the other two being present.

Heinrich Hitzinger sensed that his destiny was at hand. He slowly, carefully and precisely removed the eye patch from his eye and dropped it. From a pocket he withdrew a pair of spectacles and put them on. He regarded the captain in silence for a few seconds and then inhaled.

'Heinrich Himmler!' he announced politely, with a slight bow of the head.

It was like a bombshell! For a moment the captain was taken aback and just stared at 'Himmler'.

'Perhaps you ought to inform a more senior officer?' 'Himmler' himself suggested.

The British captain informed British Intelligence in Lüneburg by phone and they sent someone to Kolkhagen. Meanwhile, 'Himmler' was requested to sign his name. Hitzinger duly obliged – a simple task for Hitzinger – and it was checked against a specimen brought from Lüneburg.

'Himmler's' clothing was carefully searched and his body was externally checked. The British provided something to eat and drink, but 'Himmler' consumed it all without any problem. It was suspected he had poison on him, but nothing yet indicating where it might be.

Later the same evening, 'Himmler' was taken by car to a house in Lüneburg, specifically set aside to receive prominent

133

Nazi prisoners. At this time, his trousers had been taken away, and his shoes. He wrapped himself in a British Army blanket over his shirt, socks and underclothes. He was already in some pain from his stomach 'cancer' but he needed a little longer before the final scene was played and he was determined to choose his moment.

Now a British Army doctor was summoned to examine 'Himmler'. Several people were in the room, whilst the doctor examined 'Himmler' in detail, particularly the anus and other orifices. The doctor asked 'Himmler' to open his mouth and glimpsed an object inside, between teeth and one cheek. Suspecting poison, he poked a finger into Himmler's mouth to extract the 'object'. 'Himmler' probably acted reflexively and closed his mouth, biting the doctor's finger hard.

The doctor yelled in pain, and 'Himmler' grabbed the doctor's hand and yanked the finger out of his mouth. Nursing his finger, the doctor shouted to others in the room that 'it' was in his mouth.

As the others froze for the moment of time needed to digest this information, Hitzinger culminated his only performance as Heinrich Himmler, Reichsführer of the SS. He stepped back a pace and raised his chin slightly. Pulling back his shoulders and standing up straight, he let his gaze sweep over the representatives of a country which had been at war with his own for six years, with contempt. At the same time, as if moving a sweet in his mouth, he positioned the poison capsule between his rear teeth.

Whilst the people in the room began to move closer, 'Himmler' crunched the glass phial in his mouth. It shattered and he swallowed its contents. When the British soldiers reached him to grab hold of him, 'Himmler's' face contorted in a grimace. His body weight caused him to drop to the ground, although supported by the soldiers.

Everyone frantically made efforts to try and save 'Himmler's' life with stomach washes and artificial respiration, but it was useless. 'Heinrich Himmler' died in the late evening of May 23rd 1945.

The few British Intelligence officers and men at the house in Lüneburg were far from happy. They had had the most important surviving Nazi delivered to their custody and now he was dead.

Eventually 'Himmler's' body was left on the floor of the room in which he died, as the officers and soldiers went off to their quarters to sleep. Two men were posted as a guard on the room overnight.

The guards were not in the best moods. Hostilities had been over for about two weeks and now when they felt that they deserved a good rest, they had been ordered to stand guard over a dead body. Surely, they reasoned, the body was not going to get up and walk away, neither was anyone likely to break in and steal it. Only a few people yet knew of the body's presence there. The guards thought their duty was a waste of time.

Dividing the quietest hours of the night between them, they agreed to take turns having a sleep whilst the other stood guard. The guard on duty kept post outside the doorway of the room, with the door left ajar so that he could glance inside from time to time. He had a storm lantern to see by.

Well before reveille, Lance Corporal Benjamin Green, known to his mates as Benny, entered the house, intending to start heating water for the officers billeted there, for both washing and tea making.

The guard recognized Benny and called to him softly, 'Benny! Come over here quietly and I will show you something that you may tell your grandchildren about!' hissed the guard.

'Is that you, Ernie?' Benny replied. 'What are you up to now?'

'Have a look at this, Benny!' exclaimed Ernie, as he opened the door of the room wider, illuminating the interior by holding the lantern up high.

'Who's that?' queried Benny, glimpsing the body of a man on the floor of the room. 'Is he dead?'

'Well, if he isn't dead, then he's been giving a good impression. He's dead all right. The question is, guess who he is?'

They both entered the room and the guard lifted the blanket from the body's head. He held up the storm lantern, so Benny could see clearly.

'There you are, Benny! Any guesses? He was a top Nazi! Have a closer look at the face and see if you can see who it is. He was very well known, but used to have a moustache,' Ernie continued.

Benny looked closely at the face, but could not visualize who it was supposed to be. It couldn't be Hitler. He had shot himself in Berlin, and the Russians held the city.

'Sorry, Ernie! I have no idea who it is,' Benny ventured at last.

Ernie chuckled and announced quietly, 'This is Heinrich Himmler, who was chief of Hitler's SS. They brought him here last night and he managed to take poison. That's why all these bowls are here. They tried to wash out his stomach to try to revive him, but it was no use.'

Benny continued to stare at the body of 'Himmler' as it lay in front of him. Giving voice to his thoughts, he said to Ernie, 'It seems a bit odd to me. I would have thought that it was obvious that Germany would lose the war some time ago and of all the top people, I'd have thought Himmler would have made plans to get away and save himself.'

Ernie just shrugged his shoulders and replied, 'Not a word of this to anyone. You have not been in this room and you haven't seen Himmler's body this morning. If a word slips out, we'll both be in big trouble!'

'Don't worry!' replied Benny. 'I can keep my mouth shut. I'll go and boil the kettle and bring you a mug of tea in a few minutes.'

Benny went off to his duties and Ernie awoke the second guard, so it would appear that they had both been on duty all night.

During the day, United States and Russian representatives were summoned to view the body. The edges of 'Himmler's' mouth seemed to be upturned in a faint smile.

The following day, May 25th 1945, the body was photographed and a brief autopsy was performed. It was perfunctory. If someone kills himself in front of others, so near that people can smell the cyanide, it is hardly necessary.

Moreover, if anyone had detected that arsenic was present in the stomach besides cyanide, what difference would it make? The man was seen to have taken poison and the man was dead. What type of poison he had used had no relevance.

Benny Green was acting as 'batman' (servant) for two intelligence officers two days later, when he heard them discussing the

Himmler suicide. As he moved the officers' freshly laundered clothes and made tea, he eavesdropped on their conversation as closely as possible.

He heard one officer state that Himmler had actually announced his presence to the British camp commander for detained persons. Prior to that, no one realized that they had captured the SS chief.

Benny thought that this sounded even more odd. Eventually he could not keep quiet any longer, although he was not going to admit having seen Himmler's body.

'Permission to speak, sir?' Benny enquired.

'Permission granted, Green,' replied one of the officers.

'I have been sorting out your laundry and putting things away. I haven't been deliberately listening, but I couldn't help hearing you talk about this Himmler chap. May I ask a question, sir?'

'Go ahead, Green.'

'Well, sir! Begging your pardon, but if I was a high-ranking Nazi and I got captured by the enemy, if the enemy did not know who I really was, why should I tell them?'

For a moment there was silence and then one of the officers replied, 'Because he was not very clever, Green!' Both officers laughed.

Benny Green smiled and nodded and carried on serving the tea. He did not pursue the matter, but he thought it highly unlikely that a man who 'wasn't very clever' had risen to be in charge of the whole SS and remained in that position throughout the war. His doubts nagged at him. Why was he the only one who seemed to perceive something was not quite right with this whole Himmler suicide story?

Finally, the British were left with the problem of what to do with the body. If they cremated it, the ashes might be kept in secret by Nazis. If they buried it in a normal cemetery, it could provide a grave and focal point for remembrance by any future Nazi sympathizers. The British finally decided to bury the body in secret and took steps to keep journalists well away.

After 'Himmler's' death by suicide, the BBC broadcast the news over the radio.

With the millions who died during this war, no one had particular reason to remember the name of Heinrich Hitzinger.

He was one of thousands who, according to records, died on the Eastern Front over a year ago. As for Heinrich Himmler, the world knew he was dead – the BBC had reported it, so it must be true.

No one had any reason to believe otherwise. The two men who did know, Dr Josef Mengele and Erich Koch, were not about to tell anyone. Neither were they in a position to do so. They both believed themselves to be wanted men. Certainly Mengele's name was on a list of persons wanted for war crimes.

As for the Allied forces, there were still Nazi 'bigwigs' at large to look for. Those that had already been captured, or had surrendered to them, were to be gathered together in a camp, nicknamed Camp Ashcan.

Already the biggest names in the Nazi hierarchy had gone – Adolf Hitler, Heinrich Himmler, Josef Goebbels – all dead. Luftwaffe chief Hermann Göring was in custody, together with Rudolf Hess, who had been in England for most of the war. The remainder of the high-ranking Nazis to be eventually tried for war crimes were largely unknown to the general populace.

Perhaps ninety kilometres from Lüneburg, Heinrich Himmler sat in the bunker with me. It was fairly cold, but not unbearable. After we entered the bunker some days before, we had unpacked the crates of the items immediately required, by the light of the storm lanterns. The one-wheel bicycle had been assembled on a stand with a belt around the tyreless wheel. This produced electricity from a small generator, which the belt drove. In turn the generator charged several large batteries to give us a power source. It was sufficient for lighting, to power the electric fans to circulate air in and out, and to operate the radio transmitter/receiver (when required). The storm lanterns were now extinguished and left for emergencies.

Himmler had insisted that I now dropped his Reichsführer title and asked me to call him Heinrich. He would address me as Erich. We had enough food, largely in tins, to last about nine months, a water supply and kerosene for operating the stove. Initially we left the stove unlit, although it would also have provided us with heat.

The daily operation of the bicycle generator was a routine

138

chore. We took turns at gentle pedalling for ten-to-fifteen minute periods to charge the batteries. This exercise helped to keep us fit. For several days we remained completely sealed in the bunker whilst we listened to BBC radio broadcasts at regular intervals, using earphones. I was the main listener, as I was fairly fluent in English, but Himmler also listened to try and understand what was being said. He had some knowledge of spoken English, but was out of practice.

Time passed slowly. Himmler asked me to teach him some more English. Question and answer sessions took place – such as:

'Are you thirsty, Heinrich?'

'Yes, I am thirsty, Erich. I would like a drink of water. Where is the mug?'

We had weapons amongst the supplies, a machine pistol, two pistols (one had a silencer) and ammunition. These were only to be used in emergencies. The bunks and bedding provided adequate sleeping arrangements and at first Himmler and I took shifts, one sleeping whilst the other kept watch. The chemical toilet was certainly useful, but not desirable long term in the confined space of the bunker, however good the air extraction was.

After a few days, whilst listening to the radio by earphone, I heard the BBC radio announcer state amongst the news headlines that Heinrich Himmler was dead. I urgently beckoned Himmler over and he took up another single earphone. He listened intently, but did not understand everything. Himmler heard the announcer say, 'British Forces in Northern Germany announce that Heinrich Himmler, the former leader of Hitler's SS, was captured in the last few days. During questioning, Himmler took poison, which had been concealed in his mouth, and committed suicide.'

There was a short pause and the announcer continued, 'In London the Government have announced further measures concerning food rationing…'

Himmler put down the earphone and asked me what the announcer had meant. I translated what I had understood into German for Himmler to digest. Himmler looked thoughtful, but made no immediate reply.

After a while, he mused, 'Hitzinger actually did it! He was a very brave man indeed. We must continue to listen to the news broadcasts,' he stated. I just nodded and continued to listen to the radio.

After five days in the bunker, Himmler decided to 'surface'. Periscope watch had determined that no one came to this remote wood, which is why it had been picked in the first place. The lid was carefully lifted and placed on the flat rock. At first Himmler and I only moved a few paces away from the bunker entrance, standing in silence and listening intently.

There was nothing to hear but the wind in the trees. At Himmler's suggestion, we began to explore a few hundred metres in each direction. On two of these sides was the edge of the wood and we avoided approaching the treeline. The woods were fairly thick and we could not see the fields around, from where we were. Likewise, logic determined no one in the fields could see far enough into the woods to see us.

We wore loose-fitting camouflage jackets and trousers from our clothing supply crate. Our boots had smooth soles, as opposed to the hobnailed military variety, to be quieter and less harmful to the grasses and ferns. We moved slowly and carefully to avoid leaving tracks and avoided any muddy patches.

There was little to see or learn that was useful from our surroundings. There was a faint path or track in one part of the wood, but it showed no sign of recent use. The air smelled clean and pure and brought no odour of smoke or tobacco. We moved around like slow motion walkers, turned back to the bunker entrance and sat on a fallen tree trunk nearby.

Himmler turned to me and announced quietly, 'You know this reminds me of stories which Adolf Hitler told me about his early years. When he was a boy, he often liked to play games in the woods with his friends. He claimed that he became very good at stealthily creeping up on his "enemies" in the woods without them noticing. In fact in later life, when he fought for Germany in the First World War, it came in useful.'

'How do you mean?' I enquired, quite fascinated.

'Well!' continued Himmler, 'Adolf Hitler was an Austrian and he volunteered to fight for Germany and was accepted into the 16th Bavarian Infantry Regiment. After a while, he was made a runner to carry messages from various parts of the line. This could be a very dangerous job and very often these runners had to crawl along flat on their bellies in order to avoid being seen and shot at by the enemy. You can see that it was part of his lifestyle. He could become obsessed with doing something so well that he was almost fanatical. He was always a serious man and he was awarded the Iron Cross 2nd Class quite quickly and was promoted to corporal.

'I think that he must have discovered his ability to bluff his way through situations around that time. You remember when he sent German troops back into the Rhineland. If the French had opposed us with their military forces, we would have had to retreat. Hitler's bluff worked, and more than once, I tell you.

'Sometimes his colleagues thought he had a charmed life because of the risks he took. Yes, my friend, some guardian angel seemed to sit on Hitler's shoulder and saved him from numerous attempts on his life. It was as if he had a sixth sense.'

Himmler remained silent for some minutes, as if in contemplation. 'OK, my friend, shall we return to our "burrow" now?'

He led the way down into the bunker and I replaced the lid carefully.

It became the daily pattern. We would emerge in the early morning, after a good check around by periscope, and also in the early evening.

One day, Himmler produced some wires and pads from a crate. He explained that it was a security device to detect anyone approaching the bunker. The pads could even alert us if anyone approaching was out of sight of the periscope. Taking our time, we buried the wires just under the surface of the ground, with the ends leading back down into the bunker through the 'rabbit hole'. We led the wires out in various directions and finally buried pressure pads in areas, where anyone moving towards the bunker might step on them.

Inside the bunker, we connected the wires to batteries and small bulbs. If someone stood on a hidden pad, the extra pressure would cause the appropriate bulb to light up. I tested the pads and Himmler drew a sketch on the bunker wall, with locations for the pads. The bunker now had an additional early warning security device.

We made toilet arrangements on the surface by each of us digging a latrine. They were dug a considerable distance from

141

the bunker within bushes. This was infinitely better than using the chemical toilet in the bunker, unless absolutely necessary. Within the bunker, we used buckets for urine, which could be emptied daily.

As time progressed, both of us sought to entertain the other by stories of our lives, or amusing anecdotes.

I was fascinated by Himmler's stories of his early days with Hitler.

'Can you imagine, Erich, Adolf Hitler was only a corporal in the First World War? Yet he became the leader of officers like Göring, Hess and Röhm. I myself was an officer cadet at the end of the First World War. You have heard the Führer make speeches to the party faithful, but in the early days, he had hecklers throwing beer mugs and people trying to shout him down. It was some experience, I tell you. When that man started to speak, he had the full attention of the crowd within a few minutes. It was if he put a spell on them. He calmed them down, he used language they understood and he was on their "wavelength". You should have seen the women particularly, he entranced them and he fascinated them. Within a short time our corporal would be talking with generals and field marshals. Yes, our Herr Wolf was quite amazing!'

'Herr Wolf?' I queried.

'Oh! Yes! I need to explain,' replied Himmler. 'Adolf Hitler sometimes used the name Herr Wolf in his earlier days as an alias. In fact the eastern headquarters at Rastenburg was known as *Wolfsschanze* (Wolf's lair). Wolf was a nickname for Hitler in his private circle, chiefly among those we called the "Mountain men", those people who were with him at the Obersalzburg Berghof. Even his sister Paula used the name, and Eva Braun.'

'Who is Eva Braun?' I asked.

'She is, or was, if she is now dead, the Führer's mistress for many years,' replied Himmler.

'But I have never heard of her, nor seen any photograph of her,' I retorted.

'That is what the Führer intended. Women might desire the attention of the Führer, thinking him unobtainable, but he had his creature comforts all the time. Eva Braun was at the

Berghof at Obersalzburg for most of the war, but she came to the Berlin bunker to be with Hitler at the end.' Himmler was again silent for some moments.

'Do you think that Hitler is dead, Heinrich?' I ventured, slightly nervously.

'Yes! Himmler relied emphatically. 'You can be sure of that, even though I was not there. The man was exhausted by the war and totally burnt out. He had run out of strength, run out of ideas, run out of time. There was no way he would ever allow himself to be captured by his enemies and he would certainly not surrender. No one, who had ever met the man, or spent time with him, could think otherwise. Adolf Hitler was very strongly principled. He would control his final destiny, and others would follow his example. Although history may condemn him, this world is not going to see anyone coming close to Hitler as a leader for decades, possibly centuries, to come.'

'Was this war worth it?' I asked.

Himmler smiled. 'It depends how you judge things, my friend. In time of war some things, such as weapon and medical technology advance at a huge rate. Those things may help mankind in the long run. The huge wastage of men, women and children in all war zones, may be one of nature's unseen weapons of control of the population of this planet. In the same way famine, fire, flood, disease and earthquake may control, or affect populations from time to time, in other areas. Who is to say? I rode the crest of a wave with Hitler and others for years. Now the wave has crashed and circumstances have changed dramatically.

'I got to my position as Reichsführer through hard work. As a student at university, others might say "leave it to Heinrich to organize. He is reliable". I was reliable. I was a good organizer. I could be again, but the circumstances will never be the same. I believe our destiny lies in a country other than Germany, after a decent time has gone by. I plan to travel initially to Britain. We both need to build new lives and I have the money in Swiss numbered bank accounts to facilitate that.'

'Would the authorities discover your identity, if you go elsewhere?' I queried.

'Whose identity, Erich? If we get to Britain successfully, you will be Eric Cook and I could be Henry, no – Harry Fowler. If you were thinking of Heinrich Himmler, then that man is dead, as the world already knows. Kaminski told me that people may look for a man that they believe could be dead, but no one looks for a man that they know to be dead. It makes sense, doesn't it?'

I could only nod my agreement at the logic.

'But what if Hitzinger's real identity was discovered by the British?' I continued.

Himmler smiled. 'I don't know what they thought, because I wasn't there. However, I apply the same sort of logic as they have, hopefully. The war is over. The Allies are searching for high-ranking Nazis, and they find some of them alive. Others are dead. One day, they discover a man. He tells them, during questioning, he is Heinrich Himmler, Reichsführer SS. They look at him. Some will see the resemblance. Others may look at photos of Himmler. They may ask him questions, ask for his signature, compare it. At some time, this "Himmler" takes poison and dies, possibly in front of them. After he dies, they may even compare dental records against his teeth. They will correspond too.

'So let us examine the situation – a man claiming to be named Heinrich Hitzinger reveals that he is actually Heinrich Himmler, who is wanted by the Allies. Himmler commits suicide. All checks with records on Himmler correspond. So the logical man should conclude Heinrich Himmler is dead. Why should anyone think for a moment that the man is really Hitzinger, who claims to be Himmler and then kills himself, whilst pretending? No, my friend. It is like the conjurer. You tend to believe that which you see with your own eyes.'

I went further, 'What about the real Hitzinger?'

'Perhaps the real Hitzinger died in the final months of the war. He was missing presumed dead. Perhaps that fellow Himmler knew that and decided to pick on his identity to assume at random,' smirked Himmler.

Himmler realized that I did not know that Hitzinger had been officially dead for some time now, according to records in the SS personnel bureau.

I said nothing. It sounded reasonable to me. Himmler walked over to the periscope and looked around the area above us. It was empty of animal or human life, as he hoped it would remain. He turned to the carbon dioxide level instruments on the wall and examined them. The level was rising, but was not dangerous. Nevertheless he turned on an electric extraction fan for a while until the CO_2 level dropped substantially. Mounting the bicycle, he began steadily cycling to charge the batteries and I lay on my bunk to rest.

I still felt uneasy, for some reason. I lay on my bunk with my hands under my head, as it rested on a pillow. Somewhere in the recesses of my mind lurked an unanswered question that could affect Himmler's logic. As I thought back over past events, I suddenly remembered the comments Himmler had made to me about Rudolf Hess, long ago. It whirled around my mind until I could hold my tongue no longer.

Sitting up on the bunk with my feet on the floor, I called across to Himmler, who was examining a pistol.

'Heinrich. You once told me that there were certain things that I must not ask. That was during the war. Now that it's finished, may I be allowed to ask you further questions?'

'Why not indeed, Erich. Go ahead!' replied Himmler. He put down the pistol and sat on a chair facing me.

'Can you explain the position with regard to Rudolf Hess, please?' I asked.

'Certainly!' Himmler replied. 'I can see why it should interest you. From the start of the war, Rudolf Hess felt his power gradually erode as Deputy Führer to Hitler. He therefore came to the conclusion that he must try to pull off some amazing feat that would raise his status again. As you know, Hess was an officer in the First World War and a pilot. He continued to fly as a hobby, even after the war started, and his friend Willi Messerschmitt was in a position to help him with aeroplanes.

'Hess used to consult astrologers, so did Hitler and so did I, but our Kaminski was someone in a league of his own. Anyway, it was relatively simple to put the idea to Hess that he should fly in secret to Britain with proposals of peace. You must remember that we did not declare war on Britain, but Britain and France declared war on us. Hitler never wanted to fight the British. Our two countries have too much in common.

'At the time, we were developing "doubles" for Hitler, and logically Hess also had a double – and by coincidence he was also a pilot. His name was Weiss. The idea originally was for

145

Hess to fly to Britain with peace proposals. His double would be kept under wraps in Germany. If the proposals failed, we would produce the double, claiming he was the real Hess and that a double had flown to Britain. Things would carry on as normal in Germany, with the double in the Hess role, and at some point we hoped to exchange Hess (who the British would believe to be a double) for British prisoners of war. We could delay this, if we wished and keep the real Hess in Britain out of the way. At that time, the chance of Germany losing the war was not considered.

'Now Rudolf Hess, the real one, had a passion for fast cars and as sod's law happens, he crashed and died of his injuries, on his way to Augsburg to make the flight to Scotland. Fortunately, my own men who escorted him were brilliant. The accident was covered up and no member of the public saw Hess's body. We whistled up the double, who was also in the area, being kept close to Hess.

'Weiss was briefed and given the flight plans. He was not stupid and he sensed if he was suddenly being sent, then the real Hess was dead. He literally gambled his life on a phone call to me. He gave me an ultimatum – tell me what is really going on, or I don't fly.

'He won, because too much was riding on this plan. I told him I understood that Hess had died in a car crash and that I wanted him to go ahead with the flight. If he failed to get our peace proposals accepted, the Führer would claim he (Hess) was mad. If that happened, Weiss was advised to feign memory loss and insanity, until we could exchange him for British prisoners. The real Weiss was an orphan and over the war years his former Luftwaffe colleagues were killed in action.

'As you know, he flew to Scotland, but the peace proposals failed. I persuaded the Führer that to ease Hess's situation, he should declare him mad. Hitler did this and the British had their "Hess" safely locked up for the rest of the war.'

'What will happen to him now?' I queried.

'God only knows!' retorted Himmler. 'He may choose to go on playing the part of Hess. If he suddenly says he is actually Weiss of the Luftwaffe, who will believe him? It would be seen as another symptom of insanity. Alternatively, if he succeeded in convincing the British that he wasn't Hess, they might be so

146

embarrassed, that an accident would happen to Weiss. He has enough intelligence to work things out for himself.

'One thing is certain, my friend, now that the war is over, he will never leave prison for freedom alive, because the real Rudolf Hess knew too much. There were still members of Churchill's cabinet trying to make peace with Germany long after this war started, behind Churchill's back. You have my word on that.

'Weiss was a brave man. He could have flown to the Irish Republic and possibly sat out the war, but he did what was asked of him, as his duty. If he had succeeded, Germany could have had Britain out of the war completely, by agreement. It was a huge gain against a sacrifice of just one man, if it failed. We all die sometime. Weiss is presumably in prison. Whether the future for him is long or short, he will always be closely supervised, I imagine. I salute his effort.

'Now you see why it was so secret, Erich?'

I murmured my understanding and lay back on my bunk uneasily, as I tried to analyse this information. I understood what I had been told, but also realized that it could cost me my life if I ever told anyone whilst 'Hess' was still alive. They would wonder who exactly I was, how I had this information, and who told me. It was a secret that could never be told, or at least not for many years.

Himmler smiled to himself. He knew that if I ever considered trying to hand him over to the Allies, all he would have to do to doom me, would be to declare what he knew about me. Namely, that I had had British prisoners of war executed and I had also personally executed Georg Elser (the man that tried to blow up Hitler before the war). I believed that there was undoubtedly documentary evidence secreted in some safe place to support this. Now he could add that I knew the truth of the Hess flight, if any British officers ever asked him questions.

Himmler needed me and I needed Himmler. We were a mutual support team and it was already working.

The days and weeks began to pass. There was no further comment on Himmler on the BBC radio news. In fact under a barracks in Bavaria, Allied troops had found a huge cache of currency that was thought to have been Himmler's escape fund. Himmler had intended that it should be found, because the actual volume of money would have needed a truck or two to move it. Secondly, it was found in Bavaria, where Himmler originated from and, as it remained untouched, it would give greater credence to his own suicide. Himmler was probably on his way back to Bavaria to recover it when he was caught – one might think.

Himmler had briefed his group of this intention, before most of its members were caught in Bremervörde. He had intended that they should be, because they had been given false demobilization papers, which stated that the holder was a soldier of a certain rank, and regiment, but that he had been detached to the GFP (SD). This last designation of letters meant that the holder had been a member of the Secret Field Police. This was an automatic arrest category amongst those that the Allied troops were vetting.

In common parlance, Himmler had set the group up.

At times and intervals and on varying frequencies known only to Himmler, he sent brief messages to someone and listened for the replies on the radio transmitter/receiver. Himmler was aware that the Allies could pick up these messages. However, unless an operator was able to sit for several weeks and hear all frequencies, it was unlikely that anyone could get a 'fix' on our position. In addition, at this stage after the war, the Allies were beginning to get suspicious of one another. Even if a message was heard, the Allies might initially suspect one another. What with black marketeers and Allied undercover agents and official radio messages, Himmler's messages were not the only ones on the airwaves.

Himmler was not in a hurry to go anywhere. He was methodical, organized and quite tidy. By contrast, I was becoming bored with the inactivity, the limits on where I could move on the surface and the repetitive food.

We had a few books with us in the bunker, which we had read and re-read many times. Himmler had tried to anticipate most things, including headache tablets, a first aid book and bandages and ointments, amongst the bunker's stores. We had made up a board and pieces for playing draughts, but he could invariably beat me.

Himmler seemed to sense my mood.

'Tell me, Erich. Did they ever show you how to snare a rabbit in your survival training?' he asked.

'Yes they did, but that was a long time ago,' I told him.

'Well, can you show me how it is done? If we are lucky, we might catch a rabbit or two to vary our diet,' Himmler enthused.

'We would have to light the stove to cook them,' I added.

'So be it, Erich! We have seen no one in these woods since we have been here. I think it's about time that we risked it. After all, when it gets colder, we will need the heat and it gives us a chance to try the stove out.'

Himmler checked the surface through the periscope and we lifted the bunker lid and emerged. Moving some distance away from the bunker, as carefully as usual, I made snares of string with a slipknot. I placed these in locations where I thought rabbits might pass. We had both seen rabbit droppings in the wood, previously.

Success was not immediate, but we finally caught a rabbit, which I had to skin, gut and cook. The kerosene stove worked, although initially the chimney smoked as a few layers of spiders webs were burnt. Himmler checked the chimney on the surface. He could not smell kerosene fumes. As he walked away from the chimney, he noticed that the wind seemed to dissipate the fumes that emerged. I even found that salt had been included in the supplies, together with pepper. I began to cheer up, as my cooking started to give off an appetizing aroma. Both of us sat down to our first hot food in quite a while, later that day. It was another milestone in our existence.

Chapter 9

At the abandoned farm on the river Ems, Humbert had made himself comfortable over the weeks since he arrived to secrete the Seehund midget submarine in the dock.

He had also discovered pressure pads and wires amongst his stores and had laid them at night along the mud track from the farm to the road, just under the surface. As opposed to a bunker, he had in fact made himself a comfortable warm nest high up in an old pigeon loft in one of the barns.

He connected the ends of the pressure pad wires into tiny bulb sockets and carried a battery up there to provide the power. The battery would last some time, because it might only be used occasionally. If any bulb lit up, it would give warning of someone coming up the track, or a vehicle approaching, whilst he was in the pigeon loft.

He used a long ladder to get up to his loft. He also had a knotted rope up there, which could allow him to escape to ground level if he thought it was an emergency. Should anyone show any sign of moving the ladder to inspect the loft, then he could quietly open a flap in the outside wall and lower himself to the ground, via the knotted rope.

At other times of the day, when he was active on the ground, he had quietly made the farmhouse as unattractive as possible. He broke glass in windows, left windows open to the rain and removed tiles from the roof. The farm was already becoming damp, mouldy and uninviting, as he intended that it should. The last thing he wanted was some refugee deciding to take up residence. He did not, however, damage the water supply, which he needed for himself, principally for drinking water. He used the farmhouse to wash in, although not with any remnant of soap, because the smell of soap can linger in the air, the same as the smell of tobacco smoke. Fortunately he did not smoke.

150

Humbert had a radio receiver/transmitter with spare batteries, which he kept under one of the slabs in the boat shed. He had to listen for signals, on occasions and frequencies detailed in his orders. There were contingency plans for re-transmissions two days later, if anything stopped him being at the radio on time. Sometimes he took the transmitter to his loft to use there.

He too was rapidly tiring of tinned food. He thought of foraging at night for a chicken or two, but the risks might not be worth it. Humbert's motivation was the promise of more diamonds. Whoever was to come there, by arrangement with him over the radio, needed the Seehund, or they would not have had it so carefully hidden. He was a trained Seehund sailor, and they would need him to operate and navigate the vessel.

Few vessels used the river at present. So far he had seen no danger. The Allies occupied the area and were undoubtedly in Emden. He had seen British patrol boats with the white ensign flag, but only a few of them. If foot patrols had come to his side of the river, no one had ventured up to the farm. The carefully contrived look of desolation should be enough to put most people off. Nevertheless, Humbert did not want to be surprised on the ground. He fashioned several wooden clubs for a quiet method of defence and hid them in various places.

No official came to the farm and, even more important, no letters were delivered. Humbert wondered about this, but imagined that the farm owner had informed the local postman when she moved away.

He had a lot of time on his hands. He dragged the old wooden dinghy, which had a hole in the bottom, from the side of the dock and tied it to a mooring ring. The boat was pushed into the dock. It floated, despite being full of water. It set off the boathouse's appearance. A boathouse containing a large empty dock might be considered to be of use to someone. The waterlogged boat made it look more run down, desolate and unattractive.

Humbert bored a hole in the rear wooden wall of the boat-house which was conveniently disguised on the other side. This allowed him to keep a check to his rear whilst he was working on anything in the shed, such as pulling out tins of food from

151

the stores under the slabs. The last thing he wanted was to have the transmitter out if anyone walked into the boathouse without him first hearing them approach. He also had to take care that, whilst he was in the boathouse, no one spotted him from a boat on the river and came to investigate. Humbert therefore adopted extreme caution when moving about. He listened intently and sniffed the air before moving. He did this particularly in the mornings when he emerged from the pigeon loft. Humbert took a pride in moving around as quietly as a cat.

The pigeon loft had peepholes also, so that he could check the area outside the barn as well as the interior of the barn below him. The height gave him an advantage over looking out from ground level.

He had a watch and kept it wound. It was practically his only link with the real world and important for the radio signals that he needed to make. He kept a calendar of dates by scratching them on a piece of wood. He had to keep to a system and found it easiest to scratch out the previous day's date as soon as he awoke each morning.

Humbert realized the boredom and absence of human contact could make him careless. He therefore devised a programme for the day, which included periods of exercise to help him keep fit. One of his own self tests was to creep up on rabbits in the early morning or evening and see how close he could get to them before they ran off. The field near the farm that he used for this was shielded from anyone on the road by a bank of earth.

He perceived his greatest danger as the possibility of falling ill. He therefore became very careful not to get a chill from wet clothes, etc. There was some spare clothing amongst his stores, but it was limited. He needed to ensure that he got wet clothes dry before wearing them again. Fortunately the warmth of the barn and the availability of straw was a great help.

The farm yard was concreted and free of mud, which was lucky, because he would have otherwise left tracks. He took care to keep the interior of the barn tidy, or he might leave tracks in the dust, or take strands of straw outside on his clothes.

Humbert kept thinking about Bible stories and particularly temptation. He was tempted to leave the farm and go home. He was tempted to go and try to steal chickens. He was tempted to walk to the nearest village and speak to a human being once more. He was tempted to find out the latest news of what was going on in Germany. He was tempted to have a companion with him, preferably a woman. He found himself gravely tempted.

He would make excuses up, such as: if I go to the village, no one will know that I am living here. If I steal a chicken, perhaps the farmer will think it was a fox. Humbert had to wrestle with himself. So far, he had held out against temptation. At his lowest times, he would take out the diamond and look at it. That was real, that was worth money. The money would help him in the future. The promise of more diamonds to come was worth a little privation for a few months, in his opinion.

Humbert remained at the farm. He used to console himself that another day scratched from his wooden calendar meant a day nearer to his reward.

The voice sending the radio messages was still in regular contact. It was the only sign that he was not wasting his time. He stuck to his diet of tinned food, multi vitamin tablets and water. He had a few tins of tinned fruit and used these as a special treat for Sundays.

In the *Werwolf* bunker, Himmler and I at least had companionship. The difficulty with living with someone in a close environment was that little mannerisms of one person tended to annoy the other, such as scratching, belching, farting and picking one's nose. When I was engaged in some boring activity, I tended to whistle, and that irritated Himmler. Himmler was growing a full face beard as a disguise and it itched. The constant scratching irritated me.

Each of us kept it to himself, but sooner or later it would lead to arguments.

As the months progressed, Lance Corporal Benny Green found himself back in England and demobilized from the British Army. He lived with his parents in Bermondsey, London, and was working at a firm of accountants. Life was a bit dull, but

153

he had more freedom than he had had in the Army. His weekly routine was work, cinema or dance hall, and the synagogue.

Benny belonged to a Jewish ex-servicemen's organization and during late 1945, he received a form asking for details of any Nazi soldiers or officials that members had known about, either as a serviceman or as a prisoner of war. The information on the form explained how both former Nazis and evidence of any war crimes were being sought.

Benny wrote that he didn't know of any crimes, but he had been in Lüneburg when Himmler committed suicide and explained about the doubts he had had at that time. He mentioned nothing about having seen Himmler's body. He posted the form off and soon forgot about it, because there was no reply.

Unknown to Benny, the people looking for Nazis decided to keep a casual eye on Himmler's former wife and daughter, Himmler's mistress and her children and certain other people associated with Himmler. Although Benny Green's notes had not rung any alarm bells, the logic of Benny's thoughts was felt to be of interest.

Over in Germany, day followed day and we 'bunker boys' had lived quietly for several months. One day in October 1945, things changed dramatically.

I can remember this episode as if it was yesterday. About the middle of one morning, Himmler and I were sitting in the bunker playing draughts, which Himmler always won, when a pressure pad light illuminated. For several seconds both of us sat staring at it in astonishment, until Himmler reacted, surprisingly quickly. He rushed to the periscope, raised it the few centimetres to operational height and turned it in the direction of the activated pressure pad. At first he told me that he saw nothing unusual. Then he saw a man approaching and looking about. He forced himself to keep watching. The man appeared to be alone. He was looking at the ground for something.

Himmler relayed this quietly to me and I picked up a pistol and looked towards the closed hatch.

'Take the machine pistol as well,' ordered Himmler, as he

154

moved to crouch down by the cupboard which was fixed against one wall. He flung open the cupboard doors and pushed down a hidden lever inside. This raised the cupboard about three centimetres and revealed a small rubber-covered wheel on one side underneath. The action also released the cupboard from the wall at one side. Glancing back at me, Himmler saw that I was watching, goggle-eyed.

'Life is full of surprises, eh! Erich, bring the guns and the torch,' he ordered.

Himmler swung back the cupboard on its wheel. It was hinged and revealed a black opening where he had pulled it from the wall on one side. He crouched and moved into the blackness.

'Switch off the bunker lights, put your torch on and get in here quickly!' Himmler instructed.

I did as I was told and found that I could stand upright in a concrete-lined vertical rectangular 'tube' the other side of the bunker wall. I was amazed. I had opened that cupboard many times and noticed nothing. Himmler closed the cupboard and clicked another lever, which secured the cupboard tightly to the wall once more. He started to quietly mount a metal ladder, after grabbing the torch from me. At the top, he disappeared from view.

I climbed up after him, following the light, and saw Himmler crawling along a low horizontal rectangular concrete lined tube for perhaps fifteen metres. At the end it widened and I could join him. Looking up, I saw another hatch like the one in the bunker. In the corner a small pipe allowed the air in that area to circulate a little. It was already getting warmer in the confined space. Himmler held his finger to his lips for silence and we listened. At first we heard nothing, then we heard sounds of the main bunker hatch being lifted. After a few more seconds we heard the sounds of someone jumping on to the ledge beneath the bunker hatch to enter.

'Put your back under this hatch to lift it, Erich,' ordered Himmler in a whisper. 'It will be stiff, because it hasn't been opened since it was built, on my instructions. Heinrich's hidey-hole!'

I put my back under the hatch and tried to straighten up. The hatch would not move. Himmler lay on his back and put his feet under the hatch also.

'Push together on three, 'I suggested. 'One, two, three!'

We both pushed up hard. Still nothing happened. I exerted more pressure, my face contorted with the effort. We heard the grasses tearing and the hatch rose out of its rim and cool air flooded into the tube.

I passed the pistol to Himmler and kept hold of the machine-pistol.

'No shooting unless I say so,' he ordered.

I put the hatch aside gently and we both emerged amongst bushes. No one else was visible. We approached the open main bunker hatch stealthily. We could hear the sound of movement inside the bunker.

Himmler glanced at me and called out, 'You below, can you hear me?'

The noise in the bunker stopped abruptly, but there was no answer.

Himmler continued, 'Throw out your weapons, or we will drop hand grenades inside.' He repeated this slowly in English and French (besides German).

After a few seconds a frightened voice called up in German. 'I have no weapons. Do you want me to come out?'

Himmler called out, 'Are you alone?'

'I am alone, sir,' came the disembodied voice.

'Climb the ladder and stand on the ledge with your hands up,' Himmler ordered. 'We have you covered and there are six of us. No tricks or we shoot!'

'I am coming sir,' wailed the voice. 'Please don't shoot!'

Himmler and I moved to different locations near the hatch and watched it intently.

A hand appeared from below, waving what had once been a white handkerchief. After a second or so, a man's head appeared and he stood up on the ledge within the bunker. He was poorly dressed and dirty.

'Stand still. Don't move!' Himmler ordered the man, as he covered him with a pistol. Without taking his eyes off the man, he called to me, 'Search him for any weapons.'

Whilst I emptied the man's pockets and searched him, Himmler continued the questions.

'Who are you? Why are you here and how do you know of this place?' he rapped out.

156

'I am Johann Berger, sir. I came here to obtain food and shelter. I knew that the bunker was here, because I was here when it was built.'

'Explain how you were here,' demanded Himmler.

This time the answer did not come as quickly from Berger.

'I was a guard here, sir.'

'State your rank, number and regiment!'

Again the reply was hesitant. Finally Berger stated, 'Rottenführer, Number 613956, SS Bau Brigade Neuengamme.'

Himmler felt that he had to be sure. 'Take off your shirt and show me your SS blood group tattoo,' he told Berger. Berger obliged and Himmler felt convinced by the tattoo that Berger was an SS man.

As Berger put his shirt back on, he was suddenly struck by a thought.

'Besides sir,' he continued, 'you gentlemen are also here using this bunker, which was constructed under close security. I believe that only a few people know of this bunker location. You have guns and it is the death penalty for Germans to possess guns and ammunition. I think that we might belong to the same club. Am I right, gentlemen?'

Himmler countered the question with one of his own to Berger.

'Why do you address me as sir?' he enquired.

'Just a guess,' answered Berger. 'You have the bearing of an officer and these bunkers were probably not constructed for just enlisted men to use. You are also the one pointing a gun at me, sir.'

'Quite so,' answered Himmler, lowering his pistol and relaxing a little. 'Welcome to our bunker, Berger! My name is Heinrich and this is Erich. There are more of us, but they are away at present. Now you must take us as you find us. We were not expecting visitors when you happened to drop by. I expect you are hungry and thirsty. We will see what we can rustle up downstairs. Let Erich go down first and put the lights on.'

I wondered if Berger would recognize Himmler, but he genuinely did not appear to. Himmler's full face beard seemed to disguise his fairly ordinary features. I also reasoned that if Berger had heard that Himmler was dead, then logic would dictate that any similarity between the Himmler of newsreels and the man Berger saw was purely coincidental. I was quite confident that Himmler had never met low ranking guards like Berger either.

As Berger descended into the lit bunker, he looked around at the fittings which were now in use.

Himmler followed and called me across. 'Wasn't there something that you were going to tidy upstairs?' he asked quietly.

I got the 'message' and went back up the ladder to replace the hatch over what was now apparent as an emergency exit to the bunker. I put it back carefully. It fitted snugly in place. At the main entrance to the bunker I also lifted the lid that Berger had pulled up and set it on the rock. I then lifted the grass that had been depressed under the lid to help erase the mark.

Himmler had put the stove on to boil water for our guest.

'I'm afraid that we only have black tea, Berger,' he smiled. 'We are right out of cake. Now tell us all about your story from the building of the bunker to your arrival here. We are both eager for news. Make yourself comfortable.' He indicated a chair.

Berger sat down to begin his story. He relaxed and started to talk about the construction of the bunker and others in other areas and the return to Duisburg and then back to Neuengamme concentration camp near Hamburg.

He then recounted how the camp had been evacuated during the last weeks of the war. The prisoners had been force-marched out of Neuengamme and northwards to the Baltic coast. There they had been loaded on to several ships. Berger himself had the job of counting the numbers on to each. The biggest was the *Cap Arkona*, a large passenger liner, and Berger had counted over 5,000 prisoners on to this ship.

A second ship with 2,800 prisoners was the *Thielbeck*. A third, smaller, vessel was also involved. After the loading had been completed, the ships remained close to the port of Neustadt. The SS officers in charge had not informed Berger of the ships' destination, but he imagined Norway, or even Denmark.

The Allies became aware of these vessels and imagined that, with a sprinkling of small naval vessels nearby, the larger ships might be full of troops being evacuated from the front-line.

On May 3rd 1945, several squadrons of RAF Typhoon fighter

bombers, armed with either rockets or bombs took off to attack this shipping. The *Thielbeck* was attacked with rockets and sank within minutes. There were 50 survivors from the 2,800 persons on board. The situation for the *Cap Arkona* was even worse. It was hit by many rockets, which set it on fire and the fuel tanks eventually exploded. This caused the ship to sink quickly with a loss of all but about 450 persons, most of whom were not prisoners.

(In fact the 4,500 or more deaths on the *Cap Arkona* was the second largest total in history for one ship – the largest loss of life was also in the Baltic in the Second World War. By contrast, almost three times as many died on the *Cap Arkona* as on the *Titanic*.)

Berger knew the figures because his job was to count the people coming aboard. He also had to count the survivors, after he had managed to get ashore. Besides attacking these ships, which were about three kilometres off the coast, the British ground forces had also arrived in Neustadt, the same day.

The British soldiers were embarrassed to discover what had happened, and by the hundreds of bodies that drifted to the shore. After taking the town of Neustadt, one of their first tasks was to have the bodies buried quickly. They were often buried in mass graves, where they had been found on the beaches.

Berger, meanwhile was hiding with other surviving SS Totenkopfverbände camp guards. He had guessed that the RAF had not known that there were prisoners on the ships. He also imagined that the British would not take too kindly to the former guards, both for the condition of surviving prisoners, or as witnesses to what had happened.

He hid with others in isolated barns and a few days later heard news of the war's end. After wandering around for some days, he had managed to get some civilian clothing. Over the next week or so, he slowly made his way south to Hamburg. There was colossal devastation there from the bombing earlier in the war and the city was full of homeless civilians, former soldiers, former foreign workers and former concentration camp prisoners.

Berger imagined that some of the last category had been

survivors from the ships near Neustadt, because he knew of no other large camp in the Hamburg area.

He had himself witnessed 'street roundups' by British soldiers. This consisted of soldiers arriving by lorry and sealing off both ends of a street. The soldiers would then allow one or more former concentration camp prisoners to look at all the civilians in that street to try to identify former camp guards. The mere accusation of 'He was a camp guard' was enough for the man or men to be arrested. Often the people who were arrested were not camp guards and it sometimes took weeks or months to prove otherwise.

Berger reasoned that he would be safer to make his way south and hide in one of the *Werwolf* bunkers which he had seen being built. Apart from *Werwolf* people murdering the Bürgermeister of occupied Aachen before the War's end, Berger had heard nothing of *Werwolf* activity. He imagined that there were few fanatics who were still prepared to fight on. He had sheltered for some months with a lady friend, but with checks on houses and occupants, he decided that it was safest to hide in the bunker.

Himmler asked Berger if he had told anyone else where he was going. Berger assured him that he had not. Himmler decided to 'milk' Berger of recent information about what was happening in Germany over the last few months.

I prepared a meal and we all ate it and drank some tea. Berger was tired and we got another bunk ready for him and gave him some blankets. Berger soon fell asleep and Himmler talked quietly with me for some time afterwards.

The two of us decided to sleep in shifts once more, for our own security. Berger was probably what he claimed to be, a lowly guard on the run, but we did not want to take any chances. At the same time, Himmler did not want Berger to become too much of a friend, because he ultimately posed a risk to our discovery by the Allies.

Himmler took the first shift of staying awake, whilst I slept. He had been monitoring BBC radio broadcasts since he left Flensburg, but he had heard nothing of the tremendous loss of life in the sinking of these ships, yet at the same time Berger's description was hardly likely to have been made up. This was made even more definite when Berger woke up screaming.

160

That naturally woke me up with a shock, but Himmler soon calmed him down. Berger apologized for his nightmares about the *Cap Arkona*. He simply could not forget the crash of bombs and rockets hitting the vessel and the screams of the trapped and injured prisoners and guards. The infernal din had played on his mind, as he struggled to help row a boat to the shore, through a sea that was itself littered with bodies which bumped against the boat with dull thuds every few seconds.

Eventually Berger drifted off to sleep again and I did also. Himmler reviewed in his mind the questions which he needed to ask in the morning, as he waited for my shift to start for the remainder of the night.

As the two sleepers awoke in the morning, I invited Berger to do some pedalling on the bicycle generator to 'help earn his keep'. Berger seemed quite fit and helped with this chore, whilst we prepared some more of our monotonous diet for breakfast.

After we had breakfasted, Himmler asked Berger if he knew what had happened to the *Bonzen* (important people) in the Reich.

'Hitler's dead in Berlin,' Berger stated. 'The Allies say he committed suicide, so did Goebbels. Göring has been captured, Dönitz and Kaltenbrunner also.'

'What about Himmler?' asked Himmler.

'He apparently was caught by the British and took poison to commit suicide,' answered Berger.

'What of Bormann, Keitel and Jodl?' enquired Himmler.

'Field Marshal Keitel is under arrest by the Allies, but I don't know the other two men you mention,' replied Berger. 'I have also heard that some of the SS Generals have been captured, like Sepp Dietrich. There is talk of war crimes trials and the whole of the SS has been declared a criminal organization. However, at least the British have come to the realization that some of the foreign SS legions joined the SS to fight the Russian Communists. They have had the Latvian SS division survivors imprisoned in Neuengamme concentration camp since June. The locals say that some of them are as young as thirteen years old. Some criminals, eh?'

Himmler interrupted Berger's news. 'Have they got Hitler's body?'

Berger replied that he did not know, Germany had been divided amongst the Allies. The Russians held Berlin, but the other Allies had parts of Berlin. The Russians were first into Berlin and they were pretty tight-lipped about what they said.

'What about Himmler's body? What have the British done with it?' demanded Himmler.

'I passed Lüneburg on the way here and the locals say Himmler took poison in a house there. They also say the British were pretty embarrassed that he had taken poison whilst he was their prisoner. They have disposed of his body in secret, I understand.'

Himmler took a deep breath, as Berger (unknowingly) confirmed that another part in the escape plan had fitted into place. I was looking at Himmler's face and I raised my eyebrows slightly as he glanced at me. He gave a tiny nod of his head.

'Did you have any ideas about escaping to Sweden, Berger?' asked Himmler. 'I would have thought that more logical when you were on the Baltic coast.'

'Logical perhaps, my friend,' answered Berger, 'but the Swedes are actually handing back our soldiers and those from our Latvian and Estonian legions, who have taken refuge there. Sweden is certainly not a safe haven.'

Himmler nodded his head at the news. 'My friend Erich will show you how we live in here,' he said. 'I expect you will need the latrine.'

Whilst I lifted the hatch and took Berger outside on the surface, Himmler unlocked the 'emergency exit' cupboard and hid our weapons out of sight. He re-locked the cupboard in place, just before the pre-arranged radio transmission to Humbert. Using the radio quickly, he confirmed that Humbert should expect someone to arrive there quite soon. He then shut the radio down.

Our wood consisted mainly of evergreen trees and so there were few leaves to fall and spoil our cover. However with the passage of time, it was getting colder. Snow would soon fall and that would leave footprints on the surface, which could lead to our discovery.

Himmler pumped Berger on conditions locally: food rationing, travel passes, check points, etc. He built up a fund of knowledge and came to decisions which he kept to himself. His plan was

162

to move out from the bunker at the beginning of December, or by the first snowfall, if that came first. He would need the map of his intended route to his destination, food, warm clothing, a few gold rings from the bunker supplies to barter with, his good friend Koch and a slice of luck.

He also realized that Berger could not feature in his future plans and pondered what to do about him. There were few alternatives.

At length, the day arrived when Himmler had decided to leave. After Berger had gone up to the surface to perform his ablutions, Himmler briefed me and we both began our preparations.

We packed a few tins of food, a tin opener, a change of clothing, some gold rings and a blanket each into two rucksacks. Himmler spent some time considering his appearance in a mirror. His hair had grown, and with my help over the months, he had effected a change of hairstyle from his military 'crop'. He now had a full-face beard, which he kept neatly trimmed. He also had two pairs of ordinary rimmed glasses for his vision. He looked nothing like his former self, but then he had always been an unremarkable figure of a man. He still had two phials of poison, one of which was concealed in the hollow heel of his left boot and the other he kept in his pocket.

Berger returned and saw the rucksacks on the table.

'Going somewhere?' he enquired.

'Yes, we are leaving the bunker now,' retorted Himmler.

'Where are we going?' asked Berger.

'That need not concern you my friend,' answered Himmler. 'You can remain here.'

'Not on your life!' Berger said loudly. 'If you two are going, I want to come with you.'

'I rather thought that you might!' Himmler snarled, and withdrew an automatic pistol with a fitted silencer from his coat. In one quick motion and without appearing to take aim, he shot Berger once, which made him stagger back and fall on a bunk. Moving closer to the groaning man, Himmler took careful aim and shot him again. This time the shot was to the head and Berger jerked once and was lifeless.

Himmler noted the look of concern on my face and lowered the gun. I knew he was leaving, but he had said nothing about shooting Berger. Himmler was surprised at how calm he felt. He had witnessed executions, but apart from his experiences towards the end of the First World War, that was the first time that he had actually shot someone from close range.

'I'm afraid Berger was a risk to us, if he was left alive,' Himmler explained. 'However, his information was certainly a bonus. Come on! Let's get out of here and get on our way.' He dropped the pistol on to the table.

From a packing case Himmler took two walking sticks. Each had a concealed metal core. They would make an effective weapon, because we dared not risk being caught with guns. He made one last radio message to Humbert and closed down the radio.

Himmler and I left the bunker, replacing the hatch for the last time and adjusting the grasses around it. It might even turn out that we would have to return there. Not a pleasant thought, with Berger's body for company.

The journey to the south-west was made slowly, carefully and stealthily. It was cold. We had not been above ground for so long for several months. Himmler seemed to have made a study of the area's geography before the war's end. He led me across country to near the banks of the river Weser between Bremen and Bremerhaven, then we spent most of the remainder of the day resting and watching the river traffic. Himmler had in mind stealing a small boat to cross the river, but then our observation paid off. A local man owned a rowing boat, which he used to take people across the river, to the north of the town of Brake, on the other side.

The following day, Himmler and I waited for the man to appear again, in the early morning. We approached him in a friendly way.

'Good morning, my friend!' I said pleasantly. 'If you will take us both over to the other side of the river, I will give you a gold ring as payment.'

'And if not...?' queried the boatman.

'How long were you thinking of living, old man?' I snarled. I actually surprised myself at my vicious reaction. It was not like me to be so unpleasant.

164

'OK! OK!' countered the boatman. 'I'll take you both. Do you mind if I see the ring first?'

I felt in a pocket and handed the boatman a gold ring. The man examined it closely, appeared satisfied, and pocketed it.

'At your service, gentlemen. Please get in the boat.' The boatman shoved off and scrambled into the boat himself and picked up the oars. He began to row diagonally, as the current tried to force the boat upstream. Himmler and I sat in the stern, watching the river and the boatman as the boat progressed across the Weser.

'If there are more gold rings, gentlemen, then I'm your man for ferry work,' stated the boatman.

'Thank you,' replied Himmler. 'We are coming back the day after tomorrow, if you watch out for us at 17.00 hours. We have no more gold rings, but I'm sure that we can fix you up with something – cigarettes perhaps?'

'That would be fine, gentlemen,' replied the boatman. 'I will look forward to that.' He increased the pressure on the oars and the boat approached the shore and grounded. We jumped on to the shingle and walked up the river bank.

The boatman called after us, 'I would advise you gentlemen to steer clear of the British checkpoints in Wilhelmshaven and Varel.'

'Thank you!' I called over my shoulder.

Himmler had no intention of going to Wilhelmshaven, but Varel was on the route to our destination and so that was advice to be heeded.

We passed to the south of Varel and to the north of Oldenburg, which was the next large town. Himmler explained to me that the boatman probably took us for black marketeers. If the boatman intended to inform the police, then he was expecting us back the day after tomorrow. By that time Himmler hoped to be at or near his destination.

Over the next two days we moved westwards and slightly south, crossing the Elbe river between Papenburg and Leer to gain the west bank. Moving northwards, we drew close to the farm on the river bank where Himmler knew Humbert should be waiting as planned.

Himmler, as usual, was cautious. He tried to plan for any eventuality. It was a critical stage, and I could see he seemed nervous. He asked me to walk up to the farm buildings, whilst he remained on guard some distance away. I was told that there was a man waiting at the farm; his name was Humbert and he was a naval man. I should whistle a few bars of the 'Badenweiler March' and then stop for half a minute. I should then continue the same tune. The man they expected to be there would in turn whistle a little of 'Lilli Marlen' in reply. After the man appeared, I had to check that no one else was hiding in the buildings and then call for 'Harry' to come in. If the situation seemed safe, I would scratch my head. If all was not well, I would just call and Himmler would take his cue from that.

I moved off towards the farm buildings slowly. Himmler moved into bushes and watched me. He fingered the phial of poison in his pocket and considered putting it in his mouth, but decided to wait.

The faint sound of whistling came to Himmler's ears on the cold breeze from the river and he waited for me to return. After what seemed a long time, I appeared on the farm track scratching my head and calling softly for 'Harry, Harry' (Himmler). Himmler approached cautiously and saw Humbert for the first time.

'Herr Humbert, I presume?'

Humbert nodded and asked, 'Have you brought the diamonds?'

'My dear Humbert,' Himmler explained, 'we could not risk carrying a fortune in diamonds with us. I had to place them in safe keeping, in a place that our country's enemies could never find them. They are across the water in England. That is why we need your particular expertise. I trust our vessel is in good order?'

Considering the fact that Humbert had been waiting there alone for months for his reward, I thought he took this news very well. Himmler had said nothing to me about diamonds, but I had no reason to disbelieve him. Humbert looked as if he was going to protest, but he finally shrugged his shoulders and led the way over to the boathouse. Inside, I saw a waterlogged rowing boat in the dock, tethered to the side by a short rope.

Seeing my disappointed face, Himmler pointed and said, 'Our transport to England!'

166

I looked incredulously at the boat. Humbert smiled and Himmler actually doubled up in peals of laughter. It was if Himmler's nerves prior to finding Humbert at the farm needed release. He laughed and laughed, until he finally regained control of himself and offered me an explanation.

'It's good "window dressing", is it not, Koch? Our transport is not this boat in the water; it's a midget submarine under the water.'

The three of us settled down for a meal and sleep, before making a start on preparing the submarine the following day.

I noticed that Humbert had not recognized Himmler, or if he had, then he was a good actor. Himmler no longer looked like his familiar wartime image. Humbert presumably saw an ordinary person in front of him, as opposed to someone special.

Chapter 10

The next day, Humbert took charge and directed Himmler and me to assist in placing a couple of planks across the dock. At low tide on the river, we opened the lock gate paddles to reduce the amount of water in the dock. After equalizing the levels, we shut the paddles again.

The periscope of the Seehund midget submarine now revealed itself above the surface. Humbert retrieved a hand pump from the items in the stores and we started the laborious task of pumping water out of the dock. We were aided by mist from the river in the morning and evening, which hid our activities.

At last the tiny conning tower of the Seehund was sufficiently above the water to have the hatch clear. Humbert placed us on either side of the dock to push other planks firmly against the casing, in case the midget tilted to one side as he entered it. He made his way along the other planks across the width of the dock, lay down on them carefully and swung his legs from the planks to rest lightly on the superstructure near the hatch. He crouched down slowly and undid the wheel securing the hatch, and opened it. The hatch was left open for the air to freshen for several minutes.

Gripping the sides of the hatch, Humbert slowly lowered his legs inside, to drop down lightly on the metal step under the hatch. The midget submarine sat firmly in its cradle without movement. He then disappeared, as he went forward out of sight to the front crew seat and sat down. He cracked open a cylinder of compressed air slowly. As the air surged into the dive tanks to provide buoyancy, the midget rose in the water to float free of the cradle. Humbert connected the battery leads and a light came on inside the Seehund. The battery power gauge looked reasonable, considering the length of time the craft had been dormant.

Moving carefully backwards to stand upon the step again, Humbert poked his head and shoulders from the hatch.

'Push the planks near to the two towing eyes,' he ordered. 'Move along them and pick up those ropes, which are attached to the towing eyes and pull them out. There's a weight on the end. Be careful. When you have the weights, untie them and put them on the dockside.'

We did as we were asked and pulled the ropes out of the brown stained water. Having done this, we were able to pull the midget to one side of the dock, under Humbert's instruction and tie it to the mooring rings and against the dockside fenders.

I marvelled at this 'fat sausage', as the Seehund appeared, being able to destroy much bigger craft. The torpedoes (slung one on each side) could not be seen. Humbert got out of the Seehund and showed us where diesel oil drums were located under some slabs. Between us we tipped up the drums to stand on end, and unscrewed the caps. Humbert fetched a smaller hand pump and hose and connected this up. The fuel tanks of the Seehund were filled up to the brim, to replace fuel used on the journey from Ymuiden.

Putting the oil drums away again and covering them with slabs, Humbert set us to open wooden crates containing tinned food and other items. He himself collected a full compressed-air tank and replaced one of those inside the midget. Under Humbert's instruction, I collected jerrycans of drinking water from the farm supply and brought them back to the boathouse. Humbert also included an empty jerrycan and a funnel. Himmler assembled the tins of food and water on the dockside.

Everyone seemed in good spirits: Humbert, because he finally had some company and a reward for his efforts seemed in sight; and we were content to have a change of scenery and activity from the underground bunker.

Rather surprisingly, Humbert had shown no obvious curiosity as to who his new colleagues actually were. Perhaps his involvement in crime had taught him not to ask too many questions. It was clear to us that Humbert was quite competent in handling the Seehund, from what we had already seen. Himmler had already known of Humbert's navigating ability and his knowledge of the English coast before he chose him for this mission.

Traffic on the river did not come near our side, and to prevent discovery I got everyone working on painting some canvas that I had found. It was actually a lorry tarpaulin, but by painting it with diesel oil, and leaving patches of the original colour, we produced a 'canvas', which could disguise the shape of the Seehund. We tied it tightly across the mouth of the dock and over the forepart of the vessel. I trusted that, from the river, it would appear to indicate a rubble-filled interior to the boathouse. Better still, it would provide some cover from any passing river traffic when we were moving around inside the boathouse.

'As ever, you are quite resourceful, Erich!' said Himmler.

'Why thank you, Harry!' I replied, as I continued to tie the tarpaulin tautly in the entrance.

It worked two ways. The cover of the tarpaulin shielded us from the river, but it darkened the interior of the shed and made it harder to work in. Nevertheless, we progressed towards getting the Seehund ready for sea again.

Eventually, risking someone hearing the noise, we started the diesel engine, with the propeller disengaged, and let it turn over for some minutes. It seemed to go smoothly, and at the same time some more electrical charge trickled into the batteries.

'Have you actually got a date in mind to depart?' Humbert asked 'Harry'.

Although nothing had been said, he sensed the older man was in charge.

'Yes, I have a date in mind, Herr Humbert, but instead of planning to just go on that day, I think that we should ensure that the Seehund can exit the dock satisfactorily,' answered Himmler.

'Why shouldn't it?' Humbert queried, evidently surprised.

'The river may have silted up the dock entrance a little over the months.'

Humbert grunted. He seemed embarrassed that he had not considered such an eventuality.

'OK! We'll try tonight,' he announced.

'So be it then,' replied Himmler.

Humbert spent the intervening hours describing his time at the farm to us. He had been alone for so long that he presumably needed to talk – and he nearly wore his tongue out.

170

Later the same day, we checked the river in the darkness. There was no sign of any boats. We spent some time undoing the bottom of the tarpaulin, so that we could lift it when the periscope passed underneath. Moving to our pre-arranged positions, Humbert entered the Seehund. He announced that he would use the electric motor to manoeuvre out of the boat-house dock. He stood on the metal step, beneath the hatch, directing operations. Himmler and I untied the Seehund from the dockside and, whilst I held the stern still, Himmler dragged the bow of the submarine to the opposite corner diagonally across the dock. The left dock gate paddle was opened fully on the high tide of the river to raise the water level inside the dock. The Seehund rose in the water accordingly.

I opened the left dock gate fully and then Himmler tossed his rope to me on the other side. I grabbed it, and with much puffing, pulled the bow of the Seehund back to the left side of the dock. The right dock gate could then be opened fully.

Both dock gates were now fully open. We centralized the Seehund in the dock by means of ropes, so that it now faced the open river between the open dock gates.

At his signal, in turn Himmler and I tossed our rope ends to Humbert, who secured them within easy reach of the hatch. He then crouched down inside the craft and secured the hatch over his head.

The Seehund bobbed gently as Humbert, inside, got into the forward crew seat. After a few moments we heard the electric motor start; as it was engaged at low revolutions, we saw it move under power until two metres of the bow had emerged into the river Ems, beyond the dock gates, and then it stopped, with the propeller churning purposelessly. I tapped the hull with a piece of wood. Humbert stopped the motor and after a few seconds he opened the hatch.

'You were right Harry!' he called softly. 'The entrance has silted up a bit.'

Humbert untied the bow and stern ropes and tossed them to us on the dockside. We both heaved back on the ropes to pull the Seehund backwards into the dock. Nothing happened. We tried short sharp tugs on the ropes. Still nothing happened. If we couldn't move the Seehund, our entire getaway plans were finished. I could see that Himmler looked worried. Furthermore,

171

if things remained as they were, how long would the prow of a small submarine sticking out into the river remain unseen when daylight dawned? Maybe Himmler had another plan to fall back on, but if he had, he had not told me. We had only a few hours to sort out this problem.

Humbert called softly across the water to us.

'Keep pulling. I am going to try and bounce the boat if I can.'

He secured the hatch over his head, and after a few seconds the stern began to dip and rise in the water as Humbert inside commenced some rather strenuous gymnastics in the confined space. As the stern dipped and the bow rose, we pulled on the ropes. Finally we felt the midget ease backwards slightly, and we were able to pull it back into the boathouse dock completely. As the stern of the Seehund approached the rear of the dock, we ran up either dockside to arrest its progress by the ropes, so that it did not hit the rear dock wall.

We were both now fairly tired. Under Humbert's instruction, we went through the sequence to shut the dock gates and secured the Seehund to one side of the dock again.

Whilst Himmler and I rested, Humbert went searching under the slabs. He retrieved a small self-contained breathing apparatus which could prolong the diving time on the Seehund, and showed it to us. He fished out another length of unused rope and a rubber-cased torch.

Outlining his proposal, Humbert explained that he intended to try and check the extent of the silting of the entrance underwater. He tied one end of the rope to his waist and gave the other end to me. He then put on two woollen jumpers, in addition to the clothes he was wearing. Making his way to the water's edge, he waded into the almost freezing water, gasping. He seemed very determined and really motivated. As I fed out the rope, Humbert swam a few strokes, took a deep breath from the breathing apparatus and dived beneath the surface. He used his torch and felt with his hands without disturbing the mud too much.

I watched the water anxiously. After what seemed a long time, Humbert surfaced, gasping. I pulled him into the bank by the rope and hauled him out. Himmler and I half dragged him to the barn, where we pulled off his clothes and rubbed him

172

with handfuls of straw. Humbert was about all in and only semi-conscious. Strangely, Himmler seemed to know what to do. He lay close beside Humbert and told me to cover both of them with straw. I then had to lie down on Humbert's other side, after covering myself with straw as far as I could. We both lay on either side of Humbert, close to him, using our body heat and the insulation of the straw to warm him gradually and speed his recovery. Humbert fell asleep almost instantly. We initially felt damp from Humbert's cold body, but we all grew warmer quite rapidly. Himmler was quite patient; he could wait for Humbert to awaken and report when he felt ready.

At last Humbert began to wake up. He was slightly alarmed at being 'cuddled' by both of us, but our combined body heat had certainly worked. During the war years Germany had learnt much about how best to treat airmen and sailors who had been immersed in cold sea water for a long time. This had greatly aided airmen shot down into the sea and sailors whose ships had been sunk. The direct application of body heat was by far the best solution for such cases, after rescue.

Himmler knew that this research had been carried out on prisoners at Dachau concentration camp by a Luftwaffe Dr Rascher, who was executed by the Nazis before the war's end.

'There is only a little silting up in front of the gates, before the river deepens,' Humbert told us, 'perhaps only a metre.'

'Could you reduce weight by dropping a torpedo?' I asked.

'If I was in one hundred metres of water, I would consider it,' answered Humbert, 'but I would not drop a torpedo if I was sitting only a few metres above it. Torpedoes do not like being dropped!'

'Could we lift a torpedo off?' asked Himmler.

'No! They weigh about 2,000 kilos. However, gentlemen, I have another idea. I know that there is a rubber inflatable dinghy in the stores. I intend to inflate it tomorrow night, and by using most of the rope we have, then I think I could get to that Dolphin (mooring platform) in the river over there. If I can do that, then we should be able to flatten the silt "bump" by pulling on the rope against the timber leg of the Dolphin, at the same time as using the diesel engine of the Seehund,' Humbert explained.

'OK, let's get some sleep,' Himmler suggested. 'If Erich will take the first guard shift?'

I got up and went outside – going back into the boathouse and busied myself tidying up the tarpaulin that we had slackened at the bottom to allow the periscope and superstructure of the midget to pass underneath. I stood in the darkness reflecting on my life: the loss of my family in the air raid, becoming a wanted war criminal and having my 'star' seemingly firmly attached to Heinrich Himmler.

However, Himmler had shown himself to be a good organizer. If he was prepared to embark on a new life 'over the water' in England, then it was hardly likely to have been a decision made without a great deal of preparation. I was still a young man and thus a new beginning should mean new opportunities for me. What else was left for me here in Germany – no home, no relatives, no money and no job! If I went anywhere, how could I explain where I had been for the last seven months? I could hardly say the bunker, because there was a dead body there, if anyone went to investigate. I shrugged my shoulders and peered into the darkness.

The next evening, Humbert joined all the unused lengths of rope together with strong knots. He tied one end inside the boathouse and inflated the rubber dinghy with a foot pump, then he decided that he would need help, and chose me, as obviously the fitter man.

He checked the tide and walked in the opposite direction of its flow for fifty metres, carrying the dinghy with my help. After launching the dinghy carefully, we paddled out into the current and aimed towards the Dolphin. At first, it seemed as if we would miss it altogether, but then we got into slacker water and approached it. Humbert checked the smoothness of the wooden support legs and chose one of them to pass the rope around, paying out the rope, as we made our way back to the riverbank. The current took us further than the boathouse on the return journey, but we grounded and walked back to it with the dinghy and rope.

We now had a long rope secured to the Dolphin, with both ends secured in the boathouse. Humbert removed all the moveable items of any weight out of the Seehund, to lighten it as much as possible. He blew the dive tank fully and it sat visibly higher in the water.

We opened the dock gates for Humbert, and Himmler tied one end of the rope to the towing eye of the midget at the bow. We both held the slack of the other end firmly. Humbert stood on the step in the midget and announced what he was going to do. We centred the midget in the dock so that the bow faced the open river between the lock gates. He then shut the hatch and got into the rear seat to make the vessel slightly stern heavy. Starting the diesel engine, he gunned it to full revolutions before engaging the propeller. The Seehund surged forward much faster towards and through the lock gates.

There was a grating noise as it grounded and we both pulled on the rope as hard as possible. Humbert helped by bouncing the midget a little and suddenly it was through and into the river proper. Humbert felt the Seehund free and disengaged the midget's engine. It continued towards the Dolphin, slowing down as it went. Then the current caught the craft and without power it began to swing on the rope around the leg of the Dolphin.

In the Seehund, Humbert scrambled into the front seat, so that he could use the periscope to see outside. Engaging the electric motor on low revolutions, he steered it back towards the boathouse, keeping the craft parallel to the riverbank and as close to the gates as he dared. Humbert adjusted the revolutions of the motor so that the craft held its position in relation to the boathouse, and then raised the hatch carefully. He reached forward and undid the end of the craft's mooring rope from near the hatch and tossed it to me on the bank. I tied it up and Humbert switched off the motor. The tiny submarine was held in place once more, but was about two metres from the lock gates.

Humbert ordered us to close the lock gates. He then directed me to get into the rubber dinghy, which we tethered between the submarine and lock gates. Using the dinghy as a bridge, we transferred stores that we would need back into the Seehund. I then paddled to the front of it and reached up and cut the rope attached to the Dolphin, leaving the other mooring rope intact. Himmler pulled in the rope from the Dolphin and piled

175

it on the dockside. Himmler then told me quietly that he needed ten minutes to send a final message to his agent in England. He left the boathouse with the radio transmitter and carried it up to Humbert's pigeon loft to give a better signal from that height. He rapidly sent a message, which announced our intended arrival in the next few days. The message was acknowledged.

Himmler left the radio where it was, descended the ladder once more, and returned to the boathouse. Humbert had already warned me that if we both got into the Seehund where it was, then it might ground again. He proposed towing us in the dinghy and then getting us aboard at the Dolphin. I also realized that we might need the dinghy at the English coast and asked Himmler to bring the foot pump.

Himmler grabbed the foot pump and a length from the rope used on the Dolphin earlier. Passing one end to me in the dinghy, he watched as I moved the dinghy along the Seehund's hull and tied the rope's end to the rear-towing eye on the submarine above me. I then paddled to the bank. Himmler untied the Seehund from the bank and tossed the mooring rope's end to Humbert, who secured it near the hatch. Himmler then rapidly got into the dinghy.

I waved to Humbert that all was ready and he ducked down and shut the hatch. After a few moments the electric motor increased revolutions and went forwards at an increasing angle from the riverbank. I kept the rope taut and allowed it to pass through my hands, until the Seehund began to tow the dinghy slowly towards the Dolphin. Humbert steered parallel to the Dolphin and altered the revolutions to keep the craft still. He observed through his periscope until he was satisfied with his position. He allowed a little more water into the dive tanks to make the craft more stable in the water, then he opened the hatch carefully and undid his bow line end from near the hatch and wrapped it around the leg of the Dolphin. The Seehund was now secured in mid river.

It was an anxious time for Himmler and me. If Humbert had been so inclined, he could have just untied the dinghy and let us drift away. He could have then taken the Seehund where he wished. We were sitting in a tiny rubber dinghy bobbing in almost freezing waters mid-river in almost total darkness.

Luck was still with us. Humbert hauled on the dinghy rope and gradually brought us alongside the Seehund. Himmler passed Humbert the foot pump and he dropped it inside the hatch. Humbert explained how careful we would now have to be, entering the midget. He himself emerged on to the superstructure and held the periscope and the leg of the Dolphin. Himmler carefully stood up in the dinghy, as I kept it tightly against the Seehund, and pulled himself slowly up on to the superstructure. Humbert told him to take the rear seat, and he lowered his legs through the hatch until he felt the step below his feet. He sat down in the confined space in the rear crew seat.

I now stood up slowly and carefully. Humbert hooked one leg around the periscope and extended his free right hand to me. I grasped the hand and grabbed the edge of the hatch superstructure with the other, then pulled myself slowly upwards, until I could swing a leg up and straddle the superstructure. Humbert told me to get inside and crouch over Harry, out of the way, until he himself got back inside.

I did as I was told and waited. Humbert carefully dropped his legs inside the hatch and on to the step. He paused and pulled the dinghy up on the side of the midget and deflated it. This seemed to take a long time, as we listened to the prolonged hissing of escaping air. Eventually it was empty and folded up, to be stuffed down the hatch for later use. It made the space inside even more cramped.

Humbert called for a knife and cut the rope securing us to the Dolphin. He let the freed craft drift backwards for some distance from the Dolphin, then closed and secured the hatch and scrambled into the front crewman's seat. Peering through the periscope, he increased the motor revolutions and turned the rudder to make us pass the Dolphin on the far side, to avoid the cut rope from possibly fouling the propeller.

'You will have to sit on this metal step, Erich. I regret that the Seehund is a two-man vessel,' Humbert announced, over his shoulder. 'It's not designed for three people, but we can take three at a pinch. Now please sit still and be quiet both of you, because I have to do the work and concentrate. Press that red button on the right, Erich,' he ordered, as he peered through the periscope (although we were still on the surface).

I perched on a metal step under the closed hatch. I could just sit upright there, but only because the hatch was higher than the rest of the superstructure of the Seehund. I had to place my legs carefully on either side of Humbert as he sat in front of me in a seat. I had no support for my back. The whole vessel vibrated from the engine and through the metal step into my body. I had not realized how cramped it would be inside. The journey would be an ordeal.

I pressed the red button and the diesel engine that provided the main propulsion started. Simultaneously Humbert stopped the electric motor.

As we started to move nearer the mouth of the river Ems, Humbert released more air from the dive tank to present an even lower profile to anyone looking from the shore. The schnorkel device worked well and provided fresh air. He checked the fine trim of the boat by adjusting the position of the weights under his seat, and getting Himmler to do the same.

At last he seemed satisfied. Himmler started to relax, but was acutely aware of the noisy hot diesel motor directly behind him.

The Seehund began to pass Emden on the opposite bank and to head for the open sea. Electric bulbs illuminated the interior of the craft, which was largely taken up by the dive tank and compressed air bottles in the bow. The diesel and electric motors were in the stern. Pipes and instruments were along the sides of the hull. It was a little like sitting inside several filing cabinets stacked one behind the other.

As we began to reach the open sea, the motion in the boat began to increase. Himmler and I wondered how long we could bear the loud engine noise. Yet we needed the motor for the main speed of the midget and we needed its power to recharge the batteries. Humbert sat at the periscope, constantly looking to the left and the right, as we proceeded on our course. A map of the coastline and depths lay on his lap. Every five minutes, he would look carefully astern of the vessel.

Humbert glanced up at the closed hatch to ensure it was fully clipped in place properly and shouted over the engine noise behind him, 'I'm going to try a dive with the diesel on.

178

It's quicker and will cut out after a few seconds. Start the electric motor, Erich, after the diesel engine stops.'

Humbert expelled more air from the dive tank and put more power on the diesel to drive the bow beneath the waves. The bow took on a down angle, and a few seconds later the diesel stopped. I switched on the electric motor and Humbert adjusted the rear hydroplanes to reduce the bow angle. He gave the dive tank a few more squirts of compressed air gently and gradually achieved a 'trim', so that the Seehund was on an even level.

'Gentlemen, we are twenty metres beneath the North Sea,' he remarked without looking round. If he had looked round, he would have perhaps noticed that the two of us were slightly paler than before.

At that depth the motion of the boat was far less than on the surface. After running for fifteen minutes beneath the surface, Humbert ordered the electric motor to be turned off and we listened to the comparative silence.

'I can come slowly to periscope depth, gentlemen, but this is safer. There is no ship moving under power on the surface near us, or we would have heard it.'

Humbert put more compressed air into the dive tank once more and the Seehund regained the surface. Only he could see outside through the periscope, but surfacing meant that the schnorkel functioned again to freshen the air in the boat. The diesel was restarted and the Seehund increased speed and started to recharge the batteries.

We passed the Friesland Islands on the seaward side, because it meant deeper water for diving and manoeuvring.

Keeping close to the coast, apart from where sandbanks caused shallow water, we made our way south along the Dutch coast. We passed the Ymuiden harbour, from which Humbert had started his voyage many months ago.

Off the Belgian coast, we kept inshore of the huge wartime minefields – Humbert doubted that the mines would have been moved yet – and reached a position off the approaches to Antwerp. Here the cleared path across to the Thames Estuary was marked by buoys, which were illuminated at night. It was very convenient, yet it was also a busy shipping lane.

Humbert wanted to have the cover of darkness for this part of the voyage and it was still daylight, so decided to rest the

179

craft on the seabed for a couple of hours. He had picked a quiet stretch of coastline and a depth of thirty metres, with a sand bottom, and slowly let the Seehund sink deeper in the water with just negative buoyancy, until it bumped the seabed gently. He waited to see if the motion of the sea would roll the vessel slightly, but it remained motionless, as far as he could determine. Outside the hull, odd noises of the sea broke the comparative silence.

Humbert took a tin of some type of meat and opened it. He offered cans to us, but we both seemed not to be hungry. He grinned to himself, stuck a spoon in the meat and started to eat.

In the calmness of the depths, Himmler and I felt a little better after a while. We each drank some water, and tried a little food. Neither of us had huge appetites.

Humbert pointed to the time and to a carbon dioxide measurement device on the hull. He announced that he was going to try and take sleep. We were not to go to sleep, or else no one might ever wake up again. We had to keep an eye on the CO_2 level and awaken him if it rose to a certain level, which he indicated. We needed to use the breathing apparatus with oxygen which we had brought with us, so he showed us how to change the oxygen cylinders attached.

The vessel soon resounded to the sound of Humbert's muffled snoring as he tried to recharge his own 'batteries' whilst he slept. Himmler and I were used to keeping guard on rotating shifts and we divided the time accordingly. Himmler agreed to swap places with me, and we changed seats with difficulty in the cramped space. I was glad to have support for my back at last. The boat cooled rapidly with the engine switched off and moisture rolled down the metal sides of the craft. The time passed before the carbon dioxide level rose too high, and we awoke him.

Humbert set about surfacing the Seehund, and the interior soon freshened once more as the schnorkel allowed fresh air to circulate. The diesel was restarted and he began his course to enter the shipping lane from Antwerp over to the river Thames in England.

The boat was trimmed to schnorkel at periscope depth. Humbert sat alternatively examining the compass bearing, the view through the periscope and his chart. Every five minutes or less, he looked to the stern, in case any ship was approaching.

He eventually sighted ship's lights and dived to avoid a freighter outward bound from the Thames. At twenty-five metres, we heard the slow propeller noises of a merchant ship as it passed overhead. As the propeller noises receded, he paused the electric motor to see if any other vessel was approaching. Thus satisfied, it was back up to periscope depth, fresh schnorkel air and the din of the diesel engine, which was also hot, besides being noisy. Humbert had chosen night time to avoid any plume of diesel fumes from the schnorkel exhaust being seen by a ship, as it might be in the daytime.

As the time passed, I discovered what the funnel and the empty jerrycan was for. Nevertheless, we thanked Humbert for his foresight. We progressed slowly across the Channel until he sighted a warship. Diving under diesel power, he went to twenty-five metres and achieved a trim. The electric motor remained off and the diesel had stopped. The boat hung motionless in the water, as we all sat listening to the fast approaching noise of the propellers. They sounded like the hiss of a steam train, as it pounded through the sea. I even held my breath. We all looked up at the hull of the Seehund a few inches over our heads. How strong was the thin 'eggshell' of the hull, I wondered? I was terrified. I felt sure the warship would crush our flimsy hull. The pressure of being in a confined space for days, without being able to see where I was going, was nerve-racking. I felt like screaming and begging Humbert to surface and let me out of this hell.

Fortunately the sound receded as fast as it came, and there was silence once more. The Seehund again rose to the surface and the diesel was re-started. The warship had not been using its asdics, and there was no reason why it should be. We should therefore not have been detected. But it took me some considerable time to regain a normal heartbeat.

At last the Seehund reached the area of the Thames Estuary and turned northwards. Humbert kept close to the coast, unless there was shallow water there. It was now daylight again and there were radar stations on the coast also to think about. After clearing the Thames Estuary, he moved 500 metres closer to the shore than he imagined any shipping lane might be, and settled the Seehund gently on the seabed so that he could take a rest.

We did not begrudge him his rest. He was the sailor; we could not navigate the boat, although we now had some idea of its basics. We decided to give Humbert a good rest, unless the CO_2 level meant awakening him. This spot should be safe enough for us.

After some time we heard faint noises and a pinging sound. The noise grew louder, the 'pinging' more intense. We looked up at the top of the hull of our tiny craft, as if we could see through it. Whatever it was had probed our craft somehow through the depths of the sea and found us. My heart was beating fast, sweat dripped from my face. I shook Humbert awake. He blinked a few times and stretched slightly. How could he keep so calm?

He yawned and announced that it was a warship, a small one by the sound of it. As the Seehund was not using a motor and not moving, then there was no reason why our craft should not be thought to be a small wreck.

On the surface about 500 metres away His Majesty's Minehunter *Orpheus* of the Royal Navy was steaming slowly south. Its lookouts were looking for drifting mines, and the asdic operator was training a new recruit on the apparatus.

'What do you make of that, Chalky?' the operator asked Ordinary Seaman White.

'It's a small object that is stationary on the bottom, Chief,' replied Chalky.

'Yes, but what is it, you 'orrible man you?' queried the chief petty officer.

'I think that it's a small shipwreck chief,' said Chalky.

'You might be right, but it's so small it could be the fuselage of a plane. The Channel is littered with them, so remember everything on the bottom is not a sunken ship!' emphasized the chief.

The minehunter passed on and the pinging went away. On the seabed, the three of us relaxed again for a while. I wondered how much more of this I could take. By contrast Himmler seemed quite calm.

Humbert allowed plenty of time for the warship to leave the area and then came up to periscope depth for the schnorkel to freshen the air. Observation through the periscope revealed no surface craft and the diesel was started again.

Moving up the English coastline on the inner side of their belts of minefields, Humbert examined his charts. He altered course according to the depth of water, and dived the craft as we drew near known radar stations on the shore.

As we progressed, he became concerned about the amount of fuel used so far. He announced his decision to reduce weight by firing off a torpedo. Himmler suggested that he fired the right one. He gave no reason and Humbert had no cause to disagree.

He pointed the bow of the Seehund, so that it faced the open sea, away from land, and activated the motor of the right torpedo at the same time as he and 'Harry' moved the levers to release the hooks. Free of the midget, the torpedo raced away close to the surface. There was a minefield in that direction, but the torpedo finished its run and sank to the bottom of the sea without exploding a mine.

Humbert transferred some water from the diving tanks to compensate for the now uneven weight, then resuming our course, we proceeded northwards, passing Lowestoft and Yarmouth. Some of these places had lighthouses which made useful navigation landmarks.

Humbert passed to seaward of the sandbanks and this part of the voyage was without incident. We also had to swing out farther to sea near Cromer, because of shallow water. Cromer also had a lighthouse – a good landmark as we moved along the coastline, which now curved towards the West around North Norfolk's beaches.

At length the Seehund arrived off the Blakeney harbour approach. It was late on Christmas Day 1945 and the first Christmas of peace. Himmler had deliberately chosen this day as a target arrival time. He reasoned that on the first Christmas Day of peacetime most of the armed forces would be on leave and coastguard stations might not be as watchful as usual. He made a short radio transmission on the Seehund's transmitter. It was promptly answered and he inwardly breathed a sigh of relief.

In fact our journey had not come to the attention of the Royal Navy, or any other service, and that is what had been planned.

After checking the time and their position with Humbert, Himmler asked him to submerge and lie on the seabed for a while. The sea was relatively calm. We were fortunate; it is not always calm in the North Sea.

We moved slightly farther away from the shore into deeper water and gently submerged, using our self-contained breathing apparatus to prolong the time underwater. It was comparatively silent, and boring. It also quickly got cold in the craft.

Chapter 11

After receiving Himmler's radio message, Himmler's agent Christine, who was inland, waited for a while and then started her preparations.

She put the radio transmitter/receiver back in its 'hidey hole' and changed into warm clothing. She put on thick socks and trousers and rubber wellington boots, together with a thick coat, scarf and gloves, and a waterproof hat. Then she picked up a parcel from a chair.

Locking her small cottage, she walked to where she had parked her car. Christine Wilder lived in one of Norfolk's tiny villages, almost a hamlet, although it did boast a church. She had purposely left her car on the outskirts of Nordingly because she did not want other villagers to notice her late night departure. Her village had only two primitive roads and a few grass lanes. The other villagers were either still celebrating the first Christmas of peace and were indoors, or were already in bed asleep. There was no village pub and few of the villagers even possessed cars.

Walking along quietly in the darkness, Christine met no one. She arrived at her car, started it and moved off slowly towards the coast. In the back of her car, she had three fishing rods, some fishing tackle and a few fish, which had been caught earlier that day. Even on Christmas Day some enthusiasts still fished.

Christine owned a small boat at Morston, near Blakeney. Morston was also a tiny village and she passed no one as she made her way towards the boat moorings. She allowed her car to roll to a halt, switched off the engine and extinguished the lights. She sat listening for a while, but could hear nothing, but the wind.

Everyone seemed to be indoors, as they might be expected to

185

be at around midnight. Christine picked up the fishing rods, tackle, fish and her parcel from the car, and locked it. She walked down to the tidal creek, where her boat was moored, along with others. The tide was almost full and her boat floated at its mooring. Making her way up the wooden staging, she climbed aboard and put down the rods, fish, tackle and parcel. Still in darkness, she unlocked the tiny wheelhouse of the boat and moved inside. Her boat had a diesel engine, as other small local fishing boats did, but, unusually, her boat had an electric motor as well, which she intended to use.

In her head, Christine went over the moves she had practised many times in daylight. She could literally take the boat out of the creek and out of the channel to the open sea with her eyes closed. She knew the twists of the creek and the time it took at various speeds to cover the distance from the mouth of the Morston creek to the open sea. At the point where the sea sent waves through the neck of the channel, she had to turn sharply north, because there was a sandbank ahead, running towards Wells-next-the-Sea. Even in darkness, or with one's eyes closed, the motion of the boat told you when you were approaching the mouth of the channel.

From Blakeney, beyond Morston farther down the inlet, the outer coastline extended like a withered finger to create this large tidal harbour. Before the war it had been a haven to yachts, and they would surely come again now that the war was over.

In complete darkness, save an occasional glimpse of the moon behind a cloud, Christine took her boat out of the creek and along towards the mouth of the channel. She left the riding lights of her boat extinguished and steered it gently, as it purred along almost silently on the electric motor.

She was completely familiar with the waters and set out to sea for a short distance towards the Blakeney channel buoy. Sighting the rocking buoy in the darkness, she reduced speed even more, until she was able to keep station with it, neither advancing nor receding, as the waves bounced her boat. Shielding her wrist, she flashed a small torch on to her wristwatch and checked the time. It was almost one o'clock in the morning.

Christine opened the wheelhouse door and looked around on

186

either side. She could see no sign of the vessel which she had been radioed to expect. Time was on her side at present, but the tides were limited. She would have to return to Morston by a certain time, or the creek would largely empty of navigable water.

She could see little and could only hear the noise of the waves and feel the cold wind upon her face. Spray broke over the bows of her boat from time to time. It was not exactly the sort of thing one might do for fun.

At last she heard a low voice call her name from the port side of the boat. At first she saw nothing. Then her eyes caught a slight movement and she saw the top half of a man waving his arms. He looked absurd. It was as if he was standing in a metal dustbin which was somehow sitting in the waves.

Christine waved back to show that she had seen him. He bent down carefully in his 'dustbin' and after a few seconds it rose higher in the sea. Now she could see metal on both sides of the 'dustbin' as a metal 'whale' revealed its back. It seemed so odd to her. The dustbin man drew nearer to the boat, and asked if she was alone.

She confirmed that she was.

Calling down instructions, the man aided whoever was operating the 'whale' to come alongside Christine's boat. Himmler carefully got on top of the superstructure of the Seehund, holding the periscope gently to steady himself. As he held it, he was aware of the slight roughness of the wire strands on one side of the periscope which served as an aerial, in case of radio transmissions to or from the Seehund during normal wartime patrols. When he judged the moment was right, he scrambled aboard the boat.

'Is everything ready for me?' Himmler asked Christine.

She nodded and gestured to a thwart, which had the parcel underneath it. Himmler picked it up and removed the waterproof rubberized cover. It was a small apparatus for transmitting varying radio frequencies and it had been delivered to the Blakeney buoy by the earlier Seehund, some months ago, before the war's end. He placed it under a tarpaulin near the bows out of sight.

Although Christine was expecting Heinrich Himmler, this man's appearance was so unlike her mental image of Himmler that she involuntarily asked him, 'Are you...?'

Himmler interrupted her and replied 'Yes! I'm the man that you are expecting.' He spoke in an authoritative voice and so Christine believed him.

Calling my name softly, Himmler waited for me to appear. I stood on the metal step under the open hatch and hauled myself up on to the superstructure carefully. The Seehund rocked more easily, now that it had been made lighter by Himmler disembarking. I conveyed this fact to Humbert, who let a little air out of the tanks to allow the Seehund to sit lower in the sea.

Himmler called across to me. He asked me to tell Humbert to take the Seehund out to deeper water, after I had got off. Humbert should then get the dinghy out, inflate it and get into it, after he had set the Seehund to submerge and sink with the hatch left open. We would collect him in the boat.

I shut the hatch for safety's sake. As I prepared to move across from the Seehund to the boat, Himmler reached across and pulled me gently. It was enough for me to slip, and although my arms had hold of Himmler and the side of the boat, my legs received a freezing bath in the sea as I dangled over the side. Himmler and Christine heaved me aboard the fishing boat.

The Seehund bobbed alongside for a few seconds and then drew slowly away heading north-north-east to deeper water.

Himmler moved towards the bow and gazed after it as it disappeared into the blackness. After a minute, Christine began to fuss about me shivering with wet trousers. She insisted that I change them because she happened to have some dry clothes that would fit me on board. I retired to the wheelhouse. Christine faced the other way. Himmler glanced round at me. I had my back to him inside the wheelhouse. Picking up the tiny transmitter from under the tarpaulin, Himmler pulled out a telescopic aerial and pointed it in the direction that the Seehund had gone. He rapidly cranked a handle on its side and invisibly a series of differing radio frequency pulses were rapidly sent out from the transmitter. Nothing happened. Himmler continued cranking the handle and moving the tip of the aerial from side to side.

Suddenly the sky lit up and there was a tremendous roar. The varying radio frequency pulses had sent a signal down the Seehund's periscope aerial and along a wire connected to the left torpedo launching mechanism. It had triggered a detonator in the remaining torpedo, which blew torpedo, submarine and Humbert to bits in milliseconds. In fact it took longer for the pieces of metal and Humbert to fall back into the sea than it took to explode.

I lurched out of the wheelhouse, holding my dry trousers up with one hand. I was just too late to notice Himmler drop a small object over the side of the fishing boat with a slight plop into the sea, but Christine noticed. As waves created by the explosion reached us, the boat rocked violently.

'My God! What happened?' I exclaimed.

'It's incredible bad luck,' replied Himmler. 'He must have hit a drifting mine.'

Christine looked at Himmler in disbelief. Himmler casually wiped a finger across his lips in a gesture for her to keep quiet. She decided to show the boat's lights now and started her diesel engine. As she turned the boat back towards Blakeney harbour, she explained her cover story for the two men being with her.

'You both have been fishing with me tonight with fishing rods. Here they are, complete with tackle and the fish that you have caught. You are both refugees who have come to help me on my smallholding. You are originally from Poland and were in Germany as forced labourers. You don't wish to return to Poland, which is under the Russians. From Germany you came to England, after the end of the war. You have been living in a refugee camp south of London for some months now. I can give you all the details when we get back to my cottage.

Your identification papers are here. As requested, the papers are made out in your new chosen anglicized names of Harry Fowler and Eric Cook, because your Polish names are too difficult for the British. I had you brought up here from London earlier today and you wanted to go night fishing for a Christmas treat. If someone asks you a question that you can't answer, give the reply that you don't know. Hopefully we won't meet anyone. People on shore certainly heard the explosion, but explosions like that are not unknown. From time to time, mines from the minefields do explode. It's Boxing Day now and in the early hours. People are unlikely to want to investigate, because there would be nothing to see.

189

'Eric, how many fish did you catch?' she asked unexpectedly. 'Answer in English!'

'I don't know!' I replied.

'Count the fish!' Christine ordered.

I counted the fish in the basket. There were four.

'I catched three and Harry catched one fish,' I answered.

'Good!' she said, 'but it is "I caught three fish" not "catched",' she explained.

'I caught three fish,' I echoed.

'What is Boxing Day?' I asked.

'It's the British name for December 26th, the day after Christmas Day,' she explained. 'It comes from a time when it was traditional to give presents in boxes. Where were you collected from in London, Harry?' she enquired.

Himmler thought for a moment. 'I don't know,' he answered.

Christine smiled and nodded. She returned to concentrating on the return journey and entered Morston creek slowly. I was very nervous. I felt sure many people would come out of their houses to see what had caused the tremendous bang. I was convinced we would be arrested.

Later, as we drew near to the bank at the boat moorings, there was no one to be seen on shore. No one had bothered about the explosion. Christine switched off the engine, extinguished the lights and tied up to the staging.

At a quarter to two in the morning of December 26th 1945, Heinrich Himmler set foot on British soil for the first time, or to be more precise on to Norfolk mud. It was quite a feat for a man who had died seven months before in Germany.

The three of us carried fishing rods and the tackle, besides the fish that we had 'caught'. We moved quietly talking in English. We followed Christine to her car. On the main coastal road, a small car passed through Morston. Its headlights illuminated us briefly before it rounded a bend in the road. I felt sure it would stop and soldiers would come running. My heart was pumping hard, but nothing happened. The car did not stop.

We loaded the fishing gear in the car and all climbed in. We Germans had made the usual mistake of trying to get in the driver's side. The steering wheel is on the other side of the car in Germany and so the logical side for us, as passengers, was in fact the driver's side on the British car.

Christine drove off slowly, out of Morston and away from the coast. Himmler had been fingering the poison capsule in his pocket earlier that day on the Seehund, but now his nervousness had disappeared. Heinrich Himmler was dead and he was Harry Fowler, or so his papers said. He relaxed in the car.

By comparison with the Seehund, the car seat was comfortable. I, too, was glad to be on dry land. Although it was dark outside, the hedges along the edges of the fields fascinated me. In Germany, hedges are much less common in the country.

After less than an hour, our trip in the Seehund and Humbert's unfortunate death receded rapidly into our memories. We soon arrived at Christine's village, Nordingly, and parked the car. We removed the rods and fish and started to walk. Christine led the way and the two of us followed her to her cottage.

I turned to Himmler and asked, 'Is the ground tilting or is it me?' I found it difficult to walk in a straight line and lurched along like a drunk.

Christine heard me and laughed, 'It's the effect of being at sea, my friend. If you have been on a boat on the sea for some time and you are not used to it, then when you are back on dry land, your body isn't able to accept that the ground beneath your feet is not tilting from side to side.'

We now walked almost noiselessly along a grass lane to an isolated cottage, which was where Christine lived. Besides the smell of the grass, Himmler became aware of another, stronger smell – pigs.

Everyone was tired as Christine unlocked her front door and let us in. She had left an oil lamp burning in the kitchen, which revealed the cottage interior to us. She extracted a bottle and glasses from a cupboard and suggested a drink to our safe landing in Britain. Both of us smiled and agreed, and watched as she poured the bottle.

'I'm afraid that this is Scotch whisky and the best I could do for you,' she explained. 'Even this was very hard to get hold of and, I had to buy it on the black market.'

I must be honest and say that we were both so tired that neither of us really cared.

It was Himmler who proposed a toast. 'To the three of us!' he declared, and, perhaps as an afterthought, 'To our absent friends!'

I raised my glass with the others and drank to that. I reflected that 'absent friends' was an all-embracing term. Himmler might mean Humbert, who had come so far and been blown up. Alternatively Himmler could be referring to his wife and daughter back in Germany. But that marriage was over a long time ago and Himmler could have been referring to his more recent mistress and the children that he had had by her.

Whatever Himmler was thinking about, I let my thoughts turn to my own family members who had been lost in the bombing – mother, father and sister. I even thought about Lotte Durner and wondered if she had survived the war.

It seemed that everyone was lost in his or her own thoughts. Himmler caught the mood and announced, 'I'm sure everyone is tired. I know I am. I think it best if we all go to sleep now.'

Christine took her lamp and showed us where the bedrooms were. There was one each.

'Where is the toilet, please?' I enquired.

'It's at the bottom of the garden,' Christine told me. 'I will show you tomorrow. Look! This is what we use at night time!'

Christine bent down and pulled a large white pot from under the bed and held it by the handle for me to see.

'We call this a "Po", she told me. 'If you want to know about the British sense of humour, then there is a little joke about it. Everyone knows the "Po" is kept under the bed. Now what do you think Hitler said when he fell through the bed?'

'I don't know,' I replied.

'At last I am in Poland ("Po" land)!' she giggled, pointing at the 'po'.

I smiled politely. Himmler was even less amused, he realized that not so long ago in Germany, such a joke would have brought severe punishment. Times had indeed changed.

Christine showed us the clothing that she had got for each of us. Not all of it was new, but it would make a reasonable outfit for our working clothes.

'Tomorrow, you must wear these,' she announced. 'I will burn the clothes you came in, because they might have German labels inside.'

Himmler was pleased at her foresight. He realized that he had actually overlooked this possibility; although we were supposedly former forced labourers in Germany, the labels would be explicable. Christine gave us enough light to see our beds and wished us goodnight.

Himmler took off his boots and coat. He climbed into bed with his clothes on. As he straightened his feet down the bed, he yelled as his cold feet came into contact with a very hot pottery container, which had been put in to warm the bed.

In another bedroom, Christine heard the yell and correctly interpreted it. 'Oh! Yes! Sorry, I forgot to tell you about the hot water bottle,' she called.

Himmler said some rather uncomplimentary remarks about the British quietly to himself as he rubbed his feet, but he soon warmed up and fell asleep.

I lay in my own bed with my hands behind my head. I heard an owl hooting nearby, the sound of the wind in the trees and tiny creaks of the furniture. I dropped into a fitful sleep of explosions, thrashing propellers of warships, Humbert speaking without any sound and Berger's body on guard in the bunker. I tossed and turned as my brain kept the images fresh in my mind.

Later that morning, Christine arose, put water on to boil for tea and washing and then got dressed. She left us to wake up, in our own time, and went outside to a brick storehouse to light a boiler to boil up food for her pigs. She had five sows, fourteen piglets at varying stages of growth and a boar. The pigs had pigsties, but were also put out on some of her land. She had about sixteen acres.

Pigs are animals that get used to routine and they could hear the sounds that Christine was up and about. At that later than usual time of the morning, that meant food was on its way.

After boiling up the swill for the pigs, Christine let it cool down and returned to the house. I was already up and Himmler was coming down the stairs. We both wore our new clothes. By our general demeanour, Christine guessed that we needed the toilet. Beckoning us, she went outside and pointed to a brick 'privy' that stood about twenty metres away. Both of us made

193

for the privy and arrived at the door together. Himmler just looked at me and I instinctively stood aside in respect of his rank and let him use it first. I could not wait and walked into the trees to empty my bladder. Neither of us could use the 'po' in the night.

As we returned to the house, no doubt hoping for breakfast, Christine announced, 'If you are supposed to be here working for me, we will do some work first, then have some food. Go upstairs and fetch down the clothing that you arrived in, so that I can burn it.'

We complied, and followed her out to the storehouse. She stuffed the clothing one piece at a time into her solid fuel boiler. We watched as the flames consumed our clothing of the past, as if we were shedding a skin to begin life anew.

After a while, we each filled a heavy metal pail of swill, which steamed in the cold morning air. Christine showed us where to pour it into the troughs and how much in each one. We worked willingly and it was refreshing for Christine to get help in this daily chore. Some of the bigger pigs could be quite intimidating, but she told us not to be frightened of them. We soon finished and returned to the house.

Christine told us that she would make breakfast, but that she expected us to take turns in future. 'We won't be able to eat like this every day,' she explained. 'It's the day after Christmas, and I have some special food for us. You must understand that almost all food is still on ration, but I have already got ration books for you both. They took some organizing on the black market, and so did your papers.'

She began to fry some bacon with eggs and fried bread on her stove. Whilst this was cooking, she prepared a pot of tea.

'You need to drink tea, as most of the English do. Over here they drink tea with cold milk in it. You may find this not to your taste straight away, but to drink it without will draw people's attention to you.'

She left the tea to brew and placed a tea cosy over it. We observed this strange ritual in silence. The English make tea by putting hot water on to tea leaves in a pot, which they then hide under a padded cover. Christine cut some bread and put butter and jam on the table. She poured out the tea into large breakfast cups, straining the tea leaves from the brew with a tea strainer. She added a small quantity of cold milk to each cup and enquired if we wanted sugar. Both of us nodded, but unfortunately Christine found there was no sugar left. She put saccharine tablets into each cup to sweeten it.

'Now stir the tea with your teaspoon,' she instructed, and demonstrated.

We stirred our tea and picked up the cups to sip it. Himmler pulled a face, but I had tasted tea in England before the war.

Christine served up the bacon, eggs and fried bread. It was the first hot food for some time and we all enjoyed it. Afterwards there was bread and butter and plum jam. Christine showed us the English way to make a jam sandwich. It was delicious and we could have eaten it all, but could see that we would have to understand how long rations must last before getting too greedy. Our host warned us that when the butter had been used, it would be margarine in the future.

After the meal, I volunteered to wash up. Both of us had been offered more tea, but we had politely declined. We might have to get used to drinking milk in our tea, but we were in no particular hurry.

Christine showed Himmler all the newspapers she had kept since April 1945. They were all in daily order. They would help us refresh our memories and inform us of events during our months in hiding.

After a few minutes I joined him. Himmler announced, 'Let me introduce you properly now, Eric. This lady is Kristina Walder...'

'Please! Never use that name!' Christine retorted. 'My name is Christine Wilder. You gentlemen are Harry Fowler and Eric Cook. Any other names you may once have had must remain unspoken.'

Himmler looked at his agent's face for a few seconds. 'Of course you are correct,' he said apologetically.

Christine resumed, 'I'm Christine Wilder and I'm thirty-five years old. My parents are dead. I have lived here for seven years and I breed pigs for market. I also have a small fishing boat, as you have seen at Morston. I divide my time between the pigs and some fishing, when the weather allows. I use some fish or crabs to trade for other things that I need. The pigs, I sell for cash at market. This is how I make my living.'

She stopped speaking and looked at me. I took my cue from her and began, 'My name is Eric Cook. I'm a refugee from Poland. During the war I had to work in Germany and I do not wish to return to Poland. My family are dead, killed in wartime bombing. I am twenty-three years old.'

Himmler took his turn, 'My name is Harry Fowler and I have forty-five years. I am refugee from Poland also. I wish to stay in England. Not want to go Poland. I have some *Erlebnis* of farm before war.'

'Experience is the word you mean, Harry,' Christine told him.

'Ah! Yes! I have some experience of farm,' Himmler stated proudly. 'My idea is to stay here, until I can get money from Switzerland. Have money in Switz number account. Enough to help us all for future,' Himmler expounded.

(For the sake of clarity, from now on Himmler's speech is written in correct English, as opposed to what was actually said.)

'Meanwhile we have these to help us!' said Christine, as she tipped a bag of gold rings on to the table. 'They came earlier with...'

'Yes!' Himmler interrupted. 'I had these sent over to England earlier in the war.'

Christine remained silent. She realized that I did not know that they had come in the rubberized bag, together with the radio pulse apparatus, that had been left on the Blakeney buoy. Furthermore Himmler did not want me to know.

'My God!' I exclaimed. 'Where did you get so many gold rings? There must be a couple of hundred.'

'From winter relief collections,' explained Himmler. 'Some people were very generous and I decided that some should be diverted to help the *Werwolf* operation. In fact you yourself suggested this. They should help make our stay here slightly more comfortable, if one or two are sold at different towns.'

I ran some rings through my fingers and put them back in the bag. I felt slightly uneasy handling them.

'I will put the rings away safely,' Christine told us. 'Today is a holiday, so we can relax a bit. Carry on with your reading. I'm sure you are still tired from your journey. Tomorrow you can begin to learn the routine jobs to be done.' She went and busied herself elsewhere.

Himmler slapped me on the knee and said, 'You see! I brought you safely to England and already it's a holiday. Good food, St Nikolas (the German 'Father Christmas') has left us some gold rings and we have new identities. Not bad – eh?'

I confirmed that things had taken a turn for the better, then we resumed our reading of the newspapers.

A short time later, I started to see reports of the British Army finding a place called Belsen, a concentration camp north of Hanover. I asked Himmler about it. Himmler could neither read nor understand enough of the article to comment factually, but he could see the pictures of dead bodies in pits.

He reminded me that towards the very end of the war the Luftwaffe planes were rarely seen in the skies. At the same time it had become dangerous for any motorized vehicle to move by daylight, because of attack by British or American fighter bombers. In fact the Allied mastery of the air was such that they were shooting up farmers as they moved their horses and carts, because of the lack of bigger targets. Now this advantage for the Allies was a disadvantage for prisoners. If you could not even move a horse and cart in safety, how could you bring food to camps to feed the prisoners?

In addition, towards the end of the war, concentration camps in the East had been evacuated in the face of the advancing Russians. Unfortunately, thousands of prisoners arrived in the last few weeks of the war in camps like Belsen. Some of them might have been on the road for weeks and literally on their last legs when they arrived at a new camp.

The new camps did not know how many were coming, or when they might arrive. In particular, there was insufficient food to feed them, as well as their own prisoners. Bombing was also indiscriminate. Bombs might hit a munitions factory, but were just as likely to destroy water mains. Given a lack of water, people died rapidly. In such conditions, it did not matter whether the prisoners were British, German, Jews or political prisoners. Diseases like typhus started and people died like flies.

Himmler explained that he had never visited Belsen, but unlike most camps, which were work camps, Belsen was actually originally designated a 'sick' camp for sick prisoners and had no industrial function. Therefore, however the prisoners had died, they certainly had not been worked to death.

I was satisfied with what he had told me. Later I read reports about the liberation of Dachau near Munich and the discovery of dead bodies in railway wagons nearby. As I myself had been there only weeks before the war's end, I had not seen any sign of anything like this. I showed Himmler, who knew nothing of that either.

Himmler sat for some time in silence. Finally he expounded a theory to me.

'It is possible that the British and the other Allies prefer to report only the bad things about Germany in their own newspapers. For example, if in a camp you had some fit men and some undernourished thin men, then if you wanted to illustrate how bad things had been, then you would take pictures and describe the thin ones, wouldn't you?

'I remember that when we divided Poland between Russia and Germany earlier in the war, our intelligence from the Russian side indicated that they had systematically murdered 10,000 Polish officers, which they had as prisoners in the Russian sector. After we invaded their portion of Poland, we found 5,000 bodies, which we could identify as half of these officers, at a place called Katyn. Many bodies could actually be identified by name. The dead included officers of General rank. I believe there was also one female officer. We invited the International Red Cross in and they examined the bodies and tried to ascertain the means of death. Their findings confirmed that Russia had committed this crime. The Russians blamed us and said we had done it. I understood that the remaining 5,000 Polish officers were put into barges which were towed out far into the Baltic. There they were shelled and sunk by Russian naval ships. Dead men tell no tales, my friend. The Russians will still try to pin the blame on Germany.

'Germany and its forces are not blameless, as never having done anything wrong, but neither are the forces of the other countries. The difference is that they will trumpet our wrongdoings and conveniently forget their own.

'Germany lost the war. The Allies won, and to the victor the spoils. It has always been so. For example, I don't know if our rocket scientists are alive or dead. If they are alive, do you imagine an Ivan, Yank or Tommy is going to say "The war is over, go on home!" No, my friend, they will want the technology themselves and take those scientists away to their own countries, whether they want to go or not.'

I had never seen Himmler so animated. I could follow the logic of his observations and knew nothing to the contrary. I nodded and carried on reading.

Christine returned and admonished Himmler for getting 'worked up'.

'Don't forget you are a Pole now,' she reminded him. 'The Poles don't like the Germans and probably suffered under their occupation. Anything you see in a newspaper or hear in conversation that is anti German, you must remember to agree with, whether you do or not. You are hardly going to be convincing Polish refugees if you defend the Germans. If you are who you say you are, then you must play the part accordingly.

'The situation is that we each depend on the others. I have not risked my life to spy for Germany for years for nothing. I want a better future for myself than working with pigs, and you have promised that from your Swiss Bank funds. You have both only just arrived here. You must try to learn to fit in with your surroundings quickly, and that will include the people, who live around here. I will have to start introducing you tomorrow. I have told people that two refugees were coming to help me. Who is the American President, Harry?' she suddenly asked.

Himmler thought for a few seconds. 'Truman,' he replied.

'Good!' said Christine. 'Don't forget to read about what is happening in Britain and in the world, besides what happened in the war. If either of you call me Kristina Walder in front of the local people, I will kick you in the balls.' She whirled around and left the room.

After a few seconds of pregnant silence, Himmler whispered to me, 'What does she mean "balls", Eric?'

I explained to him. Himmler was quite shocked and started coughing. He shook his newspaper and continued to read headlines of articles. It must have felt odd for him now that he was no longer in charge. It was surely a very strange role change for him – from SS Reichsführer to trainee pigman.

The remainder of the afternoon of December 26th 1945 was spent in reading and resting and talking. Christine told us that we must learn to think in English, besides speaking the language. She gave us an illustration of what to say when we were introduced to people.

'Hello! I'm pleased to meet you Mr/Mrs/Miss Brown etc. My name is Eric/Harry!' We should avoid too many references to Poland, in case villagers knew of any other Poles living in the locality. Many Poles had fought in the British army against Germany, and some of them would also not wish to return to Poland under the Russians.

Later we had 'tea', which in England meant a small meal, as opposed to just a liquid drink. Christine had some cake, which was itself unusual due to the rationing of food. We were rapidly becoming aware that conditions in Britain were quite hard for its citizens, even though they were on the winning side.

Christine took us on a brief walk around the village. There was not much to see: two farms, maybe thirty houses, a larger house and the church. The nearest shops were miles away in other villages, as was a post office and banks and pubs.

The village of Nordingly was remarkably quiet. The few children who lived there could safely play on the streets, which were really only lanes. There was virtually no traffic passing through, apart from the occasional bicycle. Harry and I smiled and nodded to a few villagers, but most seemed too busy for proper introductions.

Perhaps that was fortunate. At the first meeting with a villager I had snapped to attention and clicked my heels and bowed. Christine told me to avoid these German manners, which were not practised in England, after we had moved on. She was vastly relieved that at least I had not raised my right arm in the Nazi salute. Christine also realized that the villagers would think it strange for two single men to share a house with an unmarried woman. However, she was still regarded as a foreigner even after living in the village for some years, and foreigners behaved strangely.

Himmler was less of a problem. He was used to people saluting him first. As long as he could get used to his new position in life, he should be all right.

Afterwards, we walked back to Christine's house and fed the

200

pigs, before going to bed. She encouraged us to go to bed early and gave me a clockwork alarm clock set for 6 a.m.

'I want you both up early tomorrow,' she announced. 'The sooner we all get into a regular work routine, the better.'

As we both started to exit the living room, Christine suddenly roared, 'Heil Hitler!' behind our backs.

I automatically snapped to attention and gave the salute. Himmler started to raise his right arm and then caught himself.

Turning to Christine, Himmler smiled. 'Yes! We have got to be careful that we are not caught out like that again. Some Pole, our Eric is.'

I reddened slightly, but said nothing. It was a good lesson to us both. There were certain reflex actions like that which we would have to lose.

Chapter 12

The next day, December 27th 1945, and thereafter, Himmler and I began to learn the routine of Christine's work with the pigs. She showed us how to look after them, feed them, and help the pregnant sows when they came to give birth.

Periodically, Christine arranged for a man to bring his small van with a trailer to her home in Nordingly, to take the older pigs to be sold at a cattle market. Christine would usually travel separately in her own car to see the livestock prices. She habitually wore men's trousers for work and we found that odd.

The first time after we arrived that she sent pigs to market, she took both of us to Fakenham cattle market. This was a far different experience for us. The small town had much more traffic than we were used to and there were lots of people about. Some of the women also wore trousers or jodhpurs, although most wore skirts.

Christine explained that these girls were from the 'Land Army', used during the war to help on farms around the country. Most of them had now returned home, but not all of them. At first, we felt self-conscious and thought everyone was looking at us. In reality, I suppose that we were hardly noticed at all. Most of the people attending the market were too intent on their own business. Christine met one or two people she knew and introduced us to them.

The pigs were sold by auction by a fast-talking man. The auctioneer was apparently skilled in interpreting the nods, nose scratchings, winks and head shakes of the bidders. Christine had to wait for some time and then queue up at the market office to receive her cash payment for the pigs that had been sold. She had done quite well, and took her 'boys' to a nearby café for a meal.

We had sausage, egg and chips with bread and margarine

and cups of tea. I noticed that the tea came with milk already in it.

Christine grinned at us across the table and whispered, 'When in Rome – do as the Romans do! That means whilst you are here, do as the English do. Drink up, lads!'

We 'lads' raised our teacups and swallowed a few sips. Not quite as bad as yesterday, it seemed. We tucked into the food.

As we left the cafe and began to walk back towards the car, we noticed a group of men on foot being escorted by an armed guard. They had large circular patches on their clothes.

'German prisoners of war,' Christine whispered.

We paused to watch them walk by on the road. The prisoners seemed a mixed bunch. We could see German airforce, army and naval uniforms, but no SS.

As we walked in the same direction as the prisoners, we were in time to see them climb into a lorry. The German prisoners got in the back first, and finally the single guard handed up his rifle to a prisoner, who held it whilst the guard climbed into the truck. The prisoner then passed the rifle back to the guard. Himmler and I exchanged glances – it was unspoken, but how times had changed.

Occasionally, Christine took us fishing, usually leaving one of us back at her house. The weather was not very suitable at that time of the year, but a few fish and crabs made a change from corned beef and spam. I always felt less than happy on Christine's boat on the open sea. I felt that Humbert's remains were nearby, and I was not a good sailor.

Days passed into weeks, then months. Most of the daily work was routine and both of us got used to it. Himmler had taken to strolling around some of the lanes and roads around the village, particularly on a Sunday, to take some exercise. He used to walk up the grass lane where the house was, away from the village. After a while it met a surfaced road at right angles and he would walk west for some distance, until he came to another grass lane on his right. Walking back down it brought him to the edge of the village near the church.

Himmler was not a churchgoer and the St Peter's Church was Church of England, not a Catholic church. One Sunday, as

Himmler made his 'constitutional' walk, he approached the church on his way back to the house. All was quiet. Alone with his thoughts, Himmler was feeling very homesick for his own country, which he would probably never see again.

In the church, they were probably listening to the reading of the lessons from the Bible as Himmler approached. Ten metres from the church gate, the organ sounded the first notes of the next hymn, which the vicar had just announced to the small congregation.

It was the well-known hymn 'Glorious Things of Thee are Spoken' and it has at least two tunes to which it can be sung. On this day, the organist chose the tune named 'Austria', which is almost the same tune as the German National Anthem *Deutschland über Alles*. As the notes of the first few lines sounded out loud and clear in the frosty morning air, Heinrich Himmler was drawn by an invisible irresistible force through the wooden gate and down the path to the church. He opened the heavy door and a rather surprised churchwarden got up and thrust a hymn book into his hand and gestured him towards a pew.

The congregation was mostly standing towards the front of the pews. Some glanced round to see who it was and recognized the fairly new Polish refugee. As the vicar and congregation started to sing the well-loved words to that familiar tune, Himmler struggled to keep his composure. He fumbled in the hymn book for the hymn number and felt in his pocket for a handkerchief. Holding the hymn book up high to conceal his face, the dam broke and his eyes flooded with tears, which rolled down his face from under his glasses and into his beard. Standing there, soundlessly, whilst the music and singing assailed his ears, Himmler made a great pretence at blowing his nose to wipe away the tears. The hymn has several verses and he needed the space of time to regain control. As the last notes died away, he was breathing deeply and more relaxed.

As he was almost at the back of the church, Himmler could follow by watching the people in front as they stood, kneeled or sat during the stages of the service. As the service progressed, Himmler felt better. In fact he felt a lot better. Perhaps during those moments Heinrich Himmler found God again, because truly, God had never entirely lost Heinrich Himmler.

Reality eventually dawned in the shape of the churchwarden

proffering a collection plate to him. Himmler shamefacedly showed empty pockets to the man, who smiled and moved on to the other pews.

For Himmler, the 'pièce de resistance' to the church service was the last Hymn. It was another well-known English hymn 'Now Thank We All Our God', but it is also a German hymn '*Nun danket alle Gott*'. It is fairly slow and Himmler knew the hymn. As it progressed, he joined in the English words softly. At the same time, he listened to the British pronunciation, as the congregation sang. He felt pleased with his efforts. After the final blessing and prayer, he left the pew.

At the church door, the vicar told him how nice it was to see him. Himmler could not reply, because of the emotion that choked him, but nodded dumbly. The vicar perhaps sensed the man's feelings, as he stood there momentarily in front of him. There appeared to be some inner conflict raging within this refugee. Placing his hand fleetingly on Himmler's left shoulder, the vicar said, 'Go with God, my son!'

Himmler struggled for words. 'Thank you, Father!' he replied.

Himmler walked back home to Christine's house with a lighter step in his walk. As he entered the cottage, Christine discerned the difference in his mood straight away.

'Wherever have you been?' she asked him.

'My dear Christine, I have been to church,' Himmler replied. 'You and Eric should try it!'

He went upstairs. Christine and I looked at one another, bewildered. God moves in mysterious ways, Christine thought to herself.

Thereafter, Heinrich Himmler attended the Nordingly church on most Sundays. He liked the little church. It had a cruciform shape, and the lectern was in the form of a golden eagle that held the Bible on the back of its wings. Attending church gave Himmler a feeling of well-being. It made him feel more content, more a part of the community, more at home in England.

It was now well into 1946. Christine showed me how to drive her car. I had driven a vehicle before, but I had to get used to the right-hand drive position of the steering wheel and driving on the left. After a fairly short time I took and passed a driving test. Himmler never showed any interest in driving himself, he was more used to being driven.

The ability to drive gave me the mobility to travel, and I started to sell a few gold rings in small towns to increase our funds and make life easier for the three of us. I only ever offered one or two rings to any jeweller and did not return to the same shop twice. After a while, this meant that I needed to travel much farther away from home.

Although Christine now paid us pocket money each week, we had all agreed to put any surplus money resulting from our efforts with the pigs and the fishing into the bank. The intention was to use the money to invest in the smallholding when the opportunity arose.

Christine used her initial share of the ring money to buy some more clothes and have her hair done. I also bought some clothes and shoes, but Himmler merely bought a second hand bicycle and saved the rest. He liked cycling and it helped to keep him fit. Although he would join us on trips in the car, he would also be prepared to cycle to neighbouring villages or small towns from time to time.

Parts of Norfolk are relatively flat, but there are some small hills. Himmler used the bicycle to build up a mental picture of the local geography. If he ever needed to disappear quickly, his knowledge of local grass lanes and tracks would be useful.

The few local children in Nordingly knew him as Harry the Pole, and some of the villagers, who were not fond of foreigners used to refer to him as 'Fowler the prowler'. Not that there was anything sinister about Harry, but even English people who moved into the village were regarded by the locals as 'foreigners' for many years. The village was changing slowly. Electricity was now supplied to all the houses and that was a great step forward.

Himmler had told us that at least two years should elapse before he could try to transfer money from his Swiss account to another bank. He related how during 1943, one of his clever young SS officers, Walter Schellenberg, had been sent to Switzerland to open numbered bank accounts. One was for Schellenberg himself, one was for Martin Bormann (the Nazi Party Secretary) and one was for 'H'.

The Swiss bank thought that the 'H' account was for Hitler himself. Schellenberg would not say anything to deny this and the Swiss overlooked the fact that Schellenberg's master,

206

Himmler, also had the same initial. However, Himmler did not know of this.

As the days, weeks and months elapsed, Himmler formed an idea to develop Christine's land. After studying the area that was not already used for the pigs, he announced that it could be ideal for keeping chickens on. His idea was to keep chickens in larger numbers than an average farmer would. We would thus have a source of eggs in large quantities to sell, as well as the chickens for their meat. Himmler had kept a small chicken farm in Bavaria before the war. That venture had not been a success, but it had also been a time of an economic depression and mass unemployment.

Now the situation was different in Britain in 1946. We had the land, which Christine owned, we had some experience through Himmler, we had some money and we had our own labour available.

Christine had no objections. The next time that we went to the cattle market for the pigs, she took us to look at the hardware stores where we could buy the chicken wire and fence posts which we would need.

Himmler examined the flimsy mesh of British chicken wire. 'This is no good!' he announced.

'What do you mean, it's no good?' queried Christine. 'This is what everyone uses here to keep chickens in!'

'You have foxes here in England, I think, Christine, and other small wild animals. This wire will keep chickens in one place, but it will not keep foxes and other animals out. Believe me, I know. You could have fifty chickens and then a fox breaks in one night. He only takes one or two chickens, but he kills them all before he leaves.'

Christine nodded. She had heard of farmers talking about foxes slaughtering their chickens and was inclined to believe Himmler. In any case, she had nothing to lose. We finally found some much more expensive metal chain link fencing and bought a quantity, together with fence poles and nails. It was arranged for it to be delivered.

Back in Nordingly, Christine surveyed the area Himmler had in mind for the chicken project. 'Do we just erect the posts and nail up the wire along the ground?' Christine asked him.

'No!' he replied emphatically. 'Although it may take much longer, Eric and I will dig a narrow trench and the edge of the wire will be set in sixty centimetres below the surface and packed in place firmly with stones. On to each layer of stones, as we progress, we should add a thin mix of cement or concrete to help bind them together. The fence posts must also be deeply dug in and supported by larger stones or small bricks. The whole thing will take much longer to construct, but we have all the time we need.

Over a period of time, other farmers may lose chickens to foxes, but we should not. That is, as long as the entrance gate is always locked properly. The gate must be set slightly below ground level, with a thick deep concrete step on the outside that foxes will not be able to burrow under. Lastly, if we add pieces of wood to the top of the posts facing outwards at an angle, then we can string a few strands of barbed wire along the top. That should keep out any unwelcome human night visitors.'

'You mean poachers,' Christine informed him.

'Ah! Poachers!' Himmler echoed, rolling this new word off his tongue.

At our own pace, the three of us took buckets out to the field and began to collect any stones that we came across. After the delivery of the wire, we dug a foundation and erected the posts and wire. Christine made some local enquiries and bought an old chicken coop. This was delivered by lorry and, with the help of the driver, we set it within the large partially wired space. It seemed out of place, as it only took up a small space within the intended wired confines, but Himmler was happy enough.

'We will copy this chicken coop and build others eventually,' he informed us.

By this time, I had seen newspaper pictures of concentration camps. I had the weirdest feeling that Himmler was building another camp here – for chickens. Furthermore, if foxes could not break into it, then chickens could not break out of it!

Himmler had volunteered to add the barbed wire to the wooden struts which were attached to the sides of the post tops and facing outwards at an angle. Starting at a point away from the entrance gate, he carefully unwound the reel of barbed wire and rolled a tight loop around every wooden strut. He used no nails and when he got to the gateway, then the wire was moved outwards along the wooden strut to create the next strand of wire that led back parallel to the first. In this way Himmler created a multiple spaced barbed wire barrier from one single reel of barbed wire.

After all our preparations were completed, Christine bought some adult laying hens and a cockerel from the market and brought them back to Nordingly. They were installed in their new 'realm' and the cockerel stalked about investigating his domain.

Feeding them wasn't too difficult, a slightly different food mix than for the pigs, and of course some grit.

They produced some eggs, which was a welcome addition to our diet and we could have the odd bird to eat in the future, as numbers increased.

Himmler took the project very seriously. He went out and opened up the coop in the morning, fed the chickens, gathered the eggs and shut them up again at night-time. For his own interest, he kept records of the numbers of eggs and noted any hens that did not lay. They were destined for the pot. He liked the administrative tasks because he was good at them. If he had wanted, he could have told anyone who asked the production cost of an egg.

The netting also proved foxproof and we lost no chickens – until one day, Himmler found some were missing. He discovered that someone had brought a step-ladder during the night and climbed over the fence and removed three chickens. There was no doubt about it. Himmler found the impressions of the step-ladder in the earth both inside and outside the netting.

It seemed that only one person was involved, from a footprint that he found inside the netting in some softer earth. The pattern was not from any of our boots. The poacher appeared to have brought the step-ladder with him, placed it parallel to the fence near a gate-post, and stepped from the ladder on to a fence post top. He – and it was undoubtedly a man – had balanced there, hauled his step-ladder up and over the wire (presumably with a rope attached to it) and then placed it on the inside of the wire to climb down. The poacher had entered the chicken coop, wrung the neck of several chickens and departed the way he came, taking the step-ladder with him. This also meant it was probably someone who not only possessed a step-ladder, but who also used it in his work – possibly a window cleaner.

Himmler had foreseen such an eventuality and was determined that it should not happen again. He contrived to build a hide, such as one might use for bird watching. This was on the far side from the chicken run, near a gap in the hedgerow. He then also littered the adjacent area with piles of logs and other bits and pieces in a seemingly haphazard way, but in reality to cause any future poacher to pass near to the hide on his way back from the chicken run.

The chickens were his pet project and we let him look after them. Each morning he arose early at about 5 a.m. and walked around the perimeter of the fencing. After his check, he started to make up the feed for the hens and pigs.

One morning when he went out, Himmler found out that the poacher had decided to pay another visit. In fact he was still in the chicken run. Himmler quietly made his way towards his hide with a spade, walking on the far side of the hedgerow. Concealing himself in the hide, he did not have long to wait until the poacher jogged by, puffing. Himmler hit him over the head from behind with his spade. The man fell with a thud to the ground, unconscious. Himmler used a method used by *Kapos* in concentration camps. He turned the man on to his back, dropped the haft of the spade across the man's throat, mounted it at each end and 'see-sawed'. After a few seconds, the man breathed no more.

He dragged the lifeless body into the nearby copse of pine trees by the arms, together with the step-ladder that the poacher had brought with him, and left them out of sight in a dip of the ground. Signs of blood from the body and drag marks were erased. He retrieved the dead chickens which the poacher had killed and returned to the outhouse for his routine chores.

Later that morning, Christine and I departed to go fishing, and that left Himmler several hours of time alone. After we had gone, he collected the spade and strolled down to the bottom of the field parallel to the copse. He made a few motions of cleaning the ditch under the hedge in case anyone was watching. Then, as he ostentatiously mopped his brow, in reality he looked around to make sure no one was in sight. He walked into the trees and, thus concealed, walked back towards the cottage to the part of the copse where the body was concealed. Turning the body over again, he recognized a man who lived in another village. He lived alone, was frequently seen drunk and did occasional painting and decorating jobs, which gave him an excuse to cycle around with his step-ladder. Bicycle – Himmler made a mental note to look around for the man's bicycle, if he had come to Nordingly on one.

After considering the matter, Himmler removed the man's jacket, cut away the turf under a pine tree in another part of the copse and dug a shallow grave, piling the earth carefully on the jacket. He buried the body and then dispersed the excavated earth in little piles which looked like molehills amongst the grass and pine needles. He replaced the top turf carefully and patted it down. Pulling a couple of pine branches from another tree, he brushed at the spilled earth that had fallen from the jacket on to the ground, and dispersed it.

Surveying his handiwork, he picked up the jacket and the step-ladder, and walked back towards the cottage, still within the trees. He dropped the step-ladder down in a different place to where he had first put it. Himmler carried the man's jacket to the outhouse, where the boiler fire for the pig food still burned. After a few more minutes, it was disposed of in the fire and the evidence went 'up the chimney'. Pausing for a few moments, he mentally considered a number of items: body buried, jacket burnt, step-ladder to dispose of, possible bicycle around.

Himmler then went for a stroll to see if he could find a bicycle belonging to the dead man. He did not find one in the vicinity and returned to the house.

In his own mind he had done nothing wrong. He owned chickens and had protected them from theft. Someone had tried to steal his chickens and his greed had killed him. He had merely tidied up afterwards.

He never told Christine (and only told me a great deal later) and suffered no further losses of chickens through poachers.

Over a period of time he visited the copse with a saw, whilst we were away. The step-ladder went into the boiler fire gradually, literally step by step, until nothing was left, but the hinges which he threw away.

After a while, the neighbours of the poacher noticed his absence and reported it to the police. Nothing was discovered, despite local enquiries being made. It appeared that no one knew of the man's nocturnal habits.

Over a period of time, the number of chickens being kept by Himmler rose and he and I constructed some more chicken coops. We were now able to sell some eggs within our own village and to shops in other villages, although of course other people also kept hens. After a while, chicks were born. When they had developed to adult size, we sent some of them to market. Things were going well.

Harry and I were familiar faces now in our small community. Certainly we were foreigners, but the locals tolerated us.

Christine tried to broaden our knowledge of English life. During the summer, she took us to a cricket match one Saturday. Both of us waited for something to happen ... and waited...and waited. Finally Himmler fell asleep and I got bored and went for a walk. She did not take us again – we were both pleased about that.

Another very minor incident occurred when Christine convinced us that we needed a haircut. She took us to a small town called Holt, where she went shopping sometimes, and indicated a barber's shop.

'Ask for a short back and sides,' she advised. 'Ask them to leave your beard alone, Harry. When you go inside, count how many people are waiting, including whoever is in the barber's chair. When the barber has finished cutting the hair of that number of people, then it will be your turn.'

We merely smiled and nodded. Both of us could have worked that out for ourselves. Christine left us outside the barber's shop, telling us that she would see us later outside the bank.

The barber's shop had a tiny counter inside the door and the actual hair cutting was done in a separate room off the entrance area. We both entered and sat down. A group of five men and

212

boys surveyed the strangers for a few moments, then continued to read magazines or comics.

As the numbers in front of us diminished, we both saw that the customers went into the entrance area to pay the barber at the counter, after having a haircut. Himmler had his haircut before me and instructed the barber, 'Short back and sides and leave the beard,' as he had been told. As he did not know his customer, the barber was rather limited on 'small talk' and Himmler decided to be reticent.

After he had finished the haircut and brushed the customer's shoulders, the barber went to his counter and Himmler followed to pay him. By now Himmler could speak and understand a fair bit of the English language, but innuendo was still beyond him.

He proffered his money to the barber, who took it and gave him his change.

'Something for the weekend?' the barber enquired.

Himmler looked puzzled. He understood the words, but could not interpret the meaning.

The barber reached under his counter and showed Himmler a small packet, which still conveyed nothing to Himmler. In desperation Himmler called me from the other room. I sized up the situation and whispered in Himmler's ear.

Realization dawned in Himmler's face and he managed a 'No thank you, sir!' and left the shop hurriedly.

Himmler was not in the best of moods when Christine joined her newly-shorn farm labourers later. Christine perceived this and asked me what was the matter with him.

I explained that Harry was embarrassed because the barber had asked him if he had wanted 'something for the weekend.'

Christine tried hard to stifle the laughter which welled up inside her, but it finally erupted in peals.

Himmler was not amused and walked back to where we had parked the car.

At around this time, I asked Himmler one evening about the huge numbers of deaths of Jews during the war. Stories about this had been reported in the British newspapers, and there had been claims of gas chambers having been used.

After a pause, Himmler said, 'I will try to explain what

213

happened, but it's a long complex story. During the period leading up to the war, amongst the mountain of daily mail that was addressed to the Führer Adolf Hitler was a particular letter. A man had a son who was severely mentally and physically retarded. He wrote to Hitler to ask if his son could be 'put to sleep'. The father merely wished to save the family further anguish in the future years.

'Hitler would never even have seen the letter if an official who dealt with his mail had not brought it to his attention. After giving the matter some thought, Hitler agreed to give his permission. He was probably thinking that this was just one person's life to be brought to an end. However, an official in one of the Ministries created a "Hitler Order" out of this single decision. A "Hitler Order" meant that what the Führer had decreed, should now apply to all such cases.

'Thereafter, a few centres were created in secret, located in various parts of Germany and Austria. Ordinary general practitioners were encouraged to send their "hopeless" cases there. At these centres, a small staff, including doctors, examined the "patients" on their arrival, administered lethal injections and buried the bodies within the grounds. Their relatives would receive a letter stating that the patient had died of pneumonia, or some other cause, a few days after their arrival.

'After a while, this became difficult, both in numbers and particularly in space for burials. Therefore, some of the establishments had a special airtight room made, where the patients could be gassed by carbon monoxide fumes from the engine of a heavy lorry. A crematory oven and chimney were also installed in each establishment. This meant that perhaps twenty or thirty patients could be gassed at a time and then their bodies were cremated.

'This speeded up the process and reduced the strain on the staff. Death became more remote. It was far easier to turn on an engine and walk away from a sealed room than to physically inject patients one by one. Thus, in secret, a programme of euthanasia, or mercy killings, had been brought into being. Nationally this secret group of staff, code name T4, numbered only 96 persons. There was an establishment at Hadamar, north of Frankfurt am Main and at Castle Hartheim in Austria (to mention two locations).

214

'This new system also had another benefit. Relatives could be told that cremation of the body had been necessary to prevent disease, but they could purchase the ashes, if they wished. You might think that this was terrible, Eric. Personally, I feel sure that there will come a time when the population of a country becomes so huge that it will seek a reduction in the population. They will do this by selecting those that are not best suited to remain alive by their physical and/or mental states. By that time, they may evolve different means to carry this out. Euthanasia will come to our planet at some time, unless wars and natural disasters perform a similar role.

'At a later stage Hitler decided that he wanted the Jewish question to be sorted out, once and for all. He appointed Reinhard Heydrich (who was one of Himmler's subordinates) to oversee it and Heydrich convened a meeting at Wannsee near Berlin. I had nothing to do with this meeting.

'The meeting decided to register all the Jews in countries occupied by us and then gradually to deport them to work in the East, mainly in Poland. In Poland itself, Jewish communities in smaller towns were brought to larger towns and cities, where a number of special Jewish ghettos were created. The Jews worked within the ghettos at various types of work, particularly making military clothing.

'Rations were tight, people died, particularly the old. Finally someone decided to create four extermination centres at remote areas within Poland. Three of them were near the Bug river – Treblinka, Sobibor and Belzec. The fourth one was at Chelmno, but that was not a proper camp. The same 96 T4 personnel of the former euthanasia programme were divided into groups of 24, with 200 Ukrainian guards, per camp. The camps were situated in remote spots, usually with railway access and gas chambers were built within the three camps to gas those arriving by train from the ghettos. Chelmno used special lorries to gas the people inside them. The exhaust fumes were piped into the sealed interior of the lorry to gas the Jews by carbon monoxide. This happened as the lorries drove en route to the woods, and there the bodies were cremated.

'It was all done in great secret and as far as possible by deceiving the Jews as to what was going to happen. From most transports arriving by train at the extermination camps, certain strong or skilled Jews were kept alive to sort the clothing, or to burn the bodies after gassing. It was an almost continuous daily process. The trains arrived. Selections of skilled prisoners took place from the new arrivals. The men were separated from the women and children. They were taken to separate undressing barracks and in turn herded along a screened barbed wire fenced path to the "bath house" for disinfection. They were locked inside the sealed room, and the lorry or tank engines were started to introduce carbon monoxide and gas them. Afterwards the bodies were burnt on grids of railway lines.

'The officer in charge, usually an SS untersturmführer (second lieutenant), could neither stop the trains coming, nor feed the newcomers, nor send them back. He had to "process them". He need have nothing to do with the actual process himself, but he was in charge and responsible. Most of the SS involved were scharführer (sergeants) who had charge of certain sections of the process. The bulk of the guards were Ukrainians.

'I myself could not stop the process once it had been started. Those extermination camps existed for eighteen months before I could have them closed as the Russians advanced. What was far more useful to the Reich was to have prisoner workers contributing towards the war effort. I geared the concentration camps to that end, and all the major camps had big industrial complexes attached to them after a while – Dachau, Sachsenhausen, Buchenwald and Ravensbrück and others in Germany, Maidanek and Auschwitz in Poland. These places made huge contributions to the war effort.

'It was with the help of Jewish workers that we produced the V1 and V2 rockets at the underground tunnels of Dora near Nordhausen. They constructed the Messerschmitt 262 jet planes and produced synthetic rubber after our Far East supplies dried up. Yet even then, we could not transfer the workers and continue to feed the old and the young in other places. So principally at Auschwitz in Poland, which had many satellite work camps, the trains arrived with families of Jews and went through a selection process. The people suitable for work were kept alive and the others were gassed.

'By that time, they had replaced the carbon monoxide method with a chemical known as Zyklon B, which worked in seconds. It was the same formula for those in charge, as I have described.

216

You could not stop the trains coming, you could not send them back, or feed everyone.

'It was therefore reduced to simple mathematics. For example camp capacity 50,000, camp prisoners 48,000 – some trains arrive with 5,000 more people in total, and so 3,000 must be eliminated. What would be kinder: a quick death, or a prolonged one from starvation?

'Was it a crime? It depends how you regard things – in isolation, or with other things.

'For example, Allied bombers dropped bombs on the city of Dresden towards the end of the War. There were no military targets there. The city was full of refugees. The bombs killed 50,000 people, mainly civilians. Most of them were old people, women and children. The bombs created a fire storm and the tar on the roads caught fire. People could not run away, they caught fire and burned where they stood, like candles. Others suffocated, because the fire consumed all the oxygen, so that they could not breathe.

'Who is the criminal – the bomber pilots, the bomb aimers, the bomb makers, the aircraft makers, the officers who ordered the raid? In our example, who is the criminal – the men who filled the trains, the train drivers, the camp commandants, the selection doctors, the men who made the gas, the men who administered the gas, the men who gave the orders? I am sure at the time people believed that they were doing the right thing and obeying orders. Is everyone concerned just as guilty? Let me give an example – the Jews of Paris were rounded up for deportation mainly by the French police, not by us!

'Are we guilty as Germans for having lost the war, or for committing these killings? If it is these killings, then Stalin has surpassed them threefold in his own country. Will he be brought to trial? The Finns fought with Germany until late in the war. Will they be tried too? How about Hungary, Bulgaria and Rumania?

'The British have hanged William Joyce ('Lord Haw Haw'), who broadcast for us on the radio during the war, as a traitor. How could he be a traitor? William Joyce was not even a British citizen.

'Are they going to hang everyone who fought against them? Well, they better have a lot of rope. We had almost 1,000

217

Indians in the SS. Some fought the Allies in Normandy. An army of well over 10,000 Indians fought with the Japanese against the British for years, in the hope of freeing their country from British rule. In the same way, Estonians, Latvians and Lithuanians and tens of thousands of Russians fought with us against Communist Russia. They fought and died with us, in order to have their own countries free in the future. Are they criminals, or freedom fighters? Who is to decide – the victors?

'Germany largely abided by the Geneva Convention in our treatment of prisoners of war. When we captured Polish or Czech pilots who had flown against us with the Royal Air Force, we treated them as prisoners of war. We did not shoot them. We did not treat the Russian prisoners of war well, because the Russians were not signatories to the Geneva Convention. That of course can cut two ways. As non-signatories of the Geneva Convention, why should the Russians respect those rights for our own men who fell into their hands? If my memory is correct, at Stalingrad the Russians took almost 200,000 of our men and our allies prisoner. I wonder how many of those, if any, will ever return?'

I had never seen Himmler so animated. What he had told me in those few minutes was a genuine revelation. I could only nod my head in bewilderment.

'How many Jews were put to death?' I finally asked Himmler.

Himmler answered, 'I have no idea of any accurate number, but it must be several million.'

'Several million?' I exclaimed unbelievingly. 'Surely that cannot be true!'

'No,' replied Himmler emphatically. 'It may be hard to comprehend, but several million were put to death over several years.'

I decided to go for a walk to clear my head of the monstrous image of millions being put to death. Himmler remained in the cottage. Christine was out visiting someone in Blakeney.

Chapter 13

The year of 1946 advanced. International war crimes trials were started at Nuremberg in Germany. An American judge presided and death sentences were handed down to the bulk of those Nazis indicted – chief of whom was Hermann Göring. Life sentences were handed down to a few – chief of whom was Rudolf Hess. Others received sentences of 20, 15 and 10 years' imprisonment. Three of those indicted were acquitted, despite the Russians demanding the death penalty for all. Martin Bormann was tried and sentenced to death in his absence.

Those sentenced to death were hanged within the prison at Nuremberg. Hermann Göring committed suicide, by taking poison, during the night before execution. As a final irony, the bodies of those executed were taken in secret to the former Dachau concentration camp and cremated in the ovens there. The ashes were dumped in the river Isar, which runs through Munich.

Other war crimes trials were held at other locations and at other times for mainly less well-known personalities. Some SS officers and Wehrmacht officers were handed over to other countries to be tried for war crimes committed there.

There were trials in Britain too. John Amery had been put on trial for treason and pleaded guilty. There was only one penalty, and he was sentenced to death and hanged. One of the senior surviving SS Britisches Frei Korps's men was also sentenced to death.

Himmler realized that most of the major war criminals would inevitably be sentenced to death, as he would be, should he become a prisoner. The most senior SS officer to stand trial at Nuremberg had been Ernst Kaltenbrunner and he had been hanged. Others such as Grand Admiral Raeder of the Kriegsmarine (navy) had been retired for most of the War, but had still received a life sentence at Nuremberg. Newspaper reports claimed that 'Rudolf Hess' was mad and he thought of Hess's double, Flug Kapitan Weiss, with his lonely secret, locked in Spandau prison. The other non-lifers in Spandau were Albert Speer and Baldur von Schirach sentenced to twenty years, Von Neurath fifteen years and Grand Admiral Dönitz ten years.

The trials also brought the subject of the Jews up again.

'Couldn't you have stopped these killings?' I asked Himmler.

'No!' he replied without elaboration.

'Surely, if you were in charge, then you could have given the order,' I insisted.

'I fully understand that from your position, that might seem obvious. Let me try to explain the reality of things to you. Let us take Auschwitz, as an example. It was set up initially as a concentration camp to hold prisoners who could work at a variety of jobs for the war effort. The actual *Stammlager* (base camp – Auschwitz I) was relatively small, covering only seven hectares. It was the holding camp for prisoners to sleep in. Almost all of the prisoners were employed to work outside the camp. They might be building, or mending roads. Others would be working on munitions in nearby buildings. Yet others would be working in coal mines in the area. Some might be involved in making clothing and footwear. Naturally some were employed in the camp itself to cook, or work in the laundry, or the camp *Revier* (hospital). The prisoners themselves carried out most of the administration under minimal supervision by guards.

'After we went to war with Russia, we discovered that the Russians had been shooting German prisoners who had paybooks indicating that they were NSDAP (Nazi Party) members. They were also shooting our SS men who were taken prisoner. We found out that the Russian commissars and *politruks* (political officers) were being ordered to create sabotage and unrest in prison camps if they were captured.

'In the face of all this, Hitler issued an order that all commissars and *politruks* taken prisoner should be shot. This applied not only to new prisoners, but those that had been in camps for some time. The existing camps were trawled through and the commissars and *politruks* were removed. Subject to

220

where they were located, many in Poland were sent under guard to Auschwitz. They were housed within the base camp, in cells beneath Block 11, which was a barrack block used by the Gestapo. Following the order, Soviet commissars and *politruks* would be shot within the courtyard between blocks 10 and 11. There were walls at each end of the courtyard.

'The first commandant of Auschwitz was a man named Rudolf Höss (author's note – not to be confused with Rudolf Hess, who flew to Scotland). Under his administration, commissars and *politruks* were shot, as I have described. At one time, Höss was away from the camp.

'Whilst he was away, his deputy, I do not remember his name, decided to see if he could gas the prisoners under sentence of death in the bunker cells en masse. The windows of the underground cells at ground level were blocked up. A guard wearing a gas mask introduced Zyklon B, a strong disinfectant, based on cyanide, into the cell block corridor. The guard closed the door to the corridor behind him, and the Zyklon B vaporized in the air. After twenty minutes the door was opened and aired, and all the prisoners were dead. They thus could kill numbers of people quickly, quietly and without bullets being fired.

'It was virtually by accident that this system was found. The deputy told Höss on his return and it was demonstrated to him on a new batch of prisoners. The sealing of the cells was inconvenient because they were also needed to house those not condemned to death so the location was then changed to the old mortuary room, which was adjacent to the crematorium, outside the camp's perimeter.

'By modifying the doors of the mortuary so that they could be hermetically sealed and bolted, several hundred people could be gassed at the same time, and the location was right next to the crematory ovens in the same building. The Zyklon B was introduced inside from a vent in the roof, which was then "capped".

'Höss had stumbled across a new method of killing people en masse. It was much more reliable than carbon monoxide from petrol or diesel engines, which had been used at the extermination camps in Poland.'

'Even so, surely you could have stopped it?' I demanded.

221

'There is one vital fact that I have not yet mentioned.' answered Himmler. 'In most hierarchies, there is always in-fighting as people jockey for position. I told you that Rudolf Hess's star was on the wane before he thought about flying to Britain. The same thing happened with Göring as the war progressed. If you could not deliver, then Hitler would get someone who could.

'I will tell you the reason why I, as SS Reichsführer, could not halt these things at Auschwitz. By one of the strange twists of fate, Rudolf Höss, the commandant, was a personal friend of Reichsleiter Martin Bormann. They had been at school together. Martin Bormann was closer to Adolf Hitler and more influential than I was.

'No, my friend, you might think that I could stop things, but in reality my neck would have been on the line if I had. Many things happened which I did not necessarily personally sanction but could not stop happening. Martin Bormann would have loved to see me fall from grace.'

'Did you visit this Auschwitz place yourself?' I queried.

'Yes, I visited the Auschwitz camp on several occasions during the war, Eric', Himmler answered. 'You must understand that when a general inspects a military camp, everyone knows that he is coming. Everything is tidied up and he is only shown what his minions want him to see. It was the same for me, although my rank was higher than a general. I imagine that I was only shown what people wanted me to see. I visited the Buna factories for producing artificial rubber at Monowitz (Auschwitz III camp). It was of more importance for me to see what was contributing to the war effort. If conditions were very bad in some places, I was not shown them. Then the commandant could not be criticized. In fact I had to promote Höss to obersturmbannführer (lieutenant colonel).

'Höss had visited Sobibor and perhaps other extermination camps. The old mortuary room at Auschwitz I was not an ideal location for a gas chamber. Two of the former farmhouses near the outskirts of the Birkenau camp, a couple of kilometres away, were modified to be gas chambers. You must understand that all the local population in the camp's vicinity had been moved out of the area compulsorily. Birkenau had small woods on its outskirts which provided a natural screen. The Jews from

222

incoming railway transports, who were not needed for work, or who were unable to work, were gassed there.

'Still later, four purpose-built gas chambers with crematoria were built. They were at the far end of the Birkenau camp complex and were many times larger than the original at Auschwitz I. From a chance discovery with Zyklon B, the whole thing grew to gigantic proportions. Jewish ghettos could be gradually emptied and the work force utilized at Auschwitz. Those unable to work were eliminated and any workers who died could be replaced. It became almost a production chain of life and death. The Reich desperately needed workers to help the war effort, and the Jews were a prime source of labour.

'Now there is something that I have not yet made clear, Eric. In this camp and all the others, the internal administration was by the prisoners themselves. In fact it was quite rare for a guard to shoot a prisoner for trying to escape, yet the *kapos* (fellow prisoners who were foremen) would constantly urge the prisoners in their care to work harder by beating them with stout walking sticks or clubs. Höss told me that the *kapos* instigated a reign of terror amongst the worker prisoners. If a man was not working hard enough, a *kapo* might knock him to the floor with a spade over the back of his head. Whilst the prisoner lay stunned, the *kapo* would place the spade shaft across the prisoner's throat, mount each end and 'see-saw'. This crushed the prisoner's throat and killed him. Naturally this caused the remaining prisoners to redouble their efforts. The *kapos* ruled by fear. They could apportion more food for themselves, and so the ordinary prisoners had less.

'Prisoners, although not exclusively Jews, fought to get the plum jobs, such as working in the Kanada barracks, sorting the clothes and belongings of those that had gone to the gas chambers. Others worked on the ramp at the train station siding, unloading the prisoners from the trains and removing their belongings.

'Höss told me that the strangest sight for him was to watch these prisoners who worked at the railway station. He noticed their behaviour when they started out to meet the first train of the day. They would march out of the camp, four or five abreast. As soon as they got to the main road, they would begin marching a little faster, without being ordered. They would march faster and faster, until they were actually jogging. Finally, they actually ran the last hundred metres to the railway station, in order to get the best positions. Some guards had to use bicycles to keep up with them. You see, these men got first pick of the food etc. brought by the people on the trains.

'These camp prisoners contributed to the process through which the Jews would be put to death. They seemed not to care what happened to their fellows. They encouraged the new arrivals to hurry and move faster! The quicker the new arrivals could be moved out meant the sooner the sorters could get their perks. Even the engine drivers wanted a share. All valuables had to be handed in, but invariably some were palmed.

'The food helped keep you alive. The valuables you could trade. Sometimes the prisoners would even trade with the SS or Ukrainian guards. Everyone wanted a share. The lorries, laden with people too old or too young to work, did not just drive to the gas chambers at a sedate pace. They were driven by prisoners and went hell for leather. Everyone wanted the job over with, as quickly as possible.

'Sometimes incoming trains brought relatives of those already involved with this work. Jews arriving at the undressing room of the gas chambers might notice a Jewish relative working there in the *Sonderkommando* (special work force) and call to them. Invariably the SK prisoner would say "I'm sorry, I'm busy. I will talk to you after you have had your bath," and then carry on working.'

'I really find that hard to believe!'

'It is true, my friend,' replied Himmler. 'Commandant Höss told me that only once did something go slightly wrong with those destined for gassing. I can't remember the exact date, but for some reason an SS guard got closer than usual to a female prisoner, within the crematorium yard. From what I was told and remember, she suddenly snatched a handful of dust and gravel from the ground and threw it in his face, then grabbed the guard's pistol and shot him several times and wounded another SS guard.

'Perhaps only five or six lightly armed SS guards were ever in the enclosed yard of the crematorium at any time. The remainder of the guards left the yard to get reinforcements. The *Sonderkommando* were male prisoners, who performed almost all the

224

duties connected with the killing process. They guided people into the "undressing rooms", helped them undress, cleared the gas chambers of the dead bodies, and cremated the corpses. These *Sonderkommando* men were left alone with the group of prisoners destined for gassing. What did they do? They forced the prisoners into the gas chambers and locked the doors!'

Himmler paused for a moment to emphasize the point.

'The men of the *Sonderkommando* including many Jews, having access to at least two weapons did nothing, but carry on unsupervised with their normal job, made even harder by a mini-revolt. They did nothing to help those prisoners escape, all of whom were Jewish. The guard, who had been shot several times, died of his wounds.

'However one *Sonderkommando* team at Crematorium IV did revolt during their time at Auschwitz. They smuggled explosives in from outside the camp and blew up the ovens, set fire to their gas chamber/crematorium building and tried to escape. No one succeeded on that occasion, but they also killed some guards.

'The more important you were in the camp hierarchy, the better you lived and the better you ate. The most important male prisoners might even be allowed to visit the brothel. Prisoners who had an easier life could only achieve this by disadvantaging their fellows. You need to understand that the people who contributed a part to the destruction of the Jews, in the final analysis at Auschwitz, were other prisoners there, including Jewish ones. I'm sure that there were exceptions to this, of course.'

'Of course!' I echoed sarcastically.

Himmler continued, 'Many of our own people were made corrupt by what they could channel into their own funds from the Jews. They might be prisoners such as camp *älteste* (elders), or *kapos*. Alternatively they could be guards, including officers. Even commandants were not immune. The commandant of Buchenwald concentration camp, near Weimar, was arrested and shot for his fraudulent misuse of money, by us during the war, and he was not the only one.

'When I was able to close down the four extermination centres of Treblinka, Sobibor, Belzec and Chelmno, I had the T4 staff transferred to anti-partisan duties near Trieste. There had been only ninety-six men in this group originally and a few had already been killed in the breakouts at Treblinka and Sobibor. The partisans killed more of them, as the war progressed.'

'Why did you transfer them to Trieste?' I queried.

For once Himmler seemed to have been caught out. It was a question that had come up unexpectedly. It took him a few moments to think of an answer. Finally he blurted out, 'I transferred them because we needed men to fight the partisans. It was also because I felt that from the beginnings with euthanasia, we had created a monstrous mechanism for killing on a gigantic scale, which was never originally intended. I felt that by transferring the T4 men, I was cutting one of the heads off the Hydra.'

I noticed that Himmler seemed different in making this last admission, but I could not decide if he was telling the truth.

The moment passed. Time moved on. Day followed day.

During 1947 Himmler started his preparations to get funds from his numbered Swiss bank account. First he opened an account in a British bank.

By using his methodical approach to problems, he watched what the bank staff did at lunch times. He became aware that a particular older male clerk seemed a bit of a loner. Himmler contrived to visit the bank often and to select a position in a queue which would ensure that the same clerk served him. A 'nodding' recognition of each other developed. This bank clerk habitually ate sandwiches on a park bench, by himself, at lunch times.

Himmler was 'accidentally' passing one day and asked if he might join the man. He had some sandwiches and introduced himself. He told the clerk that he recognized him from the bank and explained that he also used to work in banking in Poland before the war. The clerk was not terribly interested, but made polite conversation. Himmler continued that in his country there were too many experienced bank clerks and too few manager positions. The clerk agreed, and he started to describe the unfairness in the system which had deprived him of becoming a manager in his own bank. Himmler speculated that it was perhaps the same throughout the world. He continued in this manner, cultivating the bank clerk's friendship and interest.

'Tell me, my friend, where is the smart money invested outside of Britain, apart from Switzerland, I suppose?'

The clerk thought for a moment and then said quietly, 'Well, if I had a little money to invest, I would consider a British offshore bank somewhere. It would earn a little more interest and the banks are very discreet, I understand.'

'Offshore?' queried Himmler.

'Yes! You know the Isle of Man, the Channel Islands, Gibraltar, the Bahamas and so on.'

'Ah! Of course, of course!' echoed Himmler. He made further pleasantries and then made an excuse and left.

Although it was only two years since the end of the war in Europe, it was still possible for people to have a holiday. In fact the Norfolk coastal resorts of Hunstanton, Wells-next-the-Sea, Sheringham, Cromer and Yarmouth, besides a few smaller locations, had always been popular with people for holidays. North Norfolk was an area where during the summer the cornfields would be red with the poppies which grew there in profusion. The railways helped bring holidaymakers from the inland towns and cities. It was quite an event for many of them just to see the sea.

It was also possible to travel farther afield, and Himmler made enquiries about travelling to the Channel Islands. He chose Guernsey. It was nearer, smaller and less populated than Jersey. He found out that he could travel by steamer from Weymouth and that he could reach Weymouth by rail, after changing trains in London.

He decided to sell half of his stock of chickens and, with other money he had saved, he had a modest amount to invest in a new bank account in the Channel Islands.

I borrowed books from a library and read about Guernsey and got an idea of the island's geography. Fortunately, the Channel Islands are part of the United Kingdom and no special permit was required, for us registered aliens to travel there.

This all took some time, but in September 1947 we were both ready to embark on our 'holiday'. Christine drove us to the railway station in Norwich, although we could have got there by a local train. She saw us on to the train and wished us good luck with a quiet '*Hals und Beinbruch*' (happy landings).

The train chugged on towards London, with a constantly changing scene outside the carriage window. The urban sprawl of houses increased in density, until at last we reached London's Liverpool Street Station. I suggested a taxi to cross London to Waterloo Station, which we needed for Weymouth. Himmler agreed, because he wanted to see if London had been badly damaged by the bombing of the Luftwaffe. He was disappointed. Although there were 'bombsites' and buildings damaged by bombs, the greater part of the city that we saw, was largely intact. Compared with where we lived, London was full of people, vehicles and bustle. (Compared with conditions today, it was comparatively empty.)

Arriving at Waterloo station, we found that we had plenty of time before our train departed, and spent some time looking around the station complex. After a while, Himmler's attention was drawn to two uniformed British soldiers. They were unobtrusively escorting a smaller older man with grey hair. This man walked with a military bearing and was dressed in ordinary civilian clothes. As they drew nearer, Himmler gasped and quickly turned his head, as the former Field Marshal Von Rundstedt of the German Army walked by, about five metres away. Von Rundstedt could certainly recognize Himmler, having met him many times. However, the new Himmler had a full-face beard. Von Rundstedt walked on and Himmler breathed more easily. It had been an unexpected shock.

The moment passed.

We boarded the train for Weymouth and embarked on the steamer, at the harbour. It was to be an overnight crossing and we had something to eat and headed for our cabin.

Next morning, the island of Guernsey appeared and the boat docked at St Peter Port harbour. We disembarked and walked into the town to look around. Apart from the sea, it was like any other small town, with a selection of shops, banks, cafes, hotels, etc.

We first looked at the price of property for sale on the island

and then Himmler selected a bank at random. It was not yet open for business and so we killed time having breakfast at a cafe nearby.

After breakfast, we entered the bank that had been chosen. Himmler told a clerk that he wished to open an account with them and the clerk fetched a more senior person to deal with our requirements. He brought us into a side office, away from the main counter and completed the necessary forms. Himmler deposited one hundred pounds, which was a fairly large sum in those times. The name and address that he gave were false ones. He told the clerk some story about wishing to move to Guernsey to live, and about the potential transfer of funds held in a Swiss bank to his new Guernsey account. The clerk seemed pleased to have gained an important new client for the bank. Himmler enquired about the passing of bank-to-bank instructions concerning his numbered Swiss account and then we left to 'look at property for sale'.

In reality, we left the bank, got a taxi and went to the small hotel near to Fermain Bay which we had booked for our stay.

For a few days, we acted out the part of people wishing to move to Guernsey. We made enquiries about property and actually visited some houses that were for sale.

On the day of our departure back to Britain, Himmler had already made an appointment with the bank, in order to instruct them about transferring funds from his Swiss bank account. He arranged the appointment for shortly before the end of banking hours. In this way the actual mechanics of transfer would be done the next day, and for safety's sake, we would have already left the island.

Himmler wrote down the numbers of the account, the Swiss bank address and telephone number, and various code names to be quoted. The Guernsey bank employee was quite intrigued. Himmler spun him some tale of estates in Poland, now lost to the Russians. He had requested the transfer of 100,000 Swiss francs.

After the conclusion of our bank business, the arrangement was that the new customer would telephone from Britain in a week's time to enquire about the transfer of funds. A code word was also agreed to verify the identity of the caller.

229

We left for the ferry back to Britain and embarked with our luggage the same afternoon from St Peter Port.

The following day, in Guernsey, the bank processed the application for a transfer of funds from Switzerland. On receipt of the application in the Swiss bank, a clerk took it to a more senior staff member. This man consulted a large ledger of numbered bank accounts and raised his eyebrows. He made a phone call to Guernsey to check the details. Then he used the internal telephone to ring the bank president in his top floor office and spoke rapidly to him.

The bank president appeared to recognize a potential problem with this particular transfer and called the bank clerk up to his inner sanctum. His senior clerk gathered up the transfer request from Guernsey and the bank ledger and rushed up two floors. He paused, wiped his hand over his hair, straightened his tie and knocked on the heavy wooden panelled door of the president's office.

'Come in, Zimmerman!' boomed a voice from within and Herr Zimmerman entered the office and walked across to the desk, behind which the bank president sat. Herr Gustav Braendle regarded his clerk for a few seconds.

'Sit down!' he instructed.

Zimmerman sat, and passed the transfer request to Herr Braendle, who perused it. 'Have you checked that this is authentic?' he enquired, raising his head to regard Zimmerman.

Zimmerman nodded rapidly and told his superior that he had personally spoken with the bank involved.

Braendle picked up the bank ledger and checked slowly all the numbers in the account and the code words against the transfer request. He did this twice, as if willing for an error to be found, but there was none. All details agreed.

'This cannot be, Herr Zimmerman!' he breathed. 'This is an authentic request to transfer funds from the "H" account, which Schellenberg opened during the war. He has used his own account since the war, with its modest contents, but the accounts for Martin Bormann and "H" have remained untouched since the ceasing of hostilities. If, as they claim, Bormann is dead, then that would explain that. However, if this "H" account can

230

only have been Hitler's, then as he is also known to be dead, that would explain why nothing has happened to the account before. Dead men make no transactions.'

'With respect, Herr Braendle, someone knows the account details and code words and has made an authentic request for transfer of a portion of the funds. What do we do now?' enquired Zimmerman.

Braendle said nothing. He arose from the desk, paced up and down the large office a little and then gazed out of the window for some time.

Finally, he turned round to Zimmerman with a smile on his face.

'Herr Zimmerman, I have decided what to do. We shall do nothing, except to inform the bank in Guernsey that we hold no funds in that account.'

'But we do hold funds, Herr Braendle!' exclaimed a bewildered Zimmerman.

'Yes, yes,' Braendle countered. 'You and I know that, but Guernsey does not know what is in this numbered account. If this account belonged to Hitler, then if Hitler is dead, he cannot make withdrawals. If someone else knows the account details, then they are trying to make withdrawals falsely from someone else's account. It will do our bank no good, if the world finds out that we hold an account for Adolf Hitler, and yet if we retain the money which is in the unused account, our own bank is that much richer.

I want you to deal with this matter personally and to instruct the other clerks to pass to you any further requests for transfers from this account which may arrive. I wish you to tell Guernsey that there are no funds in this account. It is my considered opinion that either nothing will happen, or the applicant will come here himself to make enquiries. Should that person be Adolf Hitler, then you have my permission to call me to pay him out personally!' Braendle scoffed.

Zimmerman scurried away to do his master's bidding.

About one week later, Himmler travelled all the way to London in order to make a phone call to the bank in Guernsey. He could have done it from a local town, but preferred the security of London.

When he phoned the Guernsey bank, the news astounded him. He simply could not believe his ears – no money in the account! The bank clerk in Guernsey asked if he wished to repeat the transfer request. Himmler thought for a few seconds and reluctantly said 'No!'

He went for a walk along the embankment of the river Thames, mulling over things in his mind. A Swiss bank account was safe. No one but him had the combination of numbers and words to make withdrawals. Therefore the money must be there in the 'H' account. Suddenly, he realized that the Swiss may have interpreted the 'H' account as being Hitler's account. With Hitler dead, that is why the Swiss were stalling. He couldn't very well travel to Switzerland and tell them that the account was not Hitler's, but Himmler's, because Himmler was also 'dead'. He had been caught out by a circumstance, which he had not foreseen.

He crossed the road and caught a taxi to Liverpool Street railway station, in order to return to Norfolk.

Christine and I were not at all pleased. We had all counted on Himmler's funds to make life easier for us all. Initially I distrusted Himmler, but when I saw how disheartened he was, I became convinced that he had told us the truth.

Himmler did not contact or revisit Guernsey again. His account, under a false name and address, may still exist there.

Unknown to Himmler, Christine and Erich, although few people knew about these Swiss accounts, others were interested in any movement of this money deposited by high-ranking Nazis.

Since the war's end, discreet information concerning the existence of these accounts and others had reached Jewish Nazi-hunters. They had a friend in the Swiss bank concerned, who reported that an attempted withdrawal from the 'H' account had been made from a Guernsey bank. Further information was requested and the friend provided the name and address of the Guernsey bank and the name of the account holder in Guernsey requesting the withdrawal.

The Jewish group was open-minded as to who had requested the withdrawal. Whilst it almost certainly was not Adolf Hitler, they concluded that it was not some unknown German clerk or former soldier either.

It took them two weeks to research their friends in Guernsey who could help them. For once they were lucky; not only did they have a friend in the Guernsey bank concerned, but also it was the same man who had opened the new bank account for the Polish gentleman.

A member of the group agreed to travel to Guernsey to talk to their friend and obtain all the details. It all took time, but time and patience the group had in abundance. It was now early in 1948. Before he departed, the group's agent, Schlomo, was given a number of photographs and personal details of prominent Nazi figures. The photographs included Adolf Hitler, Heinrich Himmler and Martin Bormann. Whilst the first two were believed to be dead, the group was taking no chances.

After he eventually arrived in Guernsey, Schlomo arranged to see the banking friend one evening. The bank employee brought details of the Polish man's name and British address in London with him. Schlomo noted these details and then began to carefully question the bank official about a description of the man who had opened this new account recently.

The bank official recounted: 'Male, height about five feet nine inches, weight about ten stone, age between mid-forties and early fifties. He had dark hair, but not black, with a centre parting. It had receded from the front forehead a little with age. He wore glasses with fairly thick frames. He had a full beard, but it was not long in length. He wore a suit with a shirt and tie. He had fairly thin lips, but there were no scars or marks on his face.' He could not remember the colour of his eyes. He also described the much younger man who was with the other Pole.

'That's fine, my friend!' observed Schlomo. 'Is there any other detail of what you saw, or the man said, which you feel I should know?' he asked.

'Nothing comes to mind at present,' replied the bank official. 'Can you tell me what all this is about?'

'I'm part of a group which is searching for Nazis,' answered Schlomo. 'That doesn't mean this man is a Nazi, but he is certainly worth investigating. I want to return in a day or two, but until then I thank you for your help.'

Schlomo returned to his bed and breakfast accommodation in St Peter Port. The reason he had been chosen to travel to

233

Guernsey was because he was a gifted artist. He sat in his bedroom reading the data on the Nazis in the photographs. Two Nazis were aged under thirty years of age and he therefore excluded them from his further researches.

Taking his time, Schlomo began to sketch the faces of various high-ranking Nazis. He did this to incorporate the features of the photographs, but with the hairstyle and full beard of the bank official's description. He could not complete these all in one evening, nor could he stay in his room all day. The following morning, he tried to unobtrusively make his sketches in cafés, or in the reading room of the library. En masse, even he could not recognize some of the personalities now, from their more familiar appearances with uniforms and medals in the photographs. He therefore numbered the photographs on the back and the corresponding sketches had the same number on their reverse side.

When Schlomo had finished, he arranged to see his bank contact again. The man agreed to meet Schlomo at his own house that evening. After Schlomo arrived he was conducted to the living room and they both sat down at a table.

Schlomo introduced his idea to the bank official. 'I have made some sketches of people that are of interest to my group for you to look at. Each sketch incorporates the features of a man from photographs of him, but my sketch shows him with a full beard and with a hair-style as you described to me. Although the man who opened your account may not be in these sketches, you can tell me if he is there. Take your time, study each sketch as I give it to you, and then when you are ready, tell me if you recognize the man in the sketch or not.'

The bank official nodded his understanding. Schlomo passed him the twelve sketches one by one to consider. They were in no particular order. Schlomo did not even look at any sketch as he passed them one by one to the man. Instead he watched the man's eyes for any sign of recognition.

Time seemed to have almost stopped now, as Schlomo waited patiently. He became aware of a clock ticking in the room, which seemed to get louder as the seconds went by. The bank official quietly said, 'Not this one!' as he pushed the first sketch aside to consider the next one. Again and again the same words, 'Not this one! Not this one!' The pile of sketches yet to be seen was getting smaller. Suddenly Schlomo saw a real flicker of recognition from the man. 'Yes!' he breathed at last. 'That is the man who opened the account. Yes! There is no doubt in my mind, it was him. His hair was a little less flat than your sketch, but the likeness is remarkable.'

Schlomo seized the sketch. He was so preoccupied that he did not even look at the face he had drawn. He questioned the man further about the hairstyle and modified it until the man agreed. It was only then that he glanced at the face he had drawn and saw it was number nine. He had drawn so many sketches that even the number did not immediately signify anything. He took out an envelope and sorted through the photographs inside from the numbers on the reverse side. Number nine. Schlomo turned the photograph over quickly, so that only he could see the image. A familiar face in peaked cap and uniform stared back at him from the photograph – Heinrich Himmler, Reichsführer of the SS!

The tension in the room between the two men was almost tangible. The bank man laughed and exclaimed, 'For goodness sake! Who is it? Please tell me!'

Schlomo sat back and rubbed his chin. At length he declared, 'My group would not want me to tell you! However, I really appreciate that you have been very helpful to us and I think I can trust you. I emphasize three things to you. This is a secret probably never to be told. Secondly, the chances of it being true and us getting our man are very remote. Lastly, if you betray my confidence, it will cost you your job.'

Before the bank official could even reply, Schlomo turned over the photograph and held it out for the man to see. After a few seconds the man laughed. 'Well, Himmler is dead, so it can't be him!' Schlomo did not reply. The man stared at the photograph again and then at sketch nine. He visibly paled. At last he breathed, 'Well, if it's not him, then he must have a twin.'

Schlomo believed him. He again emphasized that this conversation should never be mentioned. They wished each other *Shalom* and Schlomo began his preparations to return to his group in Switzerland.

* * *

It took Schlomo some time to return to Basel. He utilized the friendship of Jewish citizens on the way. Making his report to the three ruling elders of his group, he was initially enthusiastic, until he heard their reply.

'Schlomo! You have obviously been working hard in Guernsey, but we have been having a re-think since you left. We simply have not the men or money to follow up such a remote prospect,' stated Matthias, the leader of the Group. 'The British buried Himmler in Northern Germany back in 1945. Why should they mistake the identity of the man they had in custody? Even if the person who has tried to withdraw money from the "H" account seems to look similar to Himmler, why should it be him?

'We have more specific targets to go after, and some of these may still be in Europe. Our priority is to search for such men as Martin Bormann, the Nazi Party Secretary, Adolf Eichmann, the architect of the "Final Solution", Christian Wirth, who ruled the extermination camps, Franz Stangl the former commandant of Sobibor and Treblinka extermination camps and the SS camp doctors Eisele and Mengele. They are just a few of an extensive list of former Nazis, who are not known to be dead. There are doubts as to whether Müller of the Gestapo is really dead, but no one has raised any doubts over Himmler so far. We cannot afford the time to chase shadows. I'm sorry Schlomo.'

Schlomo sat silently for some moments, shocked by the news. At last he said, 'I understand what you say. My recent researches have tired me and I have news of sick relatives. I need some time off to recuperate and to help the sick members of my family before I can throw myself into this work again.'

'Of course, Schlomo,' said Matthias. 'Take all the time you need and then come back to us. We need a man of your resourcefulness in our group.'

Schlomo smiled and, after shaking the hands of everyone, he left the meeting. The Himmler image had haunted his brain since Guernsey. What if it was really Himmler? The logic indicated that it could be, as it had occurred to the British private soldier Benny Green. He tossed around the alternatives in his mind and came to the conclusion that he could never rest until he had investigated some more for himself.

Schlomo started out for England a few days later, without telling his group. In England, he went to see Benny Green, who lived in London. The group had noted his address when he first indicated his misgivings about Himmler's death. Benny and his mother made him welcome, but Schlomo only revealed his real reason for visiting England to Benny. He found him to be a fountain of knowledge concerning which organizations in England did what, and so on.

Schlomo quickly visited the address that the Pole had quoted for his Guernsey bank account. No one lived there any more. The location was a wasteland of rubble from war-time bombing. The local people called them bomb-sites, and there were many of them in London. The fact of the address being false was a clue, but it did not prove that Himmler had opened the bank account.

Benny had to work. Schlomo was a visitor to England, but he took a casual evening job washing up in a hotel kitchen to earn some money and help to pay for his stay with Benny and his mother. He used the mornings and afternoons for research. He discovered that refugees who had come to England after the war were registered as aliens. He also found out that a central register was kept of names and addresses at a building in central London, and spent a lot of time watching the employees coming in and out of the doors of the registry at various times of the day.

These days Schlomo's activities might be called 'stalking'. He decided to try and get to know several young men who looked Jewish, to see if he could get a look at the register of aliens for himself.

To reduce the time and effort spent on that part of his research alone, he finally got someone to let him look at the registers unofficially after business hours. Schlomo did not tell the registry man who he was looking for, and he took Benny with him.

The registers were huge and the number of names was enormous. People of a multitude of nationalities were listed with their names and addresses, including thousands of Poles, some of whom had served with the British Army. One set of registers was filled in alphabetically and one set by location in counties of England and Wales. Benny suggested that they both looked at different registers by county to cover the alphabet more quickly. This would permit seeing if people lived singly, or in groups. Himmler was hardly likely to be with a group of real Poles in a hostel or refugee camp. Benny speculated that if Himmler was anywhere, he was living with at the most three other people. Finally, as Schlomo and Benny began to read the lists looking for Polish aliens, Benny breathed, 'Look for anything that seems odd!'

After they both started to scribble down names and addresses, Benny asked Schlomo to stop.

'We are doing this without any logic, Schlomo. In my opinion, if Himmler came from England by ferry to Guernsey, then it is likely he lives in England. Furthermore, if he came from Germany to live in England, then we need to consider how he came and where he is likely to be. I think it extremely unlikely that he arrived by aeroplane, so that means he came by sea. I also think it unlikely that he arrived on the usual cross-channel ferries to a major British port. It's possible he arrived on a small freighter or fishing boat. He could also have been rowed ashore at an isolated spot in a ship's boat, or in a rubber dinghy.

He could be living anywhere in Britain, but I don't think that he would live in any major city like London, or even in a small town. I think that he would live in a small place, where the number of people is fewer. I suspect that he would not have landed on the South Coast of Britain. During the war, it was thought to be one of the likely invasion areas, and even now it is guarded more heavily than elsewhere.

If Himmler came by sea from Germany, I think it possible that he landed on the East Coast – Kent, Essex, Suffolk, Norfolk or Lincolnshire. I'm British and more familiar with our country's geography. Let me look at the Polish aliens' addresses living in twos, threes and fours and I will indicate the locations that are not towns or cities in those counties for you to write down. We can leave out Poles living alone because I think most of them will be Poles who have married an English girl.'

Benny started on the task, which he had set himself. In fact if his logic was correct, the numbers of Poles living in twos, threes or fours would be far fewer than those in groups in refugee camps or living in towns or cities.

Benny asked his friend who worked within the aliens' record registry to help, but the man did not want to commit his handwriting to paper. He stayed outside the office door nervously. Progress was made. Although the numbers of Polish refugees in Kent and Essex was fairly large, the numbers in Suffolk and Norfolk were much less, and in Lincolnshire fewer still. Some of the names had been anglicized, from their Polish originals.

Benny and Schlomo finished after some hours and allowed their anxious friend to lock up the registry. They thanked him and took their lists back to Benny's house to examine.

Reading through the names and addresses, Schlomo and Benny could see that it would take a large number of people a great deal of time to visit all these people listed, in order to eliminate them from their enquiries. In fact the East Coast counties were only a segment of the whole country, and Himmler could just as easily be living in Scotland, Wales or Ireland.

What they desperately needed was a piece of luck. Benny poked at the coal fire with a metal poker. Schlomo had started to read out names aloud from a page that he had been looking at: 'Czarnota, lots of people called Kololski, and Vwisniewski, Harry Fowler, Eric Cook, lots of Novaks.'

'What was that you said, Schlomo?' queried Benny.

'I said, "Lots of Novaks",' answered Schlomo

'No! The English names!' said Benny sharply.

'Oh! Harry Fowler and Eric Cook, you mean,' retorted Schlomo. 'What about them?'

'Harry Fowler! Harry Fowler!' repeated Benny. 'There's something about that name that's ringing a bell at the back of my mind, but I can't think what it is.'

'Never mind!' replied Schlomo. 'I think we should pack up and go to bed. Perhaps you will remember what it was tomorrow.'

Both men tidied away their papers and went to bed. Benny lay thinking about the name Harry Fowler. It annoyed him, because he felt the name was important in some way, but could not remember why.

The following morning Schlomo and Benny looked through the names and addresses again. Benny had not remembered any more about the name Harry Fowler. They began to mark villages where Polish refugees lived, on maps of England. It was a slow and laborious job.

Both men realized that checking out these people could take a long, long time, and meanwhile Himmler might be moving somewhere else, even to another country.

Schlomo voiced his concerns first. 'I'm sorry, Benny, but this is just not going to work. Neither you nor I can afford the time and the cost to follow up all these addresses. I'm beginning to think if Himmler committed suicide whilst in custody of the British, then the only way someone looking like him would be able to get money from a Nazi account is if he, by some miracle, is a reincarnation from another life!'

For some moments Benny stared at Schlomo and then he started to dance and yell loudly. 'That's it, Schlomo! You are right! Himmler is a reincarnation!' Benny squealed with delight.

'What are you talking about, my friend?' demanded Schlomo.

Benny calmed down and started to explain. 'Heinrich Himmler truly held the theory that he himself was a reincarnation of one of Germany's early emperors. This Emperor Heinrich lived a thousand years ago and had his remains buried at Quedlinburg in Germany. Himmler used to make pilgrimages to the tomb on the anniversary of his ancestor's death!'

'What of it?' asked Schlomo.

'Be patient, my friend. This emperor whom Himmler thought himself to be a reincarnation of, had a nickname, which was Heinrich the Fowler. If we anglicize that we get Henry Fowler. A nickname for Henry is Harry. Thus we could have the name Harry Fowler. It might be a long shot my friend but if you were vain enough to believe that you were someone's reincarnation and you had to change your own name, then you might just choose that someone's name. If we spend time looking up Poles in England, then I want one of the first to be Mr Harry Fowler!'

Schlomo had never seen his friend so animated. 'Where does this Fowler live?' he asked.

Benny consulted the list. 'He lives with someone named Eric Cook in a village named Nordingly in Norfolk.'

Schlomo and Benny brought out their maps and examined the county of Norfolk. At last they found Nordingly, and discussed a plan for checking on Mr Fowler.

Chapter 14

Life for Himmler, Christine and myself continued largely as before, until an event in 1948.

I had been travelling farther and farther from Nordingly to sell a few gold rings. I went to a small town in Suffolk and offered a small private jeweller two gold rings. As before, I told the jeweller some fictitious story about the rings' origin. I usually said that they came from my grandmother and I had been left them after her death. Usually things went smoothly. Today was to be different.

The jeweller put an eyepiece to his eye to provide magnification and examined each ring in turn against the daylight, which entered high up in his shop window.

As he examined the rings, he spoke to me without actually looking at me.

'So! You say that you are a Polish refugee now living in England?'

'Yes, sir. That is correct,' I answered.

'And these rings were your grandmother's own rings?'

'I have already told you that,' I replied.

The jeweller removed his eyepiece and fixed me with a stare.

'You don't look Jewish my friend!' the jeweller stated calmly.

'No! I'm not Jewish!' I replied firmly.

'So your grandmother wasn't Jewish either then?' continued the jeweller relentlessly.

I sensed something was wrong, but I just thought the jeweller was being awkward. 'No, she wasn't Jewish, she was a Christian!'

The jeweller smiled a wide smile and held up one of the rings triumphantly.

'Then why does your grandmother have a gold ring which is inscribed on the inside in Hebrew? Only a Jew would possess such a ring, and your grandmother wasn't Jewish!'

242

I was feeling uncomfortable and trapped. Supposing the jeweller called the police? Suddenly inspiration hit me.

'My grandmother married twice during her lifetime. Although I never knew her, that must be the ring from her first marriage. Presumably she married a Jew the first time.'

'I'm sure that you are right my friend,' said the jeweller in a much more conciliatory tone. 'I will buy your rings because they are good quality, and gold is gold. In fact, if you find more of your grandmother's jewellery, come and see me again!'

I regained my composure. The jeweller made some calculations and gave me some money for the rings. I thanked him and left the shop, going back to the car by a roundabout way. I wanted to ensure that I wasn't followed.

Satisfied that no one was watching me, I unlocked the car and then drove out of the town, and stopped at the entrance to a field. I had other rings hidden in the car, and I examined them one after another, paying particular attention to the inner surface. Himmler's words came back to me – 'The rings were collected from contributions by the German people towards the war effort'. How many people, I mused, were likely to give a ring? Was not something that small likely to be stolen by some minor official, if it was handed in?

Just then another inscribed ring caught my eye. I did not know Hebrew, but the style of letters was certainly not German, or even Russian. I would bet it was Hebrew and the ring of a Jew. Moreover, I concluded that the rings had not come from collections from the German people. These were rings stolen from the Jews and, if what Himmler had told me about the camps was true, these rings had come from Jews who were now dead.

I determined to sort this out with Himmler on my return, but events were to change my immediate priorities.

On this occasion, as I returned from Suffolk in the late afternoon, I chose the coastal road and decided to break my journey. I stopped at the small village of Mundesley on the Norfolk coast, south of Cromer.

I arrived at the Continental Hotel, which stood on the main road at the highest point of the village. It was a tall, impressive building, which had been formerly called the Grand Hotel. I merely wanted to get something to eat and drink, so I parked the car, entered the hotel and made my way into the lounge. Music and voices assailed my ears from the ballroom, where a dance appeared to be in progress. I was tired. I relaxed in a chair, consulted a menu of snacks and ordered some sandwiches and a beer. Men and women passed to and from the ballroom to the bar in the lounge where I sat. I took little notice.

I heard a small gasp and became aware of a woman standing at the side of my table. Before I had time to look up, a voice said quietly, 'Erich! Is it really you, after all this time?'

I looked up at the shapely figure and smiling face of Lotte Durner.

Before I could speak, she exclaimed, 'Surely you remember Lotte from Switzerland?' She looked deeply into my eyes.

'But of course! How is your family in Switzerland?'

'They are all quite well,' Lotte replied, her smile widening. 'I'm a nurse here at the Mundesley hospital – and what are you doing these days?'

'I didn't know Mundesley had a hospital,' I countered.

'Oh! Yes! It's out in the countryside about one mile from the village. It used to be a sanatorium. We nurses don't get much time off and the dances here are very popular with us. I have been here about eighteen months. Things were very difficult where I was and so I came over here. How is your family now, Erich?'

'I regret that they were all killed in a bombing raid, towards the end of the war. The raid killed many people and I was not allowed even to go to their funeral,' I explained bitterly.

Lotte sat with her mouth open for a few seconds in bewilderment.

'Erich!' she breathed. 'I visited your sister and both your parents in 1946. They were living in Plön and were very much alive.'

'What!' I exclaimed, so loudly that several people stopped speaking and looked in my direction.

'Calm down, Erich!' Lotte hissed. 'I'm telling you the truth. They can't have been killed in an air raid, because I saw them all alive a year after the war's end, in Germany. In fact it's you that they thought had been killed in the war. There is another

244

of our friends over here in England who I have seen. You must remember von Eichwald's son. He lives here in Britain now and calls himself Oakwood. He comes here from time to time.

'You are not in a hurry, are you, Erich?' Lotte enquired.

'No! I can please myself,' I answered unsuspectingly.

'Good!' Lotte replied. 'You can book a room here in this hotel. I have to be back at the nurses' home by 11 p.m., but you can have a lie-down and I can demonstrate my massage techniques whilst we catch up on old times.'

She ushered me in the direction of the reception area and waited unobtrusively until I indicated the room number to her. She joined me a few minutes later and I soon forgot my troubles.

I drove Lotte back to the nurses' home in time for 11 p.m. In the short periods she had allowed for talk, she had provided the answers to several questions. I had her address and her phone number at the nurses' home.

I went back to the hotel and spent the night there. Despite the recent good news about my family's survival, I was worn out.

After my overnight stay in Mundesley, I drove back to Nordingly. Again I used the coastal road, passing through Cromer to the more familiar town of Sheringham, where I had been many times. I continued along the coast road out of Sheringham towards Weybourne, having to pause at the railway bridge because of traffic coming the other way. This bridge had presumably been built at a time when road traffic was lighter. It was brick built, with an arch for traffic to pass under the railway. (Note – the bridge has been rebuilt differently and much wider since those times.)

I knew that Himmler, a creature of habit, used that road to cycle to Sheringham once a week, since he never bothered to learn to drive a car in England.

Upon my return to the cottage in Nordingly, Christine met me and I found Himmler ill in bed with suspected pneumonia. He had got soaked during an unexpected downpour. A local doctor had visited and left Christine some nursing instructions. Himmler was semi-conscious, with a high temperature. At one point it even looked as though he might die. Christine had declined treatment in hospital in case Himmler said anything whilst delirious.

I used this opportunity to ask Christine if Himmler had ever left any letters with her, in case anything happened to him. Christine confirmed that he had, and produced a letter addressed to me from a locked box. I told her that as neither of us knew how Himmler's illness might turn out, I would open it.

I went outside and read Himmler's letter in the small cottage garden. I learned that my family had not died in an air raid on Stettin and had been moved to Plön, where it was anticipated that they should be safe. Himmler explained that he had needed me as a companion and helper and, if it had not been for the bad news about the Swiss account, I would have been amply rewarded.

It also revealed that I, Erich Koch, could have had no idea that the British prisoners of war whose files I had been ordered to mark NN were in fact to be shot. The letter said nothing about the execution at Dachau.

Christine read the unease in my face when I came back inside the house. She told me that she did not know the contents of my letter, nor did she wish to. However, as the future was uncertain, she wished to share a secret with me. Christine told me that Humbert's Seehund midget submarine had not hit a mine, but had been somehow exploded electronically by Himmler. That explained why Himmler had caused my ducking in the sea, so that I would have to change my clothes. She explained that she had not known that this would happen and Himmler had signalled to her to keep quiet about it.

I kept my thoughts to myself. This latest revelation illustrated to me how Himmler had used others to preserve his own life and security.

Himmler's own aides had unsuspectingly been left with Himmler's double, to be captured together. Heinrich Hitzinger – Himmler's double – had been so carefully selected and trained. Was it not strange, that he had contracted a terminal case of stomach cancer? Hitzinger had seemed fine, until Dr Mengele had been introduced to the team. Mengele had bragged about changing Hitzinger's appearance by an operation. Surely he would have noticed if the man had been suffering from a terminal condition. Now Hitzinger was dead by committing suicide. Berger had provided local intelligence and had been shot dead by Himmler back in the bunker. Humbert had navigated us safely from the river Ems to Blakeney harbour, Norfolk, and had then been blown up by Himmler. How many others had there been?

There presumably remained only two people, who knew that Heinrich Himmler was still alive and where to find him – Eric Cook and Christine Wilder. Had the money from the Swiss bank account been transferred, as intended, to Himmler's account, then surely he would no longer need our services. Hadn't Himmler himself said 'Dead men tell no tales'?

Days passed and Himmler began to recover. I thought it unfair to demand an explanation from Himmler whilst he was still sick. I busied myself with routine jobs helping Christine with the pigs and decided to wait until Himmler was much better.

Three weeks later in London, Benny Green had a few days' holiday from work, which he intended to use to visit Norfolk with Schlomo. The two of them had put a lot of thought into preparations. Benny could drive a car, but did not own one. Fortunately, he had a relative who was willing to lend his to Benny. The relative was a salesman who had broken his leg playing rugby. He also willingly lent Benny his old suitcase and samples from a previous job as a door-to-door salesman, and gave Benny some idea of how the job was done. Benny had told his relative a false cover story and had not mentioned going as far as Norfolk. Petrol was on ration, but the car's petrol tank was full, and being laid up with a broken leg for some weeks meant that quite a few petrol coupons had been saved up.

On the evening before his holiday, Benny collected Schlomo and they set off out of London with their luggage. Benny drove through the late evening and the night to make better progress.

When he arrived at the coast of North Norfolk, Benny was tired out from the driving. He found a quiet spot in a country lane and both of them slept for some hours in the car to recover.

After they had awoken, they drove off in search of breakfast in the first café they could find. As they ate their food and drank their tea, they talked quietly about the best way of visiting the address of Eric Cook and Harry Fowler in Nordingly. Schlomo wanted to do it all himself, but Benny had other ideas.

'Let's find Nordingly first, Schlomo!' Benny breathed. 'Then we can see if there is some child about who knows where two Poles live in the village. Once we have identified the actual house, we can plan from there. My guess is that if those two live in a village, then they live with an English man, or woman, or possibly even with a family. I reckon that they need someone like that as a cover for them being there. They also need some kind of employment, either with the householder, or someone else. If they lived by themselves, having bought, or rented a house with no employment, then the local villagers would surely be suspicious as to how they managed to buy food and pay their bills. As I see it, we should only go to this house once, to try and identify if Himmler lives there. We can't keep calling and calling at the same house posing as a door-to-door salesman, until we might be lucky. We have got to think this through.'

Schlomo agreed. 'You are very sensible, Benny! There's no point in rushing into this and failing. Come on, take us to Nordingly and we can familiarize ourselves with the village.'

Benny consulted his map and drove off west along the coastal road. Some time later, he turned inland and they both looked out for signs to Nordingly. Their drive took them, after many fruitless miles, to eventually meet a main road at right angles.

Schlomo looked at the signpost and turned to Benny. 'This can't be right,' he said. 'We must have come too far. We have neither seen Nordingly nor any signposts for it. Are you sure that we are on the correct road?'

'Well, according to this map, we are!' retorted Benny. 'Never mind! We must be patient. I will turn round and we can try again.'

Benny turned the car around and drove back slowly towards the coast. They saw no village on either side, but did pass single-lane tracks leading off the road they were on. None of these had signposts to indicate the presence of any village.

Finally Benny could see the coastal road junction up ahead and so he slowed down and stopped. 'If Nordingly is where it's shown on the map, then it must be up one of those tracks. We will have to turn back and explore,' he announced.

He turned the car around once more and they set off away from the coast again. He turned left at the first track and drove along it for some distance. Only fields surrounded them and Benny took the opportunity to turn round in the entrance to a grass field that had the gate open. He drove back to the road that they had left and took the next track on the right of the road. Again they could only see fields on each side, but after a while the unsurfaced track turned to the right in a curve.

After rounding the curve, they both glimpsed the shape of houses some way ahead, and the top of a church. The buildings were almost hidden in trees and in a depression in the ground.

Schlomo turned to Benny and said, 'If this is Nordingly, my friend, then I can understand why it might be chosen to hide someone. If you didn't live here, or know the village, I suspect few strangers would ever find their way to it.'

Benny nodded, but continued driving in silence. He drove into the village and out the other side a few moments later. It was really small, just a collection of houses, a couple of farms, a larger house and a church. Benny wondered at what time Nordingly had ever been a big enough village to need its own church. He imagined that it might once have been a larger village, but then ravaged and reduced in size by the great plague of hundreds of years ago. Driving a little farther, Benny turned round and drove back into Nordingly. There were a few lanes and tracks leading out from a relatively small central area.

Neither man saw anyone moving around, until they spotted a small group of school children walking along one of the larger lanes, presumably to school. Schlomo thought of a plan and asked Benny to drive along the same lane as the children, but to stop before the next village.

Benny drove the car off the lane at the side of a large barn. He got out and lifted the bonnet, so that he would be largely concealed when the children passed. Schlomo also got out and leaned against the car to wait until the children, who were walking along the lane, arrived at the barn.

After a few minutes, Schlomo could hear the children's

chattering voices as they came slowly nearer. He stepped out on to the lane as they came within talking distance and hailed them.

'Hello, boys and girls!' Schlomo said cheerfully. 'Are you from Nordingly?'

'Why do you want to know?' asked the tallest boy, a little suspiciously, as the group paused.

'Nothing to worry about, young man!' Schlomo assured him. 'I'm looking for two old friends who are Polish and I understand might live in your village. Do you know them?'

'I don't know any Poles!' the boy stated calmly.

For a moment Schlomo was puzzled. Then he explained, 'The men who I'm looking for were refugees. I believe they came to work here after the war.'

The boy scratched his head for a moment, 'Oh! You must mean Eric and Harry!'

Another child laughed and said quietly, 'Fowler the prowler!' which amused a few of the children. 'They live with Miss Wilder, but I have just seen her driving out of the village in her car. She's probably going fishing, but she was by herself, so the others must still be at home.'

Schlomo continued, 'No, The men I'm looking for are not named Eric or Harry. But whereabouts do they live?'

'In Bluebell Cottage,' a little girl informed Schlomo.

'Where would I find Bluebell Cottage?' Schlomo asked.

'Go back to Nordingly on this lane. At the church turn right, take the next track on the left and keep straight on. Bluebell Cottage is out of the village. You can't miss it,' another child said.

'Or the smell of the pigs!' offered another child, laughing.

Schlomo thanked the children, but told them that the men he was looking for had the Polish name Czarnota and so it was probably not the men at Bluebell Cottage after all. He tossed a couple of pennies to them for their help, and the children went off hurrying to school.

After the children had disappeared from sight, Schlomo returned to Benny at the car. He repeated the directions to Bluebell Cottage, where Eric and Harry lived in Nordingly. Benny drove back along the lane towards the church and they took the turning to the right. The next left turning was such a narrow track that Benny felt it too narrow for the car to drive along.

They decided that if Benny was going to act the part of a door-to-door salesman, then Schlomo should first have a look around the area, as unobtrusively as possible.

Schlomo got out of the car to investigate the track and Bluebell Cottage, which he could not yet see. Benny moved the car up to the churchyard in order to pretend to look inside the church.

Schlomo walked casually up the track. It was grass-covered with the odd rut where some heavier vehicle had once passed. As the houses of the village disappeared behind him he found himself on a hedge-lined narrow track which wound its way towards trees in the distance. So far he could not see any house, nor could he see, or smell, any pigs. As he continued, the wind changed direction and brought the unmistakable smell of pigs towards him. At last he saw a small cottage, half hidden by trees, with smoke curling from the chimney and blowing away in the wind. No one seemed to be about, and as he drew almost level with the house, he saw the sign 'Bluebell Cottage' cut into a piece of wood. The track continued past the cottage and Schlomo walked on along it. He glimpsed pigs in a field to his right and a large chicken run. He could now hear the pigs grunting and the softer clucking of chickens. Schlomo spotted a man aged in his mid-twenties, who was working in the field. He seemed to be alone and did not see Schlomo.

If Eric Cook and Harry Fowler lived at the cottage with a lady called Miss Wilder, then if she was out and the younger man in the field was presumably Eric Cook, then 'Harry Fowler' must be in the cottage, he deduced.

Schlomo hurried back and found Benny with the car at the church. He quickly explained what he had seen to Benny, who got the door-to-door salesman's case out of the car.

[*Author's note: Erich Koch was never aware at any time of the existence or plans of Schlomo and his group. It has only been possible to chronologically describe these events over fifty years later (see Postscript).*]

Benny strolled casually towards Bluebell Cottage. At the door, he checked the contents of the case before knocking. After a few seconds, to his immense disappointment, a young man opened the door; Erich had returned to the cottage before Benny had arrived.

Beaming a broad smile, Benny launched into the patter of what he imagined a door-to-door salesman might say. 'Good morning, sir! Can I offer you anything from our excellent selection of polishes, dusters, drying up cloths, table mats, pan scourers...?'

'No thank you,' Erich interrupted him.

Unperturbed, Benny continued. 'How about some handkerchiefs, sir? They are always useful, and if you have enough yourself, then you can give them to someone else as presents.'

'No thank you!' Erich said firmly. Benny described other bargains that he had on offer, but Erich looked as if he would close the door.

'Who is it, Eric?' asked another voice that was older and seemed more shrill.

Although Benny was hoping against hope that his theory about Himmler's play on his imaginary ancestor's name 'Henry the Fowler' was true, he experienced a wide variety of successive feelings and emotions. His heart beat faster and he could hear the noise of his own blood rushing in his ears. As Erich stood slightly to one side, a hand gripped the edge of the door and pulled it open more widely.

There in the doorway, almost exactly the same as in Schlomo's drawing, stood the man who Benny instantly believed was Heinrich Himmler. He could sense the similarity between the man in front of him and the body of 'Heinrich Himmler' which he had seen some years before in Lüneburg, Germany. Benny gazed at the man responsible for the deaths of millions. Instead of being exultant at his discovery, he found his mouth had dried and he felt extreme fear. Icy fingers seemed to clutch at his spine. Benny was wearing a hat and he could feel the hair on his head starting to stand on end. He would swear that the hat was actually being lifted off his head by his own hair. All this happened in the space of a second or two and he managed to react brilliantly, in a way that a professional actor would be proud of.

Benny held his hand to his mouth and coughed twice to try and make his mouth less dry, and immediately launched into an improvised reaction.

'I'm sorry, sir, but you made me jump!' he explained. 'I was just showing this young man the excellent range of products that I can offer at very competitive prices brought right to your door. I have got handkerchiefs, dusters, washing up towels...'

Himmler raised his hand for Benny to stop. 'Enough!' he said. 'I'm sure we do not need anything, because we go to the market each week.'

'But this place is miles from any market!' protested Benny. 'That's why I'm calling on small villages. I bring the goods that people need right to your own front door. That must be better than going to market.'

'Well, the market at Sheringham has a good selection of goods, my friend,' answered Himmler.

'But Sheringham is miles away!' Benny continued to protest.

'It's not too far on a bicycle and the exercise is good for me,' explained Himmler. 'I have been ill recently, but I go there almost every week. However, I am in need of another handkerchief. How much are they?'

Benny was not really expecting to sell anything and was not too familiar with prices. He invented a price, and luckily Himmler accepted. Money changed hands and for a millisecond Himmler's hand touched Benny's. Himmler chose a new handkerchief and appeared satisfied.

As the two 'refugees' withdrew into Bluebell Cottage, Benny fastened his case and strolled back down the lane as casually as he could. He was much calmer now, yet he perceived that he needed to continue his salesman act. Instead of returning to Schlomo immediately, he called at several houses in the village to offer his products. He sold a drying-up cloth and a dish cloth, before returning to Schlomo at the car.

Schlomo was anxious for information, but Benny persuaded him to wait until he had driven out of the village and he would tell him everything.

When Benny finally stopped the car, he had to recount the story at least three times for Schlomo to make sure that he had understood every detail. Finally Schlomo erupted into laughter, exclaiming, 'You actually sold Himmler a handkerchief!'

'I'm telling you, Schlomo, when I first saw him, I got such a fright that my hair started to stand on end. I could actually feel my hat lifting off my head,' Benny declared.

That only made Schlomo laugh even more.

They found out when Sheringham held a market and had a look at that area and the roads in between. They cruised around until they had both a reasonable idea of the local geography. Afterwards they returned to London at a much more leisurely pace.

Schlomo wanted to inform his group and he needed to write them a letter. Benny's house gave him a regular address to use. He reasoned that if Himmler thought himself safe and secure in Nordingly, then he was not planning to move elsewhere yet.

Schlomo wrote to his friends in Europe:

I am sorry for the lies, but I simply had to check up on the man whom we believe visited Guernsey recently. I am working with a friend. We have found the man we were looking for. The man is the man! There is no doubt. We need your help, if we are to obtain a successful solution. Please write to tell me when you can visit London.

He then relaxed for a few days. Benny showed him round the sights of London. After all, Benny was still on holiday.

In Nordingly, Himmler had been slightly suspicious, but he said nothing to me. After Christine returned, later that day, he asked her, 'Have you ever seen salesmen before, who come to your door selling things from a suitcase?' he enquired.

'What, around here?' exclaimed Christine. 'I have never seen anyone like that in all the years I have been here!'

Himmler did not reply, but the next day he casually posed the question to the occupants of the nearest houses in Nordingly. They told him that a door-to-door salesman had called at their

254

house also, the previous day. Himmler relaxed again after hearing this.

In London two weeks later, Schlomo received a brief letter from Matthias in Basel, Switzerland. It merely said that Matthias would be arriving within a week with some friends. Schlomo had better be certain about the man he had written about.

Schlomo then realized that he was inviting the help of his group purely on the identification by his friend Benny. Schlomo had not seen Himmler himself. However, he trusted Benny and felt sure that he would be proved correct.

Approximately ten days later, Matthias and some of his group arrived at Benny Green's house in London. Benny had made some arrangements with family and friends locally, because Benny's house was too small to accommodate anyone else. These friends and relatives were not told the true purpose of the people arriving from Switzerland, but a little money smoothed the way considerably.

Matthias had to reluctantly include Benny in his future plans. He appreciated that Schlomo had great faith in Benny, yet he still needed to prove himself reliable to Matthias.

The following evening everyone met in the front parlour of Mrs Green's house. She had gone out to visit a friend. Matthias invited Schlomo and Benny to describe to the group what they had found out recently. They illustrated this information with maps of Norfolk. It took longer than might be expected, because of having to translate some of the events for the benefit of the non-English speaking members. Matthias outlined a plan he had made, and the group left the house to await instructions. As Matthias went out, he turned to Benny and Schlomo. 'There is one thing that I insist on, my friends. I must see our target with my own eyes before we try to capture him!' Benny and Schlomo agreed, and Matthias went on his way.

Chapter 15

Two weeks after their arrival in England, Matthias and his group had obtained the use of two cars, a small lorry with an enclosed rear section and plenty of fuel for their expedition to Norfolk. They also had three ex-military walkie-talkie sets and blankets and ropes. Matthias explained to the more orthodox Jewish members that they would have to work on the Sabbath (Saturday), but if all went well, they should regard their work as a duty to their faith. No one disagreed and on Friday evening the group set off for Norfolk from London. They intended to meet in Sheringham, if they lost sight of the other vehicles.

In the early hours of Saturday morning they pulled off a rural lane into heathland to the west of Lower Kelling to try and sleep for some hours. The rear of the enclosed lorry provided both the space and warmth for them all to lie down and cover themselves with the blankets they had brought. Soon the only sound to be heard, apart from the wind, was the muffled snores of the sleepers in the lorry.

Some hours before on the very same Friday evening, Erich Koch (Eric Cook) decided to tackle Himmler about the lies he had been told, particularly about his family being still alive. The writer returns to Koch's narrative.

The whole thing had been simmering inside me for weeks. Now I would demand explanations. The injustice I felt was starting to boil up once more.

I knew that Himmler possessed no weapon like a shotgun or pistol. On the evening I decided on a showdown with Himmler,

Christine was out visiting a friend. She had taken a bicycle, because the friend's house was not far away.

I had worked myself up into an angry mood as I paced back and forth in the living room of the cottage, where Himmler sat. At last I confronted him.

'It is my belief, Heinrich, that if you had managed to transfer those funds from Switzerland, then Christine and I would have been dead by now!' I roared.

Himmler was taken aback. It was the first time I had addressed him as Heinrich for many months, 'Why, Eric, how can you say such things?' he demanded.

'Because all along the way, people have been disposed of to protect you – Hitzinger, your SS aides, Berger, Humbert and others!' I declared.

'Humbert hit a mine. You know that!' Himmler countered.

'That was a convenient explanation and it was a convenient end for him. After all, there were no diamonds, or we would have used them by now!' I reasoned.

Himmler did not respond immediately.

'You are quite right,' he confirmed, speaking rather slowly. 'Humbert was a greedy man. He had already committed two criminal acts during the war and had been caught both times. Supposing I had given him a bag of diamonds, the authorities would have probably caught him very soon. He would have talked and our safety would have been compromised. I understood that fact from the start of my plan to use him, and that is why I ordered SS engineers to make special modifications to the Seehund, so that it could be exploded at the right time. I did it to protect you too, Eric! I have never had any doubts about you or Christine.'

'You led me to believe my family was dead in an air raid!' I thundered.

'But I was always going to reveal the truth to you, when the moment was right. I even wrote it down, in case anything happened to me.' Himmler said rapidly. He did not even query how I had discovered this information.

'You led me to believe that the British prisoners of war had been shot as a result of my own orders to mark NN on their records and sign them!' I accused him.

Himmler looked distinctly uncomfortable. He paused for a

few seconds before answering me. 'It was a precautionary step to ensure your loyalty. Not that I ever had cause to doubt it.'

'What about the Dachau execution I was ordered to perform and was photographed carrying out?' I demanded. 'When I think back, it was a tremendous risk to send me. I had to fly there and back and if I had been shot down, then you wouldn't have had me to help you all this time!' For the first time I also realized that Himmler must have had at least one other assistant to replace me, if I had failed to return. I wasn't with him because of his personal choice; I was with him purely by circumstance. If I had not been with him, it would have been someone else. I had merely been used like a pawn in a game.

'Well! You know me, always thorough!' Himmler retorted. 'I needed your support or otherwise you could have left me after the end of the war. I had to indulge in some trickery and lead you to believe that I hadn't given that order. You even brought the photographic film of the execution back with you in the envelope addressed to me!'

I was amazed at how brazen he was in this admission.

Himmler continued. 'However, I shot Berger and that helped keep both of us safe. I even killed a poacher here in England to help protect our new way of life.'

'I don't believe you!' I replied.

'Then I'm sure I can still find where I buried his body in the wood,' Himmler replied coldly. He described what had happened. It again revealed his ruthless streak to me. A man had stolen chickens and Himmler had killed him – for that!

'Why did Hitzinger suddenly get very ill?' I demanded.

Again Himmler paused before replying.

'He was the key to the whole escape plan. When the war was in its final days, I could not risk him disappearing one night. Dr Mengele administered tiny amounts of arsenic to his food. It was enough to make him feel ill and stay where he was. After all, he had a doctor to look after him. My original plan was to leave his dead body at the cottage, whilst my aides were asleep. However, he died by his own hand, as you know.'

I remained silent for some seconds. I could now visualize it all. Himmler had disposed of anyone who posed a threat to his survival.

'What about Dr Mengele?' I asked.

'Your logic has always impressed me,' Himmler replied. 'Mengele doesn't know where we are. In fact, both he and I truly do not know if the other is alive or dead. I feel sure his war record at Auschwitz will make him stay in hiding. If he is caught and tells anyone Heinrich Himmler is still alive, who would believe him?'

'Now that I know my family is still alive, I no longer wish to stay here. Although whether in fact I go to Germany remains to be seen. I won't betray you. Christine knows nothing of this. I will take the car and then ring Christine to tell her where she can collect it,' I announced.

Himmler looked concerned, even frightened, by this news.

'You have nothing to worry about!' I told Himmler. '*Meine Ehre heisst Treue!*' (The SS motto – My honour is my loyalty.)

Having collected my belongings together beforehand, I prepared to leave the cottage. At the door I turned back to Himmler. 'Now that everything is out in the open, please answer me one last question, Heinrich. Do you think that you could have averted what happened to the Jews during the war?'

'That is a question that I have often asked myself since you first brought it up, Eric,' replied Himmler. 'In all truth, I don't think that my power or my objection would have in any way changed the course of history. Men may think, why didn't he or she do this or that? In reality, if someone else was actually in those positions, then they would find that, despite rank and position, people are usually not free from constraints to do what they wish.'

'If you couldn't stop what happened, even though you disagreed with what was going on, then you couldn't personally have profited by this attempt to eradicate the Jewish people in Europe?' I demanded.

'No! Of course I have not personally profited from the Jews!' Himmler almost screamed at me.

'Well, Reichsführer, you are lying!' I retorted. 'The rings tell their own story. The rings came from the Jews. Some of them are even inscribed in Hebrew on the inner surface!'

I flung a few gold rings on to the table in front of him. Himmler grabbed them and looked at several, until he found one inscribed in Hebrew. His mouth opened and closed wordlessly several times. He was speechless. He had overlooked a tiny detail. He was annoyed with himself and at having been found out. He gazed at me, and the look said it all!

I left without further comment and started Christine's car. I had no clear plan. I needed time to think.

I travelled to Sheringham and booked into a bed and breakfast establishment. I spent most of the night thinking. I realized that Himmler, aged forty-eight had the prospect of a long life in front of him. It would also be a life of worry for me, in case advancing age made Himmler careless. If his real identity became known, I imagined that would lead to enquiries about me. Himmler had verbally indicated that the Dachau execution of Elser was his own order, but I had no proof of that, if it was ever investigated.

I concluded that my best course of action was put an end to the threat from Himmler. There seemed only one way in which this could be achieved. If I did not, then over the future years, Himmler might decide the same thing about silencing his former aide. After all, he claimed to have killed a poacher in England already. If he was capable of that, he was capable of anything. The prospect was to keep looking over my shoulder for the next thirty or forty years, or to do something now. I came to a decision in my mind and fell asleep.

Benny, Schlomo, Matthias and the rest of the group awoke about nine o'clock on the Saturday morning. They tidied up the interior of the lorry and left it there. No one lived along the heath road and it was not much used. They travelled into Sheringham in both cars and bought some food.

Matthias outlined his plan to the others afterwards. They would all wait to identify the target as Himmler, when he came to the Sheringham market as usual on his bicycle. After he arrived, five of them would squeeze into one car and return to the lorry, which would be backed up to the edge of the heath lane. Three of them would remain there in order to capture Himmler, when he came along the lane with his bicycle and tie him up in the lorry. In order to ensure he came this way, the other two men would leave the car near the bottom of the heath lane where the main coastal road went towards Cley-next-the-Sea. Dressed in working clothes, they would erect a 'Road Works Diversion' sign on the main coastal road, and they would be able to see him coming down the hill from the direction of Weybourne through their binoculars long before he arrived there. Matthias, Benny and Schlomo would remain on the outskirts of Sheringham after Himmler had left to cycle home, in case he unexpectedly turned back. After Himmler had turned on to the heath lane, the two men were to take down the diversion sign and park their car on the lane, as if it had broken down. This would not only stop anyone else in a vehicle following Himmler and witnessing his abduction, but it would also be the cork in the bottle, if Himmler became suspicious of the lorry being there and turned around.

Some of the men waited in the two cars and others were on foot nearby. The minutes seemed like hours, as they waited. At last Benny, who was seated in the back of a car, tapped Matthias and Schlomo, who were seated in the front, on the shoulders.

'Here comes our man!' he announced.

Schlomo and Matthias waited until the lone cyclist drew nearer. Benny ducked lower in the back seat, and finally the bearded cyclist pedalled past the car. Matthias had been pretending to be in deep conversation with Schlomo and had the best view. As the cyclist passed the car, Matthias involuntarily drew in his breath sharply. A few seconds later he exhaled with the comment, 'My God! It really is him!'

Matthias, Schlomo and another group member in the car were jubilant, but Benny told them to be patient. 'If we can pull this off, then in a week or two we may all be famous. We have waited years, but we need to be patient a little longer!'

Schlomo nodded and Matthias smiled. After a few minutes, Matthias rounded up his men, tested their walkie-talkies and sent everyone but himself, Benny and Schlomo back to the lorry in the other car, as arranged.

Within ten minutes or so, the lorry men had returned and reported this over the walkie-talkie. In three more minutes the men who were to erect the 'Road Works Diversion' sign, announced that they were in position. Matthias acknowledged the calls and they continued to wait for Himmler to begin the return journey on his bicycle.

*   *   *

After breakfast on Saturday morning, I drove Christine's car to the Weybourne road from Sheringham and parked it off the road at the side of a wood. From there I could see the Weybourne railway bridge. I patiently waited, and timed cyclists from when they appeared on the road, near the entrance to my parking place, until they reached the bridge. I did this until I had a good average idea of how long it took to cycle this distance.

Next, I timed how long that it took to drive from my parking space to the bridge. I did this several times at different speeds. I had to drive beyond Weybourne in order to find a convenient point to turn the car round, but I kept a look-out for passers by and varied my times, so that no one would begin to get suspicious. Finally I returned to Sheringham for a snack and made some calculations from the timings I had made.

At about 3.45 p.m. I returned and parked up the car at the same spot, at the edge of the wood. It was hidden from anyone coming from Sheringham, yet I could still see the road. I sat there waiting, with the engine running.

At about 4 p.m. that day, Himmler started his return journey from Sheringham by bicycle along the Weybourne road. There was no reason for him to notice the parked car which contained Matthias, Schlomo and Benny, nor did he.

After Himmler had passed by some hundred yards, Matthias alerted the others on the walkie-talkie set. 'Our friend is on his way and should be with you in perhaps thirty minutes or so! Over.'

'Message received and understood!' replied the men at the lorry and the men who were to prepare the diversion.

At about 4.15 p.m. according to his usual routine, Heinrich Himmler passed my hidden vantage point cycling towards Weybourne from Sheringham. I counted off the seconds aloud and then drove out on to the road to follow him. The driving mirror indicated that the road was clear behind me. The car began to close the distance on the cyclist, who was oblivious of

262

any danger. As the speed of the car rose, I thought that Himmler would still reach the bridge before me. However, my calculations had not let me down. As the road narrowed to pass under the archway of the bridge, I swerved the car momentarily to knock rider and bicycle into the left side of the bridge. Himmler slammed into the brickwork with a sound combining a splat and a crunch. I continued under the archway and drove away towards Weybourne, without stopping. In Weybourne, I turned left and took the road towards Holt.

Motor cars were robustly built in those days. When I finally stopped in the countryside to inspect the damage, I found it to be little more than grazed paint on the front mudguard.

By sheer coincidence, Erich Koch had decided to end the threat from Himmler, by killing him on the same day that Matthias's group had decided to abduct Himmler, in a similar area, and take him to a safe house in Leicestershire for questioning and ultimately bring him to trial. (In fact, Erich never knew of this plan or of the existence of the Nazi hunters – see editor's note later.)

On the coastal road at Lower Kelling, two of Matthias's group scanned the road from Weybourne through binoculars. Forty minutes after their last radio call, they called up Matthias on the outskirts of Sheringham.

'There is no sign of our friend coming! Over.'

'Wait another twenty minutes,' Matthias replied, calmly. 'He may have called in a shop at Weybourne, or got off his bicycle to walk up the steeper parts of the road.'

After fifteen minutes of radio silence Schlomo couldn't stand it any more. 'I think that we should go and have a look,' he said. Matthias and Benny agreed, and he drove off slowly towards Weybourne. As they did so, they scanned the road ahead and the fields and side roads on each side for a sign of the cyclist.

They passed a wood on their left and came to the downhill stretch towards the railway bridge, which was in open countryside, perhaps half a mile or more before Weybourne village.

As they trundled down the incline towards the bridge, Schlomo spotted a glint of metal on the left side of the bridge in the grass. He slowed down, and as the car came to a stop, they could see part of a bicycle. They all jumped out of the car and ran forward to the left side of the bridge, which lay in shadow from the sun. In this darkened area lay a crumpled body, and Benny guessed what he would find before he looked.

Turning the body over, he could see that it was their target, Heinrich Himmler, and that he was definitely dead, although still warm to the touch. A black mark and dirt was over a large proportion of his left temple. Schlomo, possibly a little braver than the other two, pressed on this area and felt the sponginess of the shattered skull underneath.

Benny brought the other two out of their shock by advising them that they had better go before someone called the police, who would want statements. They wasted no time in driving to the other group members. Matthias told the others over the walkie-talkie that they should all meet at the lorry, as his car drove westwards.

To say that the group was disappointed would be an understatement. Furthermore, the rest of the group could not even risk seeing the dead body of Himmler for themselves. They all sat in the back of the lorry and talked whilst they rested. Someone asked about the younger man with Himmler, and Miss Wilder, back in Nordingly. Matthias told his group that they were of no real interest. They knew of no major Nazi war criminal as young as Himmler's male companion and there might not be any proof that the lady even knew Himmler's true identity.

They had tried their best and come close to a result, but fate had dictated events otherwise. 'Such is life, my friends!' Matthias pronounced. 'At least we know that Himmler is really dead, with our own eyes. There are others still very much alive out there, and tomorrow is another day. Come on, we have to get Benny back home to London. We can never thank you enough for all your efforts, Benny. After we leave England, we must stay in touch.'

The group returned to their three vehicles and started their journey back to London. Before they left, Schlomo gave Benny the sketch, as a souvenir, which he had drawn in Guernsey of the man described by the bank employee.

* * *

Erich remained in the area for a few more days; long enough to check the local newspapers afterwards.

'Local Refugee Killed on Cycle' read the small headline of an inside paragraph. 'Harry Fowler...'

Thus it was, that during 1948, Heinrich Himmler, aged forty-eight, formerly Reichsführer of Hitler's SS in World War II, a man responsible for the deaths of millions, died in Norfolk, England. A fact, at that time, unknown to all but ten persons in the world, because Himmler had officially 'died' in May 1945.

After the local police had informed her of Mr Fowler's fatal accident, Christine got out her own 'To be opened in event of my death' letter written by Himmler.

She found that Himmler had asked to be cremated and he requested that she should preserve his anonymity, for the sake of his family in Germany. There was in fact no choice for Christine. If she revealed the truth, she could be fatally compromised.

Before Himmler's death, she should have found in her bedroom a general letter from me, announcing my departure. Himmler had told her that I had gone off to try my luck elsewhere, after she returned and found that I had gone. If she did have any suspicions about the turn of events, she kept them to herself. She did not expect me to attend the funeral.

At that time, the whole county of Norfolk had only the one crematorium. Christine was the only mourner at the funeral service in Norwich. As the curtains began to close in front of the coffin, she raised her right arm quickly, in what could have been interpreted as a wave, as she gave Himmler's coffin a last salute. She then left the chapel to go to the funeral director's car for the return journey.

Behind the curtains, where rollers had passed the coffin into the business end of the crematorium, the cremator rose from his seat, where he had been reading. He was a quiet man; a man who had lost his family and his religion years ago, in a place called Auschwitz. Josef Sussman, former Jewish Auschwitz prisoner, performed the final acts in the process of cremation. Sussman was quite unaware of the real identity of the corpse and the final irony.

As there had been no specific instructions, Himmler's ashes were scattered and blew to the four winds.

Postscript

Erich Koch returned to Mundesley and developed a relationship with Lotte Durner. She re-introduced him to his old friend Bernard Oakwood (formerly Oberleutnant Bernt von Eichwald of the German Wehrmacht – whose family had owned the estate near Stettin where Koch's family had had their home). Bernard also had no reason to return to Stettin and was building up a haulage business in Norfolk. He gave Erich a job driving lorries for him. The relationship with Lotte did not last. She went to America.

Erich married an English girl and they returned to Germany to live in the 1950s. Erich had meanwhile established contact with his family by post, but did not see them until his return.

Before leaving for Germany, Erich Koch wrote down his story, which he gave to Bernard Oakwood (my uncle). His stipulation was that the story should not be made public until after his (Koch's) death. His prognosis was that even if published, most people would not be able to bring themselves to believe that such a well-known person as Heinrich Himmler, who was supposed to have died and been buried in Germany in May 1945, had actually died in Norfolk, England, in 1948. His final advice on the story was to change a few names, write the truth and declare it to be fiction.

Erich Koch died with his wife in October 1997, in Germany in a car accident.

After making a few copies of the first draft of this story, in order to seek opinions from some people who are interested in military history, I was approached on behalf of an ex-British Army man who wished to be known as Benny Green. It is with his permission that I recount the description of the attempt to abduct Himmler in order to bring him to trial. 'Benny' provided details of facts only known to myself, which proved the authenticity of what he described to me. He also gave me the sketch drawing of Himmler in 1948.

'Benny Green' has also died since I commenced this revised story.

I have no further information on Matthias and his group, or of Krauss (the second Seehund crew member with Humbert).

In 1954, German forestry workers found the hidden bunker that Himmler had used, as they cleared trees in the area. Had it not been for the artificial tree stumps and particularly the periscope, they might never have found it. As it was, it took them a considerable time to find the entrance. Johann Berger's body was buried in a cemetery, as an unknown person, in an unmarked grave. There was no evidence to indicate by whom the bunker had been used, and theories ranged from *Werwolf* units to black marketeers.

Christine Wilder met and married a New Zealander. She sold up and moved to New Zealand to live. Today Norfolk is not known for chickens, but is well known for the turkeys bred there.

In 1966, a beachcomber on the coast of North Norfolk found a small depth gauge. It was numbered in metres and of German origin. Investigations indicated that it could have come from a midget German submarine. No one could explain how it could have possibly got there.

An actual Seehund midget submarine can be seen in the German Ship Museum in Bremerhaven, Germany. Outside in a basin, various boats can be seen, including a type XXI U-boat – certainly the only one left in the world.

Memorials to the thousands of prisoners killed during the sinking of the *Cap Arkona* and *Thielbeck* by the RAF are to be found on the Baltic coast near Neustadt.

Two of the three men sentenced to life imprisonment at the Nuremberg Trials were set free before their deaths. This generosity did not extend to the third 'lifer', Rudolf Hess. Hess refused to see members of his own family for many years after the end of the war.

During his life sentence in Spandau prison, Rudolf Hess once became very ill and was admitted to a Berlin hospital. There, a British doctor/surgeon, amongst others, examined him. The doctor had access to Rudolf Hess's complete medical history and was very experienced in the effects of gunshot wounds. Rudolf Hess had been shot and wounded in the First World War. This doctor (Hugh Thomas) subsequently claimed in a book that the man he examined could not possibly have been the real Rudolf Hess. There was simply no evidence of the bullet wound, and this surgeon was well experienced in seeing the effects of gunshot wounds in Northern Ireland (see Acknowledgements).

The prisoner known as Rudolf Hess survived into his nineties. He finally became the sole prison inmate of Spandau prison in Berlin. He was found dead one day in 1987, during an exercise period in the prison grounds. The official investigation claimed that he committed suicide.

Many years before, Heinrich Himmler had correctly forecast that Rudolf Hess would never leave prison for freedom alive, because the real Hess knew too much.

After the death of Hess, Spandau prison was demolished.

As far as I am aware, bank accounts for 'H' and Martin Bormann still lie in Switzerland.

According to reports that are now accepted as true, the former SS doctor Josef Mengele of Auschwitz lived in South America for many years, after the end of the war. He eventually drowned whilst swimming in a river.

Field Marshal Montgomery used a double on occasions during World War Two. A film and a book have appeared on this subject since the war.

On occasions, one natural twin (of the same sex) has impersonated the other twin. This has been happening for years all over the world.

Some years ago, a trial was held in Israel of a Ukrainian who had been deported from the USA. It was claimed that he had been a guard known as 'Ivan the Terrible' at Sobibor extermination camp in Poland during World War Two. From as near as ten feet away from the defendant in the courtroom, survivors of the breakout from Sobibor were sure that the defendant was 'Ivan the Terrible'. It was conclusively proved after the trial that he was NOT this man, although there was a resemblance.

Do we not usually accept that people are who we are led to believe they are?

Acknowledgements

Thanks are gratefully extended to:

United Kingdom

Mr Bernard Oakwood (deceased) – for passing the story to me.

The man who wished to be known as 'Benny Green' – for his invaluable contribution.

Mr Charles Whiting, the author of many military books – for his interest and advice.

Mr John Isherwood (deceased) – for construction advice.

Mr Chris Dry (deceased) – for military advice.

Mr Duff Hart-Davis – for permission to use information from *The Murder of Rudolf Hess* by Hugh Thomas, published by Hodder and Stoughton.

British War Museum, London.

'Colin's Guided Walking Tours of North Norfolk.'

Miss Sharon Penhallurick – for tireless editing.

Germany

German Ship Museum, Bremerhaven.

Wreck Museum, Cuxhaven-Duhnen.

German Naval Memorial, Laboe.

Herr Wilhelm Lange of Neustadt – for permission to use information from his leaflet on the Cap Arkona tragedy.

KZ – Gedenkstatte Dachau.

KZ – Gedenkstatte Dora-Mittelwerke, Nordhausen.

KZ – Gedenkstatte Neuengamme.

KZ – Gedenkstatte Sachsenhausen.

Poland

Auschwitz-Birkenau State Museum.

Polish Travel Agency ORBIS – for arranging guide and driver.

Everyone who contributed to the writing of this book – for their invaluable help.